FIRST STEPS TOWARD SPACE

Proceedings of the First and Second History Symposia
of the International Academy of Astronautics at
Belgrade, Yugoslavia, 26 September 1967, and
New York, U.S.A., 16 October 1968

EDITED BY

Frederick C. Durant III
and George S. James

SMITHSONIAN INSTITUTION PRESS

City of Washington

1974

A Bibliographic Note

The series *Smithsonian Annals of Flight* terminates with the present issue, number 10. A new series—*Smithsonian Studies in Air and Space*—will present the future publications of the Smithsonian Institution's National Air and Space Museum. Following is a complete list of the previous titles in the old series:

VOLUME 1, NUMBER 1. "The First Nonstop Coast-to-Coast Flight and the Historic T-2 Airplane." Louis S. Casey. 90 pages, 43 figures, appendix, bibliography. Issued 17 December 1964.

VOLUME 1, NUMBER 2. "The First Airplane Diesel Engine: Packard Model DR-980 of 1928." Robert B. Meyer. 48 pages, 38 figures, appendix. Issued 30 April 1965.

VOLUME 1, NUMBER 3. "The Liberty Engine 1918–1942." Philip S. Dickey III. 110 pages, 20 figures, appendix, bibliography. Issued 10 July 1968.

VOLUME 1, NUMBER 4 (end of volume). "Aircraft Propulsion: A Review of the Evolution of Aircraft Piston Engines." C. Fayette Taylor. 134 pages, 72 figures, appendix, bibliography (expanded and arranged by Dr. Richard K. Smith). Issued 29 January 1971.

Volume designation terminated; issues hereafter referred to only as "numbers."

NUMBER 5. "The Wright Brothers' Engines and Their Design." Leonard S. Hobbs. 71 pages, frontispiece, 17 figures, appendix, bibliography, index. Issued 27 October 1971.

NUMBER 6. "Langley's Aero Engine of 1903." Edited by Robert B. Meyer, Jr. 193 pages, frontispiece, 44 figures. Issued 30 March 1971.

NUMBER 7. "The Curtiss D-12 Aero Engine." Hugo T. Byttebier. 109 pages, frontispiece, 46 figures. Issued 10 May 1972.

NUMBER 8. "Wiley Post, His *Winnie Mae,* and the World's First Pressure Suit." Stanley R. Mohler and Bobby H. Johnson. 127 pages, 139 figures, appendix. Issued 22 November 1971.

NUMBER 9. "Japan's World War II Balloon Bomb Attacks on North America." Robert C. Mikesh. 85 pages, 90 figures, appendixes, bibliography, index. Issued 9 April 1973.

OFFICIAL PUBLICATION DATE is handstamped in a limited number of initial copies and is recorded in the Institution's annual report, *Smithsonian Year.* SI PRESS NUMBER 5003.

Library of Congress cataloging in Publication Data
Symposium on the History of Astronautics, 1st, Belgrad, 1967.
First steps toward space.
(Smithsonian annals of flight, no. 10)
Supt. of Docs. no.: SI 9.9: 10.
1. Astronautics—History—Congresses. 2. Rocketry—History—Congresses. I. Durant, Frederick C., 1916– ed. II. James, George S., ed. III. Symposium on the History of Astronautics, 2d, New York, 1968. IV. International Academy of Astronautics. V. Title. VI. Series.
TL515.S5 no. 10 [TL787] 629.13'08s [629.4'09] 73–16298

For sale by the Superintendent of Documents, U.S. Government Printing Office
Washington, D.C. 20402 - Price $4.00
Stock Number 4705-00011

Preface

The fabric of the history of astronautics is woven of stories of individuals and small groups who developed the technologies of rocketry while dreaming of space flight. At least this was true until World War II. Since then, the complexity of guided missiles and rocket-powered aircraft has required much larger enterprises. Official recognition and financial support for such developments were difficult to obtain. Progress was made largely through the personal initiative and dedicated effort of idealists who were deeply convinced that one day man would travel through space.

Because much of the detailed history of these technical developments from 1900–1939 has not been available in the published literature, the International Academy of Astronautics of the International Astronautical Federation (IAF) commenced sponsorship of a series of symposia of the history of rocketry and astronautics. The first symposium was held at Belgrade in 1967. Subsequent symposia have been held at New York (1968), Mar del Plata (1969), Constance (1970), Brussels (1971), Vienna (1972), and Baku (1973). The proceedings of the first two symposia on the history of rocketry and astronautics form the contents of this volume of the series *Smithsonian Annals of Flight*.

The combination of memoirs and papers from the first and second symposia make it possible to present in one volume new information on the work of leading investigators of astronautics and their associates in the first third of the 20th century. Thus, the student of the history of astronautics can study independent and parallel efforts which led to the Space Age.

"Pre-1939 Memoirs of Astronautics" was the theme of the first IAA History of Astronautics symposium, organized with the cooperation of the International Union of the History and Philosophy of Science, and held on Tuesday, 26 September 1967, in Belgrade, Yugoslavia, during the XVIII Congress of the IAF. The philosophy of the organizing committee was to invite living pioneers in astronautics so that they might present memoirs. Of the 13 presentations, three were made by the men themselves: O. Lutz, F. J. Malina, and E. A. Steinhoff. The other ten authors were unable to come to Belgrade and their papers were read by other speakers. These papers appeared in *Iz istorii astronavtiki i raketnoi tekhniki: Materially XVIII mezhdunarodnogo astronavticheskogo kongressa, Belgrad, 25–29 Sentyavrya 1967* [From the History of Rockets and Astronautics: Materials of the 18th International Astronautical Congress, Belgrade, 25–29 September 1967], published in Moscow in 1970.

The second IAA History of Astronautics Symposium, "New Contributions to the Historical Literature on Rocket Technology and Astronautics, 1909–1939," was held on Wednesday, 16 October 1968, in conjunction with the XIX Congress of the IAF in New York. Of the 14 papers, three memoirs were presented by early investigators: R. Engel, C. D. J. Generales, and S. Herrick.

For reference purposes, the papers have been arranged alphabetically by the principal author's last name. The particular symposium at which a paper was presented is indicated by either (1967) or (1968) following the author's name in the table of contents.

Through the resources of the National Air and Space Museum's documentary files and library, it has been possible to add original source references for statements in a number of the papers.

We wish to gratefully acknowledge the assistance and dedication of Frank H. Winter, Research Historian of the National Air and Space Museum, in the preparation of the index. In addition, special appreciation is expressed to the staff editor, John S. Lea, and the Series Production Manager, Charles L. Shaffer, of the Smithsonian Institution Press, for their devoted efforts and assistance throughout the many stages of a uniquely difficult manuscript.

It is our hope that this volume will be useful to those persons interested in learning how the first steps were taken to advance the technologies that have opened new avenues of exploration to the Moon and beyond.

FCD III
GSJ

Washington, DC
August 1973

Contents

First Steps Toward Space

Some Jet Propulsion Formulas of Over Thirty Years Ago

ALDO BARTOCCI, *Italy*

In two articles published in *L'Aerotecnica* in 1933 and 1934,[1] some formulas were presented, together with diagrams concerning the vertical motion of a vehicle having constant acceleration and constant exhaust velocity.

It is very interesting to note that the braking effect produced by air on a rocket in vertical motion, calculated by the formulas in the above 1934 articles, coincides perfectly with results presented for the U.S. Navy Neptune (Viking) sounding rocket in a 1949 English publication.[2]

Vertical Motion by Constant Acceleration

The first formulas concern the vertical motion of a space ship with a regulated jet for maintaining a constant acceleration w; with a given constant exhaust velocity of the jet v; with the earth considered fully spherical with a radius r; and with no allowance for air friction.

The variation of mass m in the time t is given by the following formula:

$$\log m = \log M_0 - \frac{w}{cv}t - \frac{9.81}{cv}\sqrt{\frac{r}{2w}}\left[\arctan\left(t\sqrt{\frac{w}{2r}}\right) + \frac{1}{2}\sin 2\arctan\left(t\sqrt{\frac{w}{2r}}\right)\right], \quad (1)$$

where M_0 is the initial value of mass and $c = 2.30259$ is the constant for conversion of a natural logarithm into a common logarithm. The altitude x at which the motor must be turned off for reaching the altitude h is given by the relation

$$2wx = 19.62\, r^2\left(\frac{1}{x+r} - \frac{1}{h+r}\right), \quad (2)$$

and, in particular, the altitude x at which the motor must be turned off to escape from terrestrial gravity is given by the formula

$$2wx = 19.62\,\frac{r^2}{x+r}. \quad (3)$$

Applying the formula (3) to some numerical examples, it appears that the initial mass necessary for a given excursion diminishes with increasing exhaust velocity of the jet, thus producing higher acceleration values.

The air resistance in kilograms, which has not been taken into consideration in formula (1), is given by the formula:

$$R = F(V)\cdot d\cdot a^2 \cdot \frac{1000\cdot i}{g}, \quad (4)$$

where $F(V)$ is a function depending on the speed of vehicle V; d is the density of the air; a is the diameter, in meters, of the transverse section of the vehicle; and i is a shape coefficient.

Assuming for the function $F(V)$ the values in function of speed adopted by ballistics, we obtain for air resistance the curves shown in Figure 1 correlating time and acceleration.

Vertical Motion by Constant Efflux

The second group of formulas concern vertical motion of an unmanned rocket with a constant thrust (constant mass efflux and constant exhaust velocity).

Not considering air friction and considering constant acceleration of gravity during the operating time of the motor, we have formulas in which M_0 is the initial mass of rocket, M_f is the final mass at the end of the combustion, and n is the ratio be-

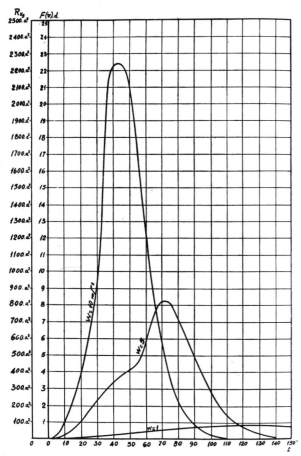

FIGURE 1.—Correlation of time and acceleration.

The initial velocity V necessary to climb by force of inertia from height h to height H, the latter reached with zero velocity speed is given by

$$V^2 = 2 g_0 r^2 \left(\frac{1}{h+r} - \frac{1}{H+r} \right),\qquad (8)$$

where r is the radius of the earth considered as spherical.

From the above formula we can obtain the value of ratio M_0 necessary for reaching a previously established altitude H with zero resulting velocity. The rocket reaches this altitude by coasting from altitude h where, at the end of the combustion, it had velocity V. For this calculation a graph has been prepared, shown in Figure 2, for a prompt solution of the problems regarding the rocket's vertical ascension without taking into account the resistance of the air.

Regarding the resistance of the air, not considered until now, and expressed by the above formula (8), this can be expressed in function of ratio M_0/m where m is the value of the mass at any given time.

In Figure 3 are shown a diagram of function $F(V) \cdot d$ of the resistance of the air; a diagram of the relative retarding acceleration W_A; and a diagram, with a linear variation, of the rocket's acceleration in the absence of air.

tween propulsion force and initial weight of the rocket.

The time T corresponding to the end of combustion is given by

$$T = \frac{v}{ng_0} \left(1 - \frac{M_f}{M_0} \right). \qquad (5)$$

The rocket velocity V_f at the end of combustion is given by

$$V_f = v \left[1n - \frac{M_0}{M_f} - \frac{1}{n} \left(1 - \frac{M_f}{M_0} \right) \right]. \qquad (6)$$

The altitude h reached at the end of combustion is given by

$$h_f = \frac{v^2}{ng_0} \left\{ \left[\frac{M_f}{M_0} \left(1n \frac{M_f}{M_0} - 1 \right) + 1 \right] - \frac{1}{2n} \left(1 - \frac{M_f}{M_0} \right)^2 \right\}. \qquad (7)$$

NOTES

1. Aldo Bartocci, "Le Escursioni in altezza col motore a reazione," *L'Aerotecnica*, vol. 13, no. 12 (December 1933), pp. 1646–66; and "Il Razzo," *L'Aerotecnica*, vol. 14, no. 3 (March 1934), pp. 255–66.

2. In a letter to the author, dated 5 July 1949, General G. A. Crocco said:

I have indeed been pleased that Professor Eula has informed me that you are the author of the interesting articles published in 1933, 34, and 38; and I was very glad to have this confirmation authenticated in writing. . . .

I am glad then to tell you that the rate of retardation (drag) introduced by the air in the vertical movement of the rocket, and which today is published by an English Review, the subject of which is the rocket "Neptune" of the U.S. Navy, coincides exactly with that which you designated certainly for the first time, in 1934.

The article to which he refers may have been that by C. H. Smith, M. W. Rosen, and J. M. Bridger, "Super Altitude Research Rocket Revealed by Navy," *Aviation*, June 1947, pp. 40–43.—Ed.

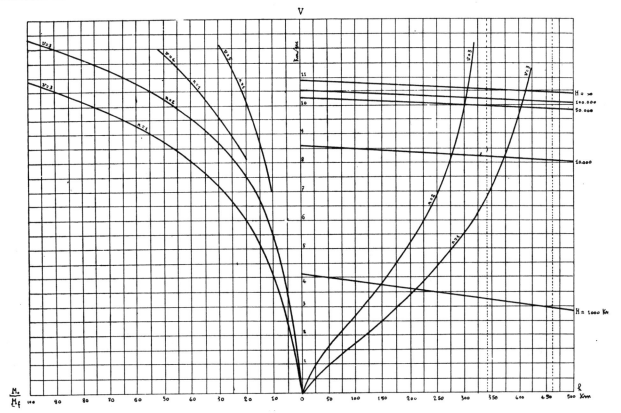

FIGURE 2.—Graph for determining relationship of various parameters during vertical ascent of rocket (omitting air resistance).

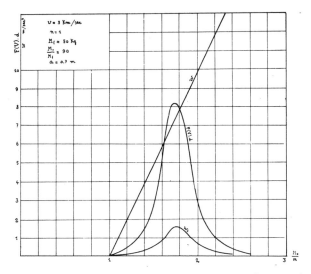

FIGURE 3.—Relationships, with and without air resistance, of rocket acceleration with drag and mass.

2

Robert Esnault-Pelterie: Space Pioneer

LISE BLOSSET, *France*

Robert Esnault-Pelterie (REP to his friends) was one of the first pioneers who, by their theoretical and experimental work, foresaw the possibilities of astronautics after those of aviation (Figure 1).

Despite his farsightedness and the broad scope of his work on space problems, however, he had to face a profound lack of understanding and overwhelming financial and material difficulties.

He received very little support from government and industry, who had no confidence in his projects.

In the light of the number and value of his original ideas, what would he not have achieved had he been understood and helped!

Son of a textile manufacturer, Robert Esnault-Pelterie, born in Paris on 8 November 1881, took a very lively interest in mechanics from his earliest childhood. At the age of 13 he built by himself an entire electrical network, including lighting, switching panel, and automatic signals, for a miniature steam train he had received as a present.[1] At 17 he transformed his small machine shop into a veritable physics and chemistry laboratory and studied wireless telegraphy.[2] His originality was already expressing itself. Instead of buying or copying, he invented the devices he needed. It was thus that he obtained in 1902 his first patent for a highly sensitive electric relay,[3] the same year that he received his science degree at the Sorbonne (botany, general physics, general chemistry). He was then 21 and immediately devoted himself to research in a field that had just been born, aviation. He supplemented his theoretical work by building and testing his own airplanes, thereby personally checking his results.

Aeronautics

Let us briefly summarize REP's contributions to aviation.

He built his first flying machine in 1904, a tailless biplane glider with fabric-covered airfoils. His glider tests included towing behind an auto (Figure 2) and tests of wing sections and other components mounted above the auto (Figure 3) at speeds up to 60 miles per hour, thereby becoming the first to undertake such direct testing.[4]

By 1906, the results of these tests enabled him to build the first all-metal monoplane, which he first flew on 19 October 1907.[5] In order that the engine

FIGURE 1.—Robert Esnault-Pelterie (1881–1957).

FIGURE 2.—Glider designed and constructed by Robert Esnault-Pelterie prior to towing test by auto, 1904.

of his plane be as light as possible, he designed it to include an odd number of cylinders axially arranged and a single cam that ensured regular ignition in each cylinder at equal intervals.[6] This system (Figures 4–5) and the theory of the metallic propeller were the subject of a report to the Société des Ingénieurs Civils de France (8 November 1907) which awarded REP its annual grand prize (gold medal).[7] Thirty years later, 75 percent of the aircraft built in the world were equipped with engines based on his principle.

FIGURE 3.—Test of airplane components from an instrumented automobile at a speed of 100 km/hr, 1905.

This 1907 airplane was, in addition, equipped with a large number of devices conceived by him and destined to become classic, notably the "joystick" (the single-lever elevator control device invented by him), a deformable trihedral landing gear consisting of two wheels without axle, oleo-pneumatic dampened shock absorbing brakes, and so on.[8]

From 1908 to 1914, he built numerous airplanes that took part successfully in frequent competitions and broke many records.[9] The photograph (Figure 5e), used for his pilot license no. 4 of the Aéro-Club de France, shows him at the controls of the REP-2 monoplane.[10] A large number of patents, in addition, show his constant concern for pilot safety: safety belts, speed indicators, parachutes which would release the pilot, double controls for pilot instruction in air-schools, static tests of planes during their construction, etc.[11] Thus he created, a quarter of a century beforehand, all the elements of modern aircraft.[12]

REP was one of the founders, 29 January 1908, of the Association des Industriels de la Locomotion Aérienne.[13] The latter combined, on 22 July 1910, with the Chambre Syndicale des Industries Aéronautiques, over which he presided for 11 years.[14] In 1909 he became president of the executive committee that organized the first international aeronautics exhibition in France, predecessor of the present Salon du Bourget.[15] In 1913, he became president of the aviation committee of the Aéro-Club de France.

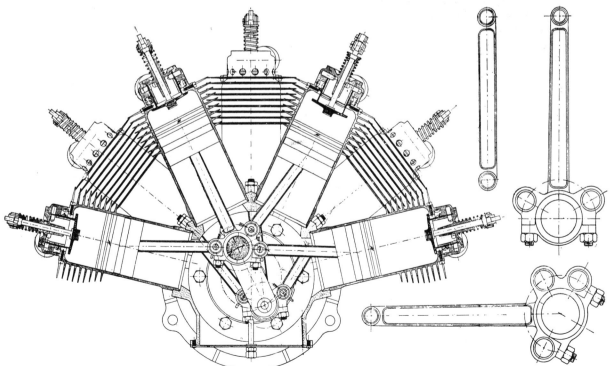

FIGURE 4.—Exterior view and cross section of 7-cylinder, 35-hp, REP airplane engine, 1907.

FIGURE 5.—*a,* The 5-cylinder, 65-hp, REP airplane engine, 1910; *b,* the 7-cylinder, 90-hp, REP airplane engine, 1911; *c,* REP at the controls of the REP-2 monoplane.

During these years, in which the future of aviation became assured, REP foresaw its extension into the conquest of outer space.

It has been said (notably by Wernher von Braun in a recent encyclopedia) [16] that the great advantage of REP over other space pioneers was that he was renowned during his lifetime.[17] This is perhaps true with respect to aviation but absolutely not with respect to astronautics. In fact, as someone once wrote, before World War II, it sufficed for a report to be signed Esnault-Pelterie for it to be filed in the wastebasket by the government officials to whom it was addressed.

Astronautics—Historical Summary

By 1908 REP had already foreseen the possibility of space travel. This early foresight is documented by Captain F. Ferber in a text dated 26 July 1908 which appeared in his work, "De Crête à crête, de ville à ville, de continent à continent," [18] where he quotes REP's studies.

Unknown to REP, on 10 June 1911, Doctor André Bing (whom he did not meet until near the end of 1912) was awarded a Belgian patent for an "apparatus for exploring upper atmospheric regions however rarefied" in which he discussed the possibility of "traveling beyond the limits of the earth's atmosphere" with "successive rockets" using nuclear energy.[19]

Shortly thereafter, first in a lecture at Saint Petersburg (Leningrad; February 1912),[20] then in a resounding report to the Société Française de Physique, in Paris on 15 November 1912, REP presented his studies and conclusions concerning the results of the unlimited lightening of engines and, in the face of sarcasm, for the first time demonstrated theoretically that it was possible for a craft with special design and equipment to travel from the earth to the moon.[21] He also predicted the realization of interstellar vehicles once atomic energy had been mastered.

As is very often the case, several scientists pursue, at about the same time and without knowing it, original works in the same field. Thus in 1912 (REP mentioned this during a later lecture[22]) Professor Robert Goddard did theoretical calculations at Princeton University regarding a method of reaching éxtreme altitudes;[23] and in 1913 and 1916, at Clark University in Worcester, Massachusetts, he carried out experiments on rockets for exploring the upper atmosphere,[24] work based on ideas strikingly similar to those of Dr. Bing.

In 1912 REP's lecture was published by the *Journal de Physique*. Because of the elimination of large parts of the text due to page limitations and editing by the secretary of the *Journal*, the author's thoughts were often hardly understandable. The secretary had in fact been shocked by the contents of the article, whose real purpose REP had prudently disguised by an inoffensive title. An English translation of the complete text was distributed at the International Astronautics Congress in 1958 (Amsterdam) as a memorial to REP and is reproduced as an appendix to this paper.

REP deplored the exaggerated condensation of the lecture, which was the cause for an apparent divergence between Goddard's and his own opinions concerning the possibility at the time of building vehicles capable of escaping from the earth's gravitation. In fact, Goddard wanted only to send a projectile loaded with powder to the moon and observe its arrival by telescope.[25] REP considered the conditions necessary for transporting living beings from one celestial body to another and returning them to the earth; his more pessimistic conclusions were based on considerations of the substantial initial mass required for a rather small

final mass, in view of the limited means available at the time.

The lecture contains all the theoretical bases of self-propulsion, destroying the myth that rockets need atmospheric support and giving the real equation of motion. Anticipated is the use of auxiliary propulsion for guidance and complete maneuverability of rockets. Also contained are calculations of the escape velocity, the phases of a round-trip voyage to the Moon, and the times, velocities, and durations, of trips to the Moon, Mars, and Venus, as well as thermal problems related notably to the surface facing the sun (polished metal or black surface). This 1912 lecture is the first purely scientific study marking the birth of astronautics. While Tsiolkovskiy had the prescience and talent to first suggest, in 1903, rocket propulsion to space,[26] REP was the first to develop the equations of the problem and to establish the mathematical theory of interplanetary flight.[27] REP is thus the founder of theoretical astronautics.

After World War I, he returned, in 1920, to his work on escape velocity,[28] but the results, later mentioned by his friend André-Louis Hirsch, were not published at the time.

On 8 June 1927, he gave a lecture at the Sorbonne on rocket exploration of the very high atmosphere and the possibility of interplanetary travel,[29] in which he presented quite clearly the theoretical basis showing the importance of the escape velocity and the ratio of initial to final mass, and presented a theory of gas expansion in a convergent-divergent nozzle.

Then REP undertook the construction of a stratospheric rocket and did numerous tests on liquid fuels, which he preferred to solids for rocket propulsion, but his means were unfortunately quite insufficient.

Since he considered liquid oxygen particularly dangerous to handle, he thought it more reasonable to use the explosive liquid tetranitromethane. Unfortunately, on 9 October 1931, this ultrasensitive explosive caused an accident that cost him four fingers of his left hand.[30] Yet the accident did move the administration finally to grant a subsidy to REP, on the initiative of General Ferrie. This support, however, was so limited that it permitted him only to study a few devices but not to undertake their fabrication. After the tetranitromethane accident, REP returned to liquid oxygen and dealt with the problem of precise and proportional flows of oxygen and fuel.[31]

As early as 1930, REP studied, with the cooperation of Pierre Montagne, the optimal theoretical conditions for reaction engine carburation.[32] This study permitted the determination of the mixture ratio of liquid oxygen and petroleum ether to provide optimum performance.

In 1932, REP, at his laboratory on Rue des Abondances, in Boulogne-sur-Seine, with Montagne and Salle, attacked the problem of constructing this reaction engine and developed a test stand at Satory which enabled him to study, from 1934 to 1937, the optimum output of his engine by injecting liquid oxygen and petroleum ether into his graphite combustion chamber. To deal with problems related to the use of graphite, REP fabricated a nozzle throat from tungsten which he smelted in a high-frequency furnace also specially designed by him for this purpose.

For these works, REP obtained a small contract from the Direction des Études et Fabrications d'Armements, which assigned Ingénieur Général Desmazières to supervise the execution of the project.

In 1937, for dignitaries visiting REP's laboratory, the engine operated 60 seconds without incident, with a thrust of 125 kg. The engine itself met the qualification standard but the subsidy to enable REP to construct the gyroscopic stabilization device that he considered necessary for his rocket was then refused. REP agreed to study a project for a finned rocket, without gyroscopic guidance, but he baptized this the "NIC" for "n'importe comment" and subsequently abandoned this project. The outbreak of the 1939 War put an end to REP's activities in astronautics.

Projects Scorned by Authorities

REP was no doubt the first to recognize the danger of rockets as weapons capable of intercontinental ranges, and this worried him. At first he thought it preferable to remain silent. But the publicity given by the press to his 1927 work, "L'Exploration par fusées de la très haute atmosphère et la possibilité des voyages interplanétaires," attracted a large correspondence from which he learned of works unknown to him: *Die Rakete zu den Planetenräumen* by Hermann Oberth (1923); [33]

Die Erreichbarkeit der Himmelskörper, by Walter Hohmann (1925);[34] and *Der Vorstoss in den Weltenraum,* by Max Valier (1925).[35]

He began to feel that it had become his duty to inform the government of his results, of the potential dangers and the means of developing methods for sending thousands of tons of projectiles several hundred miles in a few hours. Using the calculations he had first made in 1920 with two of his collaborators, Scal and Marcus, he decided to prepare a secret report which he sent on 20 May 1928 to his friend, General Ferrié, who forwarded it to his chiefs.[36] This theoretical report demonstrated that it was already possible to attain a range of 2267 kilometers with an exhaust velocity of 2667 meters per second (REP recognized later that this estimate was optimistic for the time). In addition, REP made a detailed study for the particular case of a rocket of 600-kilometer range, specifying all the mass ratios, and notably the ballistic yield (the ratio between the weight of the necessary propellant and that of the projectile for this range), both for the mixtures of gasoline and nitrogen peroxide that he had taken as examples and for the special solid propellant used by Professor Goddard.

The report ended with economic studies comparing rocket and aerial bombings and concluded that long-range rockets would be the artillery of the future.

After some months, the dossier was returned: it had aroused absolutely no interest!

No one at the time considered such works apt to give useful results and the scientist was unable to overcome the inertia of government officials who often systematically ignored anything coming from him.

In 1931 the government nevertheless assigned a lieutenant of the technical section of the artillery, J. J. Barre, to work in REP's laboratory. Barre had been collaborating privately with REP since 1927 and had helped with the calculations for the memorandum. This assignment lasted only one year, because it was not considered that "a study of rockets is worthy of the activity of an officer." In spite of this precise and prophetic memorandum, REP did not get the subsidies necessary to carry out the studies he had proposed.

The situation was different in Germany, where similar work led to the V-2 rockets. It should nevertheless be noted that in 1931 André-Louis

Hirsch visited Germany, on behalf of REP, to witness the first rocket test at Reinickendorf, near Berlin, and that these tests were in no way held secret, no doubt because the Germans did not yet believe in their military possibilities.

Because REP's work was not considered to have useful applications and since the necessary support has always been refused, when the war broke out, REP had, according to his own estimate, gone about 1/100 of the way.[37] That is, he had conducted static tests on rocket engines giving thrusts up to 300 kg for 60 seconds: this corresponds to a rocket of a total mass of 100 kg that could reach an altitude of 100 km (realized by the Americans after 1945).

REP-Hirsch International Astronautics Prize

On 1 February 1928, together with André-Louis Hirsch, REP founded the REP-Hirsch International Astronautics Prize, awarded up to 1939 to the best original theoretical or experimental work capable of promoting progress in one of the areas permitting the realization of interstellar navigation or furthering knowledge in a field related to astronautics.[38] The term "astronautique" which REP was then introducing into scientific language, had been pronounced for the first time on 26 December 1927 by the French writer, J. H. Rosny, Sr., then President of the "Académie Goncourt" and member of the prize jury (Figure 6).[39]

Note that the Société Astronomique de France, which was daring enough to sponsor the REP-Hirsch prize, was the first scientific society in the world to recognize that this new science had a future.

In the first year, the prize committee received a manuscript from Hermann Oberth, at the time a professor in a small city, and awarded him the prize.[40] This enabled him to find a publisher and, when his book was published in 1929, Oberth mentioned, on the last page, that the Société Astronomique de France had awarded him the REP-Hirsch prize and said:

It is reassuring to see that science and progress suffice to overcome national prejudices. I can think of no better way to thank the Société Astronomique de France than to pledge myself to work on behalf of science and progress and to judge people only on their personal merits.

This paragraph survived in later editions, even during World War II.[41]

The Russian, Ary Sternfeld, who won the prize in 1934,[42] wrote to André-Louis Hirsch after the launching of the first satellite to say that REP's books, translated by Rynin,[43] had exercised an important influence and that the Soviets had used his mathematical theory of astronautics in their work.

The last winner (1939) was Frank Malina, then a young student in California.[44]

REP's Important Publications on Astronautics

Oberth was the first to demonstrate that it was technically possible for rockets to eject their gases at a velocity greater than 4000 meters per second (it was for this work that he was awarded the REP-Hirsch prize). As Oberth had only stated the principle without mathematical demonstration, REP worked from 1926 to 1930 on the mathematical physics solution, which he published in his 1930 book.[45] He also computed the temperature in the combustion chamber and showed that it was much lower than Oberth had thought, because of the increase of specific heats with the temperature. From this he concluded that it would be possible to construct combustion chambers and nozzles of highly refractory materials.

Note that REP's theoretical temperature calculations were resoundingly confirmed during the stratospheric ascent of Professor Piccard.[46] The basket was a sphere polished on one side and black on the other; the black side was exposed to the sun for a certain time, during which the temperature inside the cabin rose to 39° C.[47] REP had predicted a temperature of 42° C.

In 1930, REP gathered his results in his major work, *L'Astronautique*,[48] a veritable treatise on space vehicles that served as a basis for all later works on this subject. It is a very profound theoretical study based on the thorough knowledge of celestial mechanics, astrophysics, and ballistics, as well as physical chemistry and physiology. Nothing in it has yet been invalidated.

This book is a basic text for all interested in astronautics. One needs only to scan the chapter titles to see that it is both a scientific and technical document and an encyclopedia of precious practical knowledge:

—Rocket Motion in Vacuum and in Air
—Density and Composition of the Very High Atmosphere

FIGURE 6.—A meeting of French astronautical pioneers, Paris, 1927. *Sitting, from left:* Robert
Esnault-Pelterie and André-Louis Hirsch. *Standing, from left:* Henri Chrétien, inventor of
Cinemascope; J. H. Rosny Sr., writer and president, Académie Goncourt; A. Lambert, astrono-
mer, Observatoire de Paris (or Professor Ch. Maurain, see note at end of caption); Jean Perrin,
Nobel Prize; R. Soreau, President, Société des Ingénieurs Civil de France; General Ferrié (Head,
French Army Signal Corps), member, l'Institute de France; Jos. Béthenod, founder, Compagnie
Générale de T.S.F.; E. Fichot, president, Société Astronomique de France; Em. Bélot, astronomer.
Note: this individual is identified as A. Lambert on page 217 of Andrew G. Haley, *Rocketry and
Space Exploration* (New York: D. Van Nostrand Company, 1958), and as Ch. Maurain in a
caption supplied by André-Louis Hirsch to Woodford A. Heflin in 1960 and published in
"Astronautics," *American Speech*, vol. 36, October 1961, pp. 169–174.—Ed.

—Expansion of Combination Gases Through a Nozzle
—Combustion in a Chamber
—Possible Use of Rockets (high altitude exploration, launching projectiles to the moon, high-speed travel around
   the earth, and travel through the atmosphere)
—Interplanetary Travel (with sections on the conditions
   under which trips around the moon will be carried out,
   the design of the spaceship, guidance, navigation and
   piloting devices, the conditions for habitation).

For these last points, REP states that the spaceship
could be filled with pure oxygen, which would
reduce the pressure to about a tenth that of the
atmosphere and would also serve to substantially
reduce leakages.

In the section on the guidance of a spaceship, we
already find the principle of stabilization by "three
small electric motors each one with a flywheel of
sufficient moment of inertia and placed with their
axes at right angles."

REP also suggests that the spaceship, for its return to earth, be turned and braked first by its own
engines (today's retrorockets) and then by the use
of a parachute.

In May 1934, REP published a supplement to his
1930 book in which he presented the practical conditions and the advantages of interplanetary trips.[49]
This work included a study of rocket motion
(velocity, trajectories as a function of the combustion regimes and masses); a new study of combustion gas expansion nozzles; combustion thermodynamics (referring to the thermochemical studies
of Pierre Montagne, for which the latter was
awarded the REP-Hirsch prize in 1931); prophetic
considerations on nuclear propulsion; and the use
of radioactive elements (neutrons and atomic fission
had just been discovered) and of atomic hydrogen
(REP was thus the first to consider using free
radicals to ensure the maximum utilization of
available energy for propulsion).

In addition to a study of orbital paths (corresponding to our transfer orbits), this work includes considerations on the application of relativity to energy radiation (REP anticipated photonic propulsion, study of which has been undertaken recently in some countries).

The principle of multistage rockets and the calculations of mass ratios presented by REP stimulated the work of Louis Damblanc, who in 1936 was awarded a patent for "self-driven projectiles whose propulsive charge is distributed in several combustion stages along the axis of the rocket." [50]

REP also foresaw the advantage of rockets for the study of the aurora borealis, which is the purpose of many current sounding rockets.

After the publication of the supplement to his book, REP was awarded his second annual Grand Prize by the Société des Ingénieurs Civils de France.

On 22 June 1936, he became a member of the Académie des Sciences in the division "applications de la science à l'industrie." [51]

Some Experimental Works

Let us review some of REP's experimental works that enabled him to solve certain problems in an original way (we owe the details of paragraphs 1–4 to Ingénieur Général J.-J. Barre, who sent us copies of certain of REP's reports, the originals of which have been destroyed).

1. *Method of injecting fuel and oxidizer into the combustion chamber.*—REP first tried using a device including volumetric pumps driven by a sort of gas turbine turned by part of the jet from the nozzle. This design was abandoned because of the difficulties due to pump lubrication and the poor behavior of the liquid-oxygen fittings. He then used pressurized tanks for feeding the fuel and oxidizer. This system worked by the pressure of an inert gas on the fuel and by the action of a heater that raised the pressure of the oxygen and vaporized part of it.

Figure 7 shows a particularly original device used by REP's team. It is based on the fact that the vapor pressure of liquid argon is 31.5 hpz at 140° K, while the vapor pressure of liquid oxygen at this temperature is 25 hpz. A bypass (7) operates at the pressure of the liquid oxygen tank (3) and allows the petroleum ether to pass at a rate sufficient to maintain the pressure at 25 hpz, taking into account the heat given off by the liquid oxygen to the

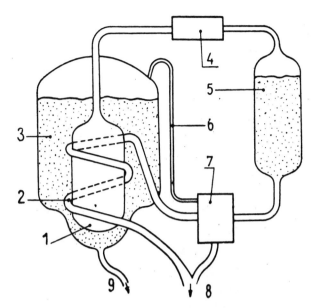

FIGURE 7.—Device for injecting fuel and oxidizer into the combustion chamber. 1, Argon tank. 2, Coil exchanger. 3, Liquid oxygen tank. 4, Release valve. 5, Petroleum ether tank. 6, Pressure gauge. 7, Heating by-pass regulator. 8, Petroleum ether outlet. 9, Liquid oxygen outlet.

argon contained in tank (1). Relief valve (4), in which the argon vapor is expanded at 25 hpz, forces the petroleum ether from the tank (5) towards the jets [52] either directly or through exchange coil (2).

For the static tests at Satory (see 5, below), compressed nitrogen was used to feed the fuel through a relief valve. This device operated very safely, provided the regulators were defrosted when necessary. The major advantage was the remarkably low dead weight, but it was not entirely satisfactory when used for cold and dense gases, the mass of which tends to become quite substantial.

2. *Vibrating volumetric feed regulator.*—REP then conceived of a vibrating volumetric feed regulator to control the liquid flow. Figure 8 shows the working of a device designed according to the principle of a double pendulum. The liquid leaves tank (K) by two cylinders (C) and the ports of the slide-valves (T) connected to pistons (P) by springs. The slide-valves (T) were fixed to the cylinder frame by springs. The entire system vibrated in resonance with tank (K), whose vibrations could be tuned to those of the piston/slide-valve assembly, by means of closed tube (A). The liquid flow was thus provided by equal and synchronous volume. This device worked quite well during its first water test.

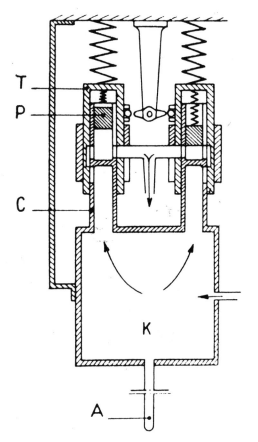

FIGURE 8.—Vibrating volumetric feed regulator.

3. *Constant pressure drop jet.*—This jet was intended to ensure a correct mixture ratio with constant pressure drop whatever the liquid viscosity. Figure 9 shows the inner surface of the jet, which is grooved. When the depth (b) of these grooves is equal to the distance (a) between them, the flow is independent of the viscosity of the fluid. Naturally, this arrangement increases the pressure drop between the tank and the combustion chamber.

4. *Means of lightening tanks.*—Light alloys proved to be particularly good material for liquid oxygen tanks because their mechanical characteristics are better at very low temperatures. Since it was not possible at this time to weld such alloys, REP designed tanks of duralumin, using thin rolled-up sheets and bonding successive layers together (Figure 10). Because of the low quality of the available adhesives, he did not continue his efforts to perfect this method at the time, but the idea was adopted very much later in other countries.

5. *Firing tests at Satory.*—A test stand was built at Satory in 1932. It was used for engines delivering thrusts up to 100 kg and later up to 300 kg. Exhaust velocities of 2400 m/sec were attained in 1936.

Figure 11 shows this apparatus in detail. The compartment on the left housed the petroleum ether tank; that in the center, the engine being tested; and that on the right, the liquid-oxygen tank.

Each of the tanks was mounted on a recording balance. The engine, with its jet directed downward, was suspended from a dynamometer having a powerful vibration damper that from the beginning worked as REP had calculated. The successive tests enabled the measurement of the time, the propellant flow, the tank pressures, combustion chamber pressure, pressure at the nozzle throat, the engine thrust, and the inlet and outlet coolant temperatures. These measurements were executed automatically in the proper sequence by a mechanical timer invented by REP. It should be noted that this assembly worked correctly from the beginning. It was necessary to add only an electric heater in order to pressurize the oxygen tank. For cooling REP at first used water.

A study of cooling by liquid oxygen was undertaken next and tests were conducted on 15 October, 3 and 16 December 1936.[53]

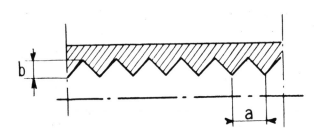

FIGURE 9.—Inner surface of injector, showing grooves.

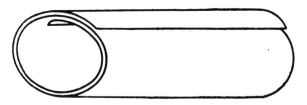

FIGURE 10.—Rolled and adhesive-bonded sheets for the manufacture of tanks.

FIGURE 11.—Experimental facility at Satory for static-test firing of rocket engines.

Figure 12 shows the system for cooling the nozzle by circulation of the liquid oxygen before its introduction into the thrust chamber. The latter was made of duraluminum and contained a block of pure copper into which were screwed six pure copper premixing chambers. The latter were equipped with four rings of jet holes.

The nozzle was made entirely of pure copper, and its outer surface had longitudinal 30° grooves which, while doubling the surface wetted by the oxygen, provided sufficient passage for the latter even in the case that the nozzle, when expanding to regulate the thickness of the cooling sheet of liquid oxygen would touch the outer ring (A).

The fuel arrived under pressure at B and, passing through the circular feeder (C), escaped by 290 small triangular slits cut 0.5 mm into the upper part of ring D, and wet the external surface of the nozzle. The flow around the nozzle is controlled by ring A, whose cylindrical bore was threaded so as to provide a rough surface that ensured a constant pressure drop. The dimensions of the oxygen passages, that is, the relative positions

of the nozzle and rings A and D, had been previously adjusted according to the results of water-flow tests.

None of the three tests was successful, and REP abandoned the idea of cooling by liquid oxygen. The reason for his efforts to cool the nozzles in this way was that he feared it would not be possible to operate without cooling.

6. *Uncooled refractory nozzles.*—At the end of 1936, REP began to work on nozzles made of ultra-refractory materials. For this purpose he built an electric furnace of his own design. After many difficulties due to the outdated equipment he was obliged to use because of lack of money, and after many experiments [54] he managed to make convergent parts of nozzles to the following dimensions: a cylinder 50 mm in diameter and 20 mm thick having, along its axis, a hole of which the diameter converged from 35 mm at the entrance to 17 mm at the throat. At that time his tests normally lasted 60 seconds. In order to fabricate with this furnace the nozzles needed, he had in vain asked the Caisse Nationale des Recherches Scienti-

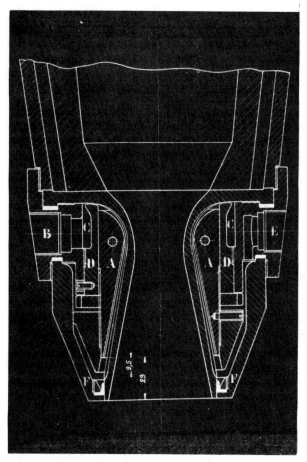

FIGURE 12.—Diagram showing method of cooling rocket nozzle
with liquid oxygen, December, 1936.

fiques for a grant that would allow him to buy a
secondhand 32,000 cycle alternator for 6000 francs
of the time, as well as various parts for measurement
instruments. In spite of the crippling conditions
under which he was obliged to work, his efforts to
improve the material for his furnace nevertheless
enabled him to construct an electric furnace of
highly original design, which he named "four-
fronde" and for which he used centrifugal force to
increase the compactness of the ceramic material
during the treatment.

It is noteworthy that he also experimented on
throatless nozzles, the cylindrical chamber opening
directly into the diverging cone.

7. *Rocket guidance.*—Some of the devices invented by REP were used in the V-2 rockets and in
the American Viking rockets derived from them.
An example is the gimbaled nozzle proposed by
REP in 1927. REP described this nozzle as "con-

nected to the control stick by a system in such a
way that the pilot would have only to make simple
instinctive movements. It would even be possible to
control the rocket automatically by means of a
system of pendulums." This idea was applied in
the V-2 integrating-accelerometer that guided the
rocket by controlling the jet deflectors. In fact this
accelerometer is composed of a gyroscopic pendulum mounted on gimbals.

Other Technical and Scientific Fields

In addition to his work on aviation and astronautics, REP applied his exceptional vision to
many other fields—metallurgy, electricity, mag-
netism, viscosity, compressibility of liquids, and
thermodynamics. He received more than 200 inventor's patents [55] and built many devices involving
new principles, such as explosion and combustion
engines, combustion turbines, mechanical and hydraulic gear systems, automobile suspensions, electromagnetic devices, hardness measuring instruments for metals,[56] and medical apparatus for
electrical shock treatments. His ballistic engine, on
which he worked from 1916 to 1921 (the energy of
the gas was transmitted to a liquid acting on a
hydraulic tank) corresponds to the first idea of
hydraulic power transmission which is only now
beginning to be applied [57] (e.g., the German Klatte
transmission).

In 1915, as a forerunner in yet another field, he
carried out extensive research on the use of tidal
energy in the Straits of Dover.[58]

It is noteworthy that REP never hesitated to go
beyond the limits of his own field as soon as he was
hampered by a lack of theoretical bases, nor did he
hesitate to carry out a number of basic research
projects, some of great value. For example, in his
astronautics work, he made careful study of a great
many ideas relating to dimensional analysis, i.e.,
the means of determining the form of equations
associating certain values.

In fact, in 1933, his work on rockets using oxygen
and liquid fuels posed the problems of designing
a small injector for a rocket engine of some 20,000
nominal horsepower that would weigh no more
than 2.5 kg and occupy a small volume. REP thus
found himself faced with a flow problem where the
equations of hydrodynamics were not easy to apply.
The only solution was to carry out a series of

measurements and to complement his experiments by theoretical study within the scope of dimensional analysis. Since he was unable to find the necessary information in existing publications, he undertook the work himself. His findings, which he communicated to the Académie des Sciences in 1933, included notably the discovery of a particular type of constant pressure drop flow ("isozemique") that, as demonstrated by dimensional analysis, is independent of viscosity.[59] The tests described above with petroleum ether and liquid oxygen, using orifices determined by these calculations, confirmed his forecasts exactly.

The final result was the publication at Lausanne in 1948 of his book on dimensional analysis, *L'Analyse dimensionnelle,* the preliminary manuscript of which was written between September 1945 and April 1946.[60]

Since we are conducting a symposium on the history of astronautics, I should like to draw attention to the fact that in an appendix to this book, REP had proposed creating in each faculty a Chair in the History of Science for the purpose of promoting a study of the errors in judgment which have had to be overcome in order to make progress possible and for comparing the various hypotheses that had to be abandoned with those that have survived; for he said that knowledge of the reasons for these choices is frequently much more useful in the training of a scientific mind than the study of texts in their definitive form, which leaves the student under the illusion that "all came about by itself."

Last Years

After the war, REP, who had retired to Switzerland unknown and misunderstood, abandoned space research. This extremely unfortunate decision was a great loss for astronautics, particularly since almost all his unpublished work was lost. Moreover, many documents in the possession of certain colleagues had to be destroyed at the time our country was occupied.

However, on 9 May 1947, in a lecture given at the Aéro-Club de France, REP returned to the results of his calculations and conclusions concerning the mixtures previously studied (solid propellants and petroleum ether/liquid oxygen) and added to these mixtures of liquid hydrogen/liquid oxygen and uranium 235 and plutonium.[61]

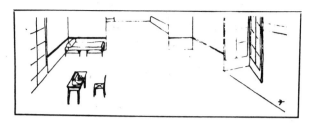

FIGURE 13.—REP's apartment at 43 Boulevard Lannes, in Paris, after attachment of his furniture by the Tax Department.

In his last years, REP experienced many trying days. He who could have made a fortune thanks to his inventions, was harassed by the tax department and his furniture was attached (Figure 13)—this on top of the indifference, the lack of understanding, and the sarcasm he had suffered all his life.

After participating in the exciting development of aviation, REP, as a space pioneer had the somewhat bitter consolation, before his death on 6 December 1957, of seeing his ideas confirmed abroad, first by the V-2 and later by the launching of the first earth satellite, Sputnik I, in the USSR.

On the day of his death, a Vanguard rocket was launched at Cape Canaveral (now Cape Kennedy) like a salute in his honor.

After looking into the laborious life of this ingenious pioneer, we salute the memory of this universal man, hardly knowing what to praise the most —the researcher's rich imagination; the theortician's rigorous reasoning; the experimentalist's capability, boldness, and intrepidity; or the engineer's concern for perfection.

I should like to express my appreciation to all those who helped me in my library research on Robert Esnault-Pelterie and in particular, Gaston Palewski, former Minister of Scientific Research; Ingénieur Général J.-J. Barré; Pierre Montagne; Alexandre Ananoff; and George S. James.

NOTES

The author of this paper, Lise Blosset, is (1973) Directeur Adjoint, Chargé de Mission auprès du Directeur Général Centre National d'Études Spatiales, 129 rue de l'Université, Paris, France.—Ed.

1. Robert Esnault-Pelterie, *Vie et travaux scientifiques* (Orleans, France: Henri Tessier, 1931), pp. 3–5 (hereafter cited as REP, *Vie et travaux*).—Ed.

2. REP, *Vie et travaux*, pp. 5–6.—Ed.

3. French Patent 318,667, 13 February 1902, Relais sensible de telegraphie sans fil.—Ed.

4. The result of these gliding and automobile-towed glider tests, conducted near Calais, and the flight performance measurements of components mounted above an automobile, during high speed runs between Vierson and Salbris (South of Orleans) were reported in: REP, "Expériences d'aviation, exécutees en 1904, en verification de celles des frères Wright," *L'Aérophile*, vol. 13, June 1905, pp. 132–138 (presented at a conference of the Aero Club of France on 5 January 1905); REP, "Communication, faite a la Société Française de Navigation Aérienne par M. Robert Esnault-Pelterie," *L'Aéronaute*, vol. 40, February 1907, pp. 31–40, and March 1907, pp. 61–72 (presented on 24 January 1907); REP, *Vie et travaux*, pp. 7–12, 47–59.—Ed.

5. "L'Aéroplane et le moteur extra-léger Esnault-Pelterie," *L'Aérophile*, vol. 15, April 1907, pp. 100–101 (editorial comments and a letter from REP, dated 22 March 1907 describing research); A. de Masfrand, "Premiers essais publics de l'aéroplane Esnault–Pelterie," *L'Aérophile*, vol. 15, October 1907, pp. 289–91; "M. Esnault-Pelterie's Experiments," *The Automotor Journal*, vol. 12, 26 October 1907, p. 1516; "The Esnault-Pelterie Flying Machine," *The Automotor Journal*, vol. 12, 2 November 1907, pp. 1533–34; 'Portraits d'aviateurs contemporains" and REP, "L'Aéroplane et le moteur extra-leger Robert Esnault-Pelterie," *L'Aérophile*, vol. 15, December 1907, cover and pp. 330–32; "Progress of Mechanical Flight, Individual Performance to Date," *Flight*, vol. 1, 2 January 1909, p. 12; REP, *Vie et travaux*, pp. 12–16.—Ed.

6. "The 'R.E.P.' Aerial Motor—A Striking Design," *The Automotor Journal*, vol. 12, 2 November 1907, pp. 1534–35, and "The 7-Cyl. 'R.E.P.' Airship Motor," 30 November 1907, p. 1719; REP, "Le Moteur R.E.P. sept cylindres," *La Revue de l'Aviation*, vol. 2, 15 November 1907, pp. 5–7; W. F. Bradley, "Advance in Aeronautical Motor Building," *The Automobile*, 13 August 1908, pp. 225–28; "Aeroplane Propellers; Table of Propellers at the Paris Salon," *Flight*, vol. 1, 9 January 1909, pp. 22–23; "The First Paris Aeronautical Salon; Engines for Airplanes," *Flight*, vol. 1, 16 January 1909, pp. 33–35, and 23 January 1909, p. 47; L. Lagrange, "L'Aéroplane REP et les moteurs REP," *L'Aérophile*, vol. 17, 15 January 1909, pp. 33–37, xi; H. Kromer, "Motor R. Esnault-Pelterie," *Deutsche Zeitschrift für Luftschiffahrt*, 30 June 1909, pp. 558–60; *Rapport officiel sur la première Exposition Internationale de Locomotion Aérienne* (Paris: Librairie Aéronautique, 1910), pp. 45–47, 48, 59–60; "Les Moteurs d'aviation; le nouveaux moteur REP (50–60 chx), "L'Aérophile*, vol. 18, 1 September 1910, pp. 401–02; "Les Moteurs à l'Exposition [illus.], *L'Aérophile*, vol. 18, 15 November 1910, p. 515; "The Vickers-R.E.P. Engines," *The Aeroplane*, vol. 1, 21 June 1911, pp. 50, 70; Paul Pouchet, "Le Nouveau Moteur 'REP'; types 50/60 et 40/50 chx à 5 cylindres," *L'Aérophile*, vol. 19, 15 April 1911, pp. 177–179; Alex Dumas, "Les Moteurs et les hélices," *L'Aérophile*, vol. 20, 1 January 1912, pp. 12–14.—Ed.

7. "L'Aviation aux ingénieurs civils; M. Robert Esnault-Pelterie lauréat de la Société des Ingénieurs Civils," *L'Aérophile*, vol. 16, 1 July 1908, p. 255; REP, *Vie et travaux*, pp. 12–14, pp. 61–86 (reprint of 8 November 1907 lecture). —Ed.

8. A. De Masfrand, "Premiers essais publics de l'aéroplane Esnault-Pelterie," *L'Aérophile*, vol. 15, October 1907, pp. 289–91; REP, "L'Aéroplane et le moteur extra-leger Robert Esnault-Pelterie," *L'Aérophile*, vol. 15, December 1907, pp. 330–32; REP, *Vie et Travaux*, pp. 12–17. Legal acknowledgment of Esnault-Pelterie's invention of the "manche à balai" (joy-stick) came, in France and other countries, only after many years of court litigation; see "Systems of Control," *Flight*, vol. 1, 2 January 1909, pp. 9–10; "The Esnault-Pelterie 'Joy-Stick' Bombshell," and "The R.E.P. Litigation in France," *Flight*, vol. 12, 12 August 1920, pp. 876, 878; "Un Grand Conflit industriel," and Charles Weismann, "Les Procès du manche à balai," *L'Aérophile*, vol. 28, 15 August 1920, pp. 251–52; "The R.E.P. Litigation," *Flight*, vol. 12, 19 August 1920, p. 915; REP, "Les Procès du manche à balai," *L'Aérophile*, vol. 28, 15 September 1920, p. 268; C. Weismann, "Les Questions du manche à balai," *L'Aérophile*, vol. 28, 15 October 1920, pp. 313–14; "The Joy Stick Litigation," *Flight*, vol. 12, 28 October 1920, p. 1136; "L'Affaire Esnault-Pelterie en Cour d'Appel," *L'Aérophile*, vol. 30, 15 November 1922, p. 339, and 15 December 1922, p. xix; and *L'Aérophile*, vol. 31, 15 January 1923, pp. 23–24; 15 February 1923, pp. xix-xx; 15 March 1923, pp. 89–90; 15 April 1923, pp. 116–17; 15 May 1923, pp. 112–13; 15 July 1923, pp. 220–22; "The 'Joy-Stick' Action," *Flight*, vol. 15, 24 May 1923, p. 280; "The 'Joy-Stick' Action," and "The French 'Manche à Balai' Action," *Flight*, vol. 15, 31 May 1923, pp. 288, 297; "The 'Joy-Stick' Claim," *Aeroplane*, vol. 24, 30 May 1923, p. 404; and "Joy-Stick," *Time*, vol. 18, 5 October 1931, pp. 30 and 32.—Ed.

9. Georges Blanchet, "Experiences de M. R. Esnault-Pelterie, le nouvel aéroplane R.E.P.–á 30 mètres de hauteur—les records du 'monoplan,'" *L'Aérophile*, vol. 16, 15 June 1908, p. 226; Fred T. Jane, *All the World's Air Ships* (London: Sampson Low, Marston & Co., Ltd., 1909) pp. 121–22, 347, 355; "R.E.P. (No. 2)," *Flight*, vol. 1, 9 January 1909, p. 19; L. Lagrance, "L'Aéroplane REP et les moteurs REP," *L'Aérophile*, vol. 17, 15 January 1909, pp. 33–37 and xi; Oiseau, "Impressions of the Paris Show," *Flight*, vol. 2, 22 October 1910, p. 862, and 29 October 1910, p. 880; Jane, *All the World's Airships* (London, 1910), pp. iii, iv, 129, 164, 424, 437, 441, 446, 457, 463; "The Last Day," and "Laurens Wins the Coupe Deperdussin," *Flight*, vol. 3, 7 January 1911, pp. 8, 17; "Pierre Marie Bournique, sur 'REP,' volé 530 kilomètres et établit les nouveaux records du monde a partir de 250 kilomèters," *L'Aérophile*, vol. 19, 15 January 1911, 28; "Latest Official World's Records," *Flight*, vol. 3, 21 January 1911, p. 57; Mervyn O'Gorman, "Problems Relating to Aircraft," *Flight*, vol. 3, 25 March 1911, p. 266; Paul Pouchet, "Les Aèroplanes REP et le moteur REP, 5 cylindres," *L'Aérophile*, vol. 19, 15 April 1911, p. 173–79; "The Latest R.E.P. Racing Monoplane, Le Poussin," *Flight*, vol 3, 13 May 1911, p. 425; "Gilbert's R.E.P., the only machine to go through [the European Circuit] with the same engine from start to finish," *The Aeroplane*, vol. 1, 13 July 1911, p. 127; "Aéroplanes REP," *L'Aérophile*, vol. 19, 1 November 1911, pp. 504–05; "The R.E.P. stand at the Paris Air Show, and the New 90 h.p. 7 cyl. R.E.P. motor," *Flight*, vol. 3, 30 December 1911, p. 1135–36; Jane, *All the World's Aircraft*, 1912, pp. 149, 178, 347, 363; "World's Flying Records," *Aero*

Club of America Bulletin, vol. 1, June 1912, p. 17; "The Latest R.E.P. Monoplane," *Flight,* vol. 4, 30 September 1912, p. 854; "The 80 hp R.E.P. hydromonoplane," *Flight,* vol. 4, 9 November 1912, p. 1028; Jane, *All the World's Aircraft,* 1913, pp. 77, 100, 11b, 7c, 1d, 25d; "R.E.P. Redivivus," *The Aeroplane,* vol. 4, 11 December 1913, p. 634; Jane, *All the World's Aircraft,* 1914, pp. 72, 92, 11b, 16d; "R.E.P.," *Flight,* vol. 6, 10 January 1914, p. 33; Jane, *All the World's Aircraft,* 1916, pp. 123 and 15b; "Le Concours de la sécurité," *l'Aérophile,* vol. 22, 1 July 1914, pp. 304–305; Owen Thetford, *British Naval Aircraft, 1912–58* (London: Putnam, 1958) p. 382 (R.E.P. Parasol). A list of the records established by REP airplanes is presented in Lucien Marchis, *Vingt cinq ans d'aéronautique française* (Paris: édité par la Chambre Syndicale des Industries Aéronautiques, 1934), vol. 1 (of 3), p. 194.—Ed.

10. "Bulletin officiel de l'Aéro-Club de France," *L'Aérophile,* vol. 17, 15 January 1909, p. 43; "Official Pilots," *Flight,* vol. 1, 16 January 1909, p. 39; "The Trials of a Pilot, Being Some Account of the Experiences of M. Esnault-Pelterie and Others in the Air," *Flight,* vol. 1, 30 January 1909, pp. 60–61; "The First Aviation Pilots to Whom the Aero Club of France Have Granted Certificates and Their Credentials," *Flight,* vol. 1, 6 March 1909, p. 131.—Ed.

11. "The R.E.P. Belt with Quick Detachment Device," *The Aeroplane,* vol. 1, 21 June 1911, p. 68; Henry Woodhouse "The R.E.P. Safety Belt," and "The R.E.P. Wings Supporting a Load of 6,250 Kilograms of Sand," (in "What is Being Done to Make Aviation Safe in Europe"), *Aero Club of America Bulletin,* vol. 1, August 1912, pp. 15–16. His aviation safety procedures and a list of his aviation patents appear in REP, *Vie et Travaux,* pp. 14–19, 98–100.—Ed.

12. REP, *Quelques reseignements pratiques sur l'aviation* (Paris: Librairie Aéronautique, 1912).—Ed.

13. "La Chambre Syndicale des Industries Aéronautiques," *L'Aérophile,* vol. 16, 1 March 1908, p. 84.—Ed.

14. "French Trade Societies Formally Amalgamated," *Flight,* vol. 2, 30 July 1910, p. 601.—Ed.

15. Philos, "1re Exposition Internationale de Locomotion Aérienne, organisée par l'Association des Industriels de la Locomotion Aérienne sous le patronage de l'Aéro-Club de France," *L'Aérophile,* vol. 17, 1 October 1909, pp. 433–34.—Ed.

16. Wernher von Braun and Frederick I. Ordway III, *Histoire Mondiale De'Astronautique* (Larousse, Paris-Match, 1968).—Ed.

17. "Esnault-Pelterie etait le plus écoute des quatre pionniers de l'astronautique, car il fut le seul a être célèbre de son vivant. Il a eu, comme Oberth, la joie de voir ses rêves entrer dans la voie des réalisations, puisqu'il est mort après le lancement des deux premiers 'Spoutnik,'" *Histoire Mondiale d'Astronautique,* p. 79.—Ed.

18. "From Crest to Crest, From City to City, From Continent to Continent," in *L'Aviation, ses Débuts—son develop-ment* (Paris, Nancy: Berger-Levrault & Cie, 1908), p. 161. REP's aviation achievements also are mentioned on pp. 132–34.—Ed.

19. Belgian patent 236,377, 10 June 1911, A Device for Studying the Upper Atmosphere.—Ed.

20. REP, *L'Astronautique* (Paris: A. Lahure, 1930), p. 20, footnote 3.—Ed.

21. REP, "Consideration sur les résultats de l'allégement indefini des moteurs [Considerations concerning the results of the indefinite lightening of motors] (Fontenay-aux-Roses: L. Bellenand, 1916). Presented to the Société Française de Physique on 15 November 1912 and originally published in *Journal de Physique,* ser. 5, vol. 3, March 1913, pp. 218–30. See Appendix for a complete translation of this work.

22. REP, "L'Exploration par fusées de la très haute atmosphère et la possibilité des voyages interplanétaires," [Rocket Exploration of the Very High Atmosphere and the Possibility of Interplanetary Travel] (Paris: Société Astronomique de France, 1928). Lecture given before the Society on 8 June 1927.—Ed.

23. Robert H. Goddard, "A Method of Reaching Extreme Altitudes," *Smithsonian Miscellaneous Collections,* vol. 72, no. 2, December 1919, Preface and pp. 5–11. REP and Goddard exchanged an interesting series of letters dating back to REP's first letter on 31 March 1920. The plans of both pioneers to meet each other were never fulfilled, see *The Papers of Robert H. Goddard,* edited by Esther C. Goddard and G. Edward Pendray (New York: McGraw-Hill Book Company, 1970), vol. 1, pp. 432, 436–37, 442, 445, 448–49, 450, and vol. 2, pp. 646–47, 651, 931, 938, 940, 947, 999.—Ed.

24. Goddard, "A Method of Reaching Extreme Altitudes," pp. 12–54.—Ed.

25. Op. cit., note 24, pp. 55–57, 67–68 (notes 19–21).—Ed.

26. Konstantin Eduardovich Tsiolkovskiy, "Issledovanie mirovykh prostranstv reaktivnymi priborami" [Investigation of Space by Means of Reaction Devices], *Nauchnoye obozreniye* [Science Review], no. 5, 1903.—Ed.

27. Op. cit., note 1.

28. Op. cit., note 20, p. 20.—Ed.

29. Op. cit., note 22.

30. REP, "De L'Aéronautique à l'astronautique," in: *Quinze ans d'aéronautique française, 1932–1947* (édité par l'Union Syndicale des Industries Aéronautiques, 1949), p. 17.—Ed.

31. Op. cit., note 30.

32. In current American usage, the term carburetion has been replaced by the term injection for the process of injecting, atomizing, and mixing the propellants of a liquid-fueled rocket engine.—Ed.

33. [The Rocket Into Interplanetary Space], Munich-Berlin: R. Oldenbourg, 1923.

34. [Accessibility of Celestial Bodies], Munich: R. Oldenbourg, 1924.

35. [Moving Forward into Outer Space], Munich: R. Oldenbourg, 1924.

36. REP, *Rapport a Monsieur le Général Ferrié,* (Paris, 20 May 1928, unpublished.

37. The appraisal given by the Germans was: "Esnault-Pelterie experimented with liquid oxygen and gasoline as propellants. He worked there (near Paris) with more or less success, until the War broke out. When the Germans later investigated his facilities, they came to the conclusion that it would have taken him several years to accomplish the first convincing result." Walter R. Dornberger, "European Rocketry After World War I," *Journal of the British Interplanetary Society,* vol. 13, no. 5 (September 1954), pp. 245–55, 262; and "European Rocketry After World War I," in *Reali-*

ties of Space Flight, edited by L. J. Carter (London: Putnam, 1957), p. 390.—Ed.

38. E. Fichot, "Le 'Prix REP-Hirsch' et les problems de l'astronautique," *Bulletin de la Société Astronomique de France*, vol. 42, February 1928, pp. 57–59; see editorial introduction to REP, "La Navigation intersiderale ou astronautique," *L'Aerophile*, vol. 36, 15 March 1928, pp. 67–70; and "Preisausschreiben für eine Arbeit uber Raumschiffahrt," *Der Flug*, vol. 10, no. 7 (April 1928), p. 130.—Ed.

39. Woodford A. Heflin, "Astronautics," *American Speech*, vol. 36, October 1961, pp. 169–74, and "Robert Esnault-Pelterie," in Shirley Thomas, *Men of Space* (Philadelphia, New York, London: Chilton Book Company, 1968), pp. 20–24, (conversation between the author and André-Louis Hirsch). —Ed.

40. A. Hamon, "Assemblée générale annuelle de la Société Astronomique de France" (5 June 1929); Gabrielle Camille Flammarion, "Les Progrès de la Société Astronomique de France," and "Prix et médailles decernes par la Société," *Bulletin de la Société Astronomique de France*, vol. 43, July 1929, pp. 301, 313, 314; and "Der REP-Hirsch-Preis Professor Herman Oberth zuerkannt," *Die Rakete*, vol. 3, 15 June 1929, p. 75.—Ed.

41. This epilogue appears on p. 576 of *Ways to Spaceflight*, by Hermann Oberth, NASA TT F-622, 1972, a translation into English of the book *Wege zur Raumschiffahrt* (Munich-Berlin: R. Oldenbourg, 1929).—Ed.

42. "The History of the REP-Hirsch Award," *Astronautics*, no. 34 (June 1936), pp. 6–7, 13; Ary J. Sternfeld, *"Initiation à la cosmonautique,"* French manuscript translated and published in Russian as *Vvedenie v kosmonavtiku* [Introduction to Cosmonautics], Leningrad and Moscow: ONTI Glavnaya redaktsiya aviatsionnoi literatury, 1937. See also Joseph Krieger, *Behind the Sputniks, A Survey of Soviet Space Science* (Washington, D.C.: Public Affairs Press, 1958), p. 351. —Ed.

43. See pp. 3–97 of *Interplanetary Flight and Communication*, vol. 3, (Theory of Space Flight), by Nikolai Alexeyevich Rynin, NASA TT F-647, 1971, a translation into English of the book *Mezhplanetnye soobshcheniya Tom 3, vypusk 8, Teoriya kosmicheskogo poleta* (Leningrad: Izdatel'stvo Academii Nauk SSSR, 1932). It contains translations of REP's "Consideration sur les résultats de l'allégement indefini des moteurs," 1913 (see note 21); "L'Exploration par fusée de la très haute atmosphère et la possibilite des voyages interplanétaires," 1928 (see note 22); and "Astronautik und Relativitatstheorie, 1928." This last paper by REP first appeared in *Die Rakete*, vol. 2, 15 August 1928, pp. 114–17; 15 September 1928, pp. 130–34; and 15 October 1928, pp. 146–48, as translated from the French by Johannes Winkler. Subsequently the paper was expanded and included as pp. 228–41 in REP, *L'Astronautique* (note 20).—Ed.

44. "Prix et medailles descernes par la Société," *Bulletin de la Société Astronomique de France*, vol. 53, July 1939, p. 296. —Ed.

45. Op. cit., note 20.

46. 27 May 1931 record flight (16,000 meters) of Professor Auguste Picchard and M. Kipfer is discussed in "Le Mois, les records," *L'Aérophile*, vol. 39, 15 June 1931, pp. 179–180, and 15 August 1931, pp. 244–47. On 18 August 1932, Professor

Piccard and M. Cosyns broke the previous record by reaching a height of 16,700 meters. "A Stratospherical Record, Balloon Ascent by Prof. Piccard, 10½ Miles Up," *Flight*, 26 August 1932, p. 798.—Ed.

47. Charles Dollfus, "L'Ascension stratospherique du professor Piccard et de Cosyns," *L'Aeronautique*, vol. 14, September 1932, p. 268.—Ed.

48. Op. cit., note 2.

49. REP, *L'Astronautique—Complement* (Paris: Société des Ingénieurs Civils de France, 1935). Lecture given to the Society on 25 May 1934.—Ed.

50. French patent 803,021, 29 June 1936, "de projectiles auto-propulseurs dont la charge propulsive est répartie en plusieurs étages de combustion superposés suivant l'axe longitudinal de la fusée" [self-projectiles with propellant charge divided into several combustion stages superimposed along longitudinal axis of the rocket].—Ed.

51. "Election à l'Académie des Sciences," *Bulletin de la Société Astronomique de France*, October 1936, p. 487.

52. American usage would define the term "jets" as injector orifices.

53. REP, "Réglage des orifices pour la première experience de refroidissement par oxygène liquide" [Adjustment of the orifices for the first experiment in cooling by liquid oxygen], Report no. 2125, Paris, September-October 1936; and "Essais de mise a feu avec refroidissement par oxygène liquide," [Firing tests for cooling by liquid oxygen], Report no. 2163, Paris, 15 October, 3 December, and 16 December 1936.—Ed.

54. REP, "Récapitulation des resultats obtenus au cours de l'anné 1937" [Review of the results obtained in 1937], Report no. 2333, Paris, 17 December 1937.—Ed.

55. A list of the French patents awarded him (to June 1929) appears in REP, *Vie et travaux*, pp. 93–100.—Ed.

56. REP, "Apparatus and Methods for Measurement of the Hertzian Hardness," *Engineer*, vol. 146, nos. 3788, 3789, and 3790, 17, 24, and 31 August 1928, pp. 180–81, 196–97, and 220–22. Paper read on 24 November 1927 before the British Section of Société des Ingénieurs Civils de France.—Ed.

57. "Moteur balistique" pp. 7–8 in Note 30 above.—Ed.

58. "Utilization de l'énergie des marées," REP, *Vie et Traveaur*, p. 38.—Ed.

59. REP, "Sur l'application de l'analyse dimensionnelle à l'étude de l'écoulement turbulent," *Comptes Rendus de l'Académie des Sciences*, vol. 196, 26 June 1933, p. 1968; "Etude de l'écoulement en régime turbulent à travers des orifices," *Chaleur et Industrie*, vol. 15, nos. 171, 172, and 173, July, August, and September, pp. 129–36, 189–98, and 235–42; and "Extension du principe de la loi-limite en analysis dimensionnelle," *Comptes Rendus*, vol. 203, 26 October 1936, p. 755.—Ed.

60. REP, *L'Analyse dimensionnelle*, Lausanne: F. Rouge, 1948. Additional publications of his concerning dimensional analysis include the following, all appearing in *Comptes Rendus de l'Académie des Sciences:* "Sur une confusion d'idées," vol. 225, 13 October 1947, pp. 606–09; "Sur une démonstration illusoire," vol. 225, 27 October 1947; "Variables de Vaschy et similitude mécanique," vol. 226, 14 June 1948, pp. 1935–38; "Action d'une variation du nombre des grandeurs choisies comme principales sur les variables de Vaschy," vol. 227 30 August 1948, pp. 493–96; "Solution d'un para-

doxe," vol. 227, 15 November 1948, pp. 994–97; "Sur les systèmes a quatre grandeurs principales," vol. 229, 14 November 1949, pp. 957–60; "Sur la distinction à faire entre systèmes de grandeurs principales et systemes d'unites," vol. 229, pp. 1041–44; "Il n'y a pas de systemes UES ni UEM, il y a des systèmes d''unités dimensionnellement amorphes dont les unités sont reliées par des coefficients indimensionnes, systèmes dont chacun peut-être fait à volonté électrostatique ou électromagnétique," vol. 229, 5 December 1949, pp. 337–41. Also, *Dimensional Analysis, Translated by the Author and Entirely Recast From the French With Numerous Additions* (Lausanne: F. Rouge, 1950).—Ed.

61. REP, *De la bombe atomique à l'astronautique* [From the atomic bomb to astronautics] (Paris: Ed. Aero-Club, 1947).—Ed.

REFERENCES

In addition to the sources mentioned in the footnotes, the following documents were helpful in preparation of this paper.

1. Alexandre Ananoff, *L'Astronautique* (Paris: Librairc Artheme Fayard, 1950).

2. Andre-Louis Hirsch, "Robert Esnault-Pelterie, génial inventeur, pionnier de l'aviation, créateur de l'astronautique [Robert Esnault-Pelterie, ingenious inventor, aviation pioneer, creator of astronautics], unpublished lecture to the Automobile Club de France, 28 March 1961.

3. J. J. Barré, *Historique des études françaises sur les fusées a oxygène liquide* [History of French Research in Liquid-Oxygen Rockets] (Paris: Imprimerie Nationale, 1961).

4. J. J. Barré, *Sur quelques particularites de la propulsion spatiale et de l'autopropulsion* [On Several Features of Space Propulsion and Autopropulsion] (Paris: Imprimerie Nationale 1961).

5. J. J. Barré, Speech in Paris on the occasion of Esnault-Pelterie Day, 18 November 1961 (unpublished).

6. J. J. Barré, Speech in Paris on the occasion of the inauguration of Ruc Esnault-Pelterie, 14 March 1966 (unpublished).

Appendix

Considerations Concerning the Results of the Indefinite Lightening of Engines

This report was presented by Robert Esnault-Pelterie on 15 November 1912 to the Société Française de Physique and published in an abbreviated version in the *Journal de Physique* (ser. 5, vol. 3, March 1913, pp. 218–30). The complete text, presented here, is the English translation distributed at the International Astronautics Congress at Amsterdam in 1958 as a memorial to REP and published in that year in *Rocketry and Space Exploration,* by Andrew G. Haley (New York: D. Van Nostrand Company, Inc., pp. 293–301).

The ideas which will be developed here in this paper have been suggested to the author by the results that have already been achieved by light engines. He has been progressively led to ask himself what could possibly result from a further decrease in weight. For instance, if the weight per horse-power could be decreased almost entirely, what possibilities would be given to man? Would this progress only be limited to greater refinements in flying or would it open new horizons? And what would be these horizons?

Innumerable authors have thought of man travelling from planet to planet as a subject for fiction. Everyone realizing without too much thought and effort the impossibility of such a dream, it therefore seems that no one has ever thought to seek the physical requirements necessary for the realization of this dream and what would be the order of magnitude of the means one had to introduce.

This is the only aim of the present study which is, it must be stressed, only a series of thoughts based on mathematical derivations.

I

The first difficulty that strikes our mind is the fact that between planets there is no atmosphere, and therefore even an airplane could not find the slightest support for flight.

Physiological difficulties will be examined later on. Let us just concentrate on our knowledge of Mechanics. If this knowledge will lead us to a realization of an engine, which would need no support for flight, it would be able to propel a body. As strange as it may seem to someone that hasn't thought about it, our knowledge gives us the answer. This engine has existed for quite a time: it is the Rocket. (The gun imagined by Jules Verne would crush the travellers as they departed and cannot qualify as an engine capable of propelling a vehicle.)

It is often said that a rocket is propelled by a jet stream "through the air." The first part of this expression is correct, but not the second. A rocket would move just as well, if not better, in vacuum than in air.

Let us take a more striking example. Let us assume that a machine gun is fixed on a car capable of sliding without friction on tracks parallel to the gun. At every shot, the machine gun will move backwards according to a well established law in Mechanics.

The respective momenta gained by the car plus machine gun and by the projectile are equal in magnitude and opposite in sign. Air resistance only enters into the phenomenon which decreases the resulting velocities.

In the rocket, the machine gun projectile is replaced by the combustion gases which are emitted continuously.

Let M_0 be the total initial mass of the rocket, M its mass at time t and dm the element of mass of fluid which flows during the element of time dt considered.

Let us first assume that the fluid emission is done with a constant velocity v with respect to the body and a constant decrease in mass per unit time μ. Let V be the body's velocity, F the propelling force and its acceleration at time t.

The calculation shows that the phenomenon is described by the equations

$$MdV = vdm = \mu vdt \qquad (1)$$

We will notice that if the whole body would be completely of consumable explosive (purely theoritically speaking, which has its importance) it would completely be used up after a time

$$T = \frac{M_0}{\mu} \qquad (2)$$

The introduction of this time limit in the formula defining V as a function of t yields the equation

$$(T - t)dV = vdt$$

thus

$$V = v \log \frac{T - t}{T} \qquad (3)$$

which gives for $t = T$

$$V = -\infty \text{ (assuming } v > 0)$$

This is no surprise for us, since the propulsion has remained constant as long as the mass was decreasing, due to the emission of the propelling gas until it vanished completely. The acceleration should therefore have increased and approached infinity.

The equation relating the displacement x as a function of t is

$$x = -v \left\{ T \left[\left(\frac{T - t}{T} \right) \log \frac{T - t}{T} \right] + t \right\} \qquad (4)$$

and the corresponding distance travelled after complete consumption would be

$$X_T = -vT$$

Aside from all external considerations, we have just seen that propulsion in vacuum is not an impossibility. However, it is not sufficient to move the body, it must be guided.

In the present case, there are no difficulties *in theory*. To alter the vehicle's direction, one need only incline the propulsor in such a way that the direction of the force it develops would be at an angle with the trajectory. If the displacement of the propulsor was not sufficient to obtain rotation in all directions, one or two smaller auxiliary propulsors would be enough to obtain complete maneuverability.

II

To remove a heavy body from the attraction of a planet, one has to spend energy.

Let us consider a mass M at a distance x from the center of a planet whose radius is R. Let γ be the acceleration of gravity at the surface of this planet. To move the body away a distance dx, it will be necessary to do an element of work

$$dZ = M\gamma \frac{R^2}{x^2} dx$$

which gives

$$Z = M\gamma R \left(1 - \frac{R}{x}\right)$$

We can readily see that to move a given mass to infinity the necessary work to be done would be finite and given by

$$Z = M\gamma R$$

Or if we let P be the weight of the body at the surface of the planet, then

$$Z = PR$$

We also see that if we consider the weight of the body as the result of the principle of universal attraction applied to body and planet, we can write after letting U denote the planet's mass

$$P = k \frac{MU}{R^2}$$

This gives for expressing the work necessary for removal of the body to infinity

$$Z = k \frac{MU}{R}$$

Therefore, if we give initially to a body on the surface of a planet a sufficient velocity to remove from the planet, this body would increase its distance indefinitely.

For the earth, the minimum velocity would be 11,280 m/s, i.e., a projectile launched from the earth with a velocity larger than 11,280 m/s (not considering air resistance) would never fall back.

This critical velocity is exactly the same as that which a body would acquire falling toward the earth from infinity and having no initial velocity with respect to the planet.

The motion of such a body would be given by the equation

$$V^2 = 2g \frac{R^2}{x}$$

We see that for $X = R$

1°)
$$V_R = -\sqrt{2gR}$$

2°)
$$\tfrac{1}{2}mV^2 = PR$$

and this velocity limit V_R for the earth is also 11,280 m/s.

It was said before, that to remove to infinity a body from a planet, P being the weight at the surface and R the radius of the planet, the work to be done will be

$$Z = PR$$

For a body weighing 1 kg on the earth, this work would be

$$Z = 6,371,103 \text{ kgm equivalent to } 14,940 \text{ cal}$$

Let us recall that 1 kg of hydrogen-oxygen mixture with appropriate fractions contains 3860 cal for 1 kg; 1 kg of a powder containing gun-cotton and potassium chlorate is equivalent to 1420 cal per kg. We can see that the hydrogen-oxygen mixture contains slightly more than a fourth of what would be necessary to escape from the earth. But 1 kg of radium, liberating during its entire life·2.9×10^9 cal, would have 194,000 times more energy than needed. We will not talk here about the efficiency of a jet engine.

If we consider a body which moves away from a planet according to any accelerated motion, we can see that at the time when its velocity will be larger than the one it would have at the same point moving in the opposite direction, falling from infinity without any initial velocity, it would be useless to give it more energy to make it go farther. Its kinetic energy would be sufficient for it to move indefinitely.

The motion of a body subject to a constant force F larger than its weight, directed vertically upwards and away from the planet would be represented by the equation

$$v = \sqrt{2Ax + \frac{2gR^2}{x} - 2R(A + g)}$$

The body would acquire a sufficient velocity to permit the stoppage of propulsion at a distance from the center of the planet equal to

$$x = R\left(1 + \frac{g}{A}\right) \quad \text{where } A = \frac{F}{M}$$

We can see that if a body could move away from the earth with an upward propelling force exactly equal in magnitude to its weight, i.e., if $A = g$, it would reach that critical speed at a distance from the center of the earth equal to twice the earth's radius at an altitude equal to the earth's radius.

This remark calls our attention to the fact that a body could perfectly well move away from a planet using a propelling force smaller than its weight. If the planet has an atmosphere, the body could in fact function first as an airplane, rising gradually and increasing its velocity as this atmosphere became rarer and rarer, until it reached the critical velocity corresponding to the given altitude.

III

Let us consider what would be the required energies if we wanted, by this method, to transport a body from the earth to the moon and back.

Let us consider that the operation will take place in three phases:

1°) The body is accelerated until it reaches the critical velocity of liberation
2°) The motor is stopped, and the body keeps moving due to its acquired velocity
3°) At the desired point, the body is turned upside-down and the motor that has been re-started diminishes the velocity until it becomes zero at the surface of the moon.

First Phase

We apply to the body a force

$$F = \tfrac{11}{10}P, \quad \text{therefore } A = \tfrac{11}{10}g$$

which seems acceptable assuming that the vehicle would carry live beings.

The critical distance is then

$$x = \tfrac{21}{11} \cdot R$$

corresponding to an altitude of 5,780,000 m above the surface.

The velocity at that instant would be

$$V = 8180 \text{ m/sec}$$

The time necessary to reach that point would be approximately

$$t = 24 \text{ min } 9 \text{ sec}$$

Second Phase

The body continues on its path due to its inertia; it is constantly attracted by the opposite gravitational forces of the earth and its satellite.

Let P be the weight of the body at the earth's surface, P_t its weight at the moon's surface and ρ the radius of the moon, $D = x + y$ the distance between the two planets; the calculation gives

$$v = \sqrt{2\left(g\,\frac{R^2}{x} + 0.165 \cdot g\,\frac{\rho^2}{y} + 0.82 \times 10^6\right)}$$

At the point where the respective gravitational forces of the earth and moon cancel each other, the velocity would be

$$v = 2030 \text{ m/sec}$$

It is the lowest velocity.

At the moon's surface it would become approximately

$$v = 3060 \text{ m/sec}$$

The velocity of the body falling freely from infinity to the moon would be

$$v_\infty = 2370 \text{ m/sec}$$

The time used to go through the second phase can be calculated approximately by neglecting the moon's action which is entirely negligible during the total journey.

It would be the same time as that taken by the body during a free fall from the moon to the point where we had stopped the engine:

$$t = 48 \text{ hr } 30 \text{ min}$$

Third Phase

One must now decrease the speed by turning the body upside-down as said before, and by re-starting the motor.

What will be the law of this slowing down?

We would establish it in the same manner as we did for the earth; but the moon's attraction being much smaller, and as we do not at this stage seek a great precision, we will deduct from the acceleration due to the propulsor, half the acceleration due to the moon, and we will assume the motion uniformly slowed down under the action of this fictitious acceleration. We find that the body has to be turned upside-down at a distance from the moon's surface equal to

$$d = 250{,}000 \text{ m approximately}$$

This point is so close to the moon, and the present calculations not being rigorous, the time necessary to reach the surface could be mistaken for the time necessary to reach the moon itself.

The time of the slowing down will be

$$t = 226 \text{ sec} = 3 \text{ min } 46 \text{ sec}$$

The total time for the whole process is approximately then:

First phase	0 hr 24 min 9 sec
Second phase	48 hr 30 min
Third phase	0 hr 3 min 46 sec

48 hr 58 min approximately

The return trip could be done by reversing the process and in the same time.

It must be pointed out that, by this means, the propulsor is used only 28 min going and the same time coming back unless the earth's atmosphere is used for the slowing down process, in which case the 28 min used for the departure, and the time necessary to orient the body properly, would suffice.

We will now consider the power actually needed to realize these minimum conditions and the resulting efficiency output of the motor with respect to the theoretical work given.

If we consider a 1000 kg vehicle out of which 300 kg are consumable; and if the engine has to work 27 min + 3.5 min and to have a sufficient flow margin 35 min

= 2100 sec, the rate will have to be

$$\mu = \frac{300}{2100} = 0.143 \text{ kg/sec}$$

and the fluid's expulsion velocity

$$v = 65,300 \text{ m/sec}$$

Therefore, by providing per kilogram of fuel

$$T = 217.2 \times 10^6 \text{ kgm} \quad \text{or} \quad 512 \times 10^3 \text{ cal}$$

one sees that the mixture $H^2 + O$ would contain 133 times too little energy and the most powerful explosives 360 times too little.

On the other hand, 1 kg of radium would contain 5.670 times too much.

The power of the motor necessary for our 1000 kg vehicle would be

$$\frac{300 \times 217.2 \times 10^6}{2100 \times 75} = 414,000 \text{ HP}$$

We could also see that the efficiency of the jet engine is in our particular case quite bad. Since to remove a mass of 1 kg from the earth to ∞, we have to apply to it 6,371,103 kgm and we have spent 217.2×10^6, so that the efficiency is

$$\rho = 0.0293$$

Moreover, to give a gas an ejection speed of 65,300 m/sec in vacuum, we would have to reach the fantastic temperature of 2.525×10^6 degrees.

In air, it would be even worse, since added to this temperature one would need a pressure of about the same magnitude.

IV

As an indication, we could assume the body moving to infinity, and also that we have kept the motor working even after the critical speed is reached, so that it eventually acquires and conserves a speed near to 10 km/sec. The times necessary to reach the closest planets as they attain their conjunction with the Earth are respectively:

> For Venus   47 days 20 hr
>
> For Mars   90 days 15 hr

These figures are merely mentioned for curiosity and we must also notice that the amount of work to cover this distance would not be much larger than the minimum necessary to remove the body from the earth. In fact, once the vehicle has reached a sufficient distance, it would keep on going due to its inertia without being slowed down by the earth's attraction which has become quite weak.

In other words, the difficulty would be to overcome the earth's attraction; but if some day this difficulty would be overcome, it would hardly be more difficult to reach a very distant planet than a close one. Subject, of course, to a cramped and hermetically closed vehicle being inhabitable for a sufficient amount of time and to another difficulty that we will consider later on.

V

In all the preceding sections we have only considered the theoretical possibility for a body with special properties to travel between the earth and the moon. This is a problem of pure mechanics which does not really answer the question of whether man will be or will never be able to leave his world to explore others.

The complete study of the question will lead to the study of the physiological conditions that must be fulfilled so that life will be possible under such conditions.

The progress made in submarines can already make us consider as quite feasible in the future the regeneration of an atmosphere which has been confined for some hundred hours.

The question of temperature deserves being particularly considered. It is often said that the interplanetary spaces have an almost absolute zero temperature. The author believes it is false.

The concept of temperature is only related to material bodies and therefore a vacuum cannot have any.

If the amount of heat absorbed per unit time by our vehicle is less than the quantity of heat that it radiates, its temperature will decrease. If the amount of heat received and absorbed is greater than the amount that is radiated, the temperature will increase.

It would therefore be possible to construct a vehicle in such a way that one half of its surface would be of a polished metal and the inside insulated. The other half of the surface, for example, would be covered of copper oxide to give a black surface.

If the polished face would face the sun, the temperature would decrease. In the opposite position, the temperature would increase.

All the difficulties that we have just considered do not seem to be theoretically impossible. But a new difficulty will arise which although a mechanical solution offers itself, will nevertheless complicate further the problem.

In fact, in the calculations related to the vehicle's journey from the earth to the moon, we have considered that we were applying an acceleration

$$A = \tfrac{11}{10}g$$

and this up to a distance of 5780 km from the earth's surface. During all this phase of the voyage, the travellers would therefore have the impression of weighing $11\!/\!_{10}$ of their weight.

One may hope that as unpleasant as this sensation may be it will not cause any disturbance to a human organism. But what is most alarming is what will happen at the instant of sudden stoppage of propulsion. At this moment, the traveller would suddenly cease to have any weight and he would have the sensation that both he and his vehicle were falling in a void.

If the human organism cannot go through such vicissitudes, we would have to replace the absence of a gravitational field by creating constant artificial acceleration produced by the motor. If this acceleration is made equal to gravity, the traveller will constantly feel he is weighing his normal weight, without any consideration of the fact that he may or may not be in the gravitational field of a planet.

It is obvious that this kind of a process would introduce a very important difficulty with regard to the amount of energy which would become necessary, and would bring us far away from the conditions of realization which were studied previously and which were already quite extreme.

If we use the formula representing the law of motion of a body acted on by a constant force due to the earth and if we assume that until we have reached the maximum velocity between earth and moon, the acceleration used is equal to $1\frac{1}{10}\,g$, then the other maneuvres will be done with an acceleration equal to gravity. The moon's influence can be neglected, it being so small. It is found that the vehicle has to be reversed at a distance from the center of the earth equal to 29.5 times the earth's radius.

The speed at this instant of time would be 61,700 m/sec, then the reversed vehicle would be slowed down by a force equal to its weight on the earth.

The time used to reach the moon would be

$$t = 3 \text{ hr } 5 \text{ min}$$

But in this new case, the work to be furnished, using the assumption of a 1000 kg vehicle of which 300 kg are consumable, would reach 67.2×10^6 cal/kg of fuel, i.e., 131 times more than in the first case.

Dynamite would be 47,300 times too weak, but radium would still be 433 times too powerful.

As to the necessary power, it would be

$$\frac{857 \times 10^{10}}{24,000 \times 75} = 4.76 \times 10^6 \text{ HP}$$

If we now assume that this method of constant propulsion is used for voyages to the closest planets and investigate what the times and velocities would be, we find for the maximum velocity:

For Venus   643 km/sec

For Mars   883 km/sec

and the corresponding times:

For Venus   35 hr   4 min

For Mars   49 hr 20 min

VI

The maximum velocities we have just considered are evidently fantastic. However, there exists at least one celestial body which reaches such velocities: Halley's comet.

Only the forces and energies which seem to be contained by molecules could produce concentrations of power and work similar to those we just considered.

If we suppose for a moment that we have available 400 kg of radium in our 1000 kg vehicle and that we knew how to extract from it the energy within a suitable time, we should see that these 400 kg of radium would be more than enough to reach Venus and come back (with a constant acceleration), so that such a formidable reservoir would be just enough for man to visit his closest planets.

3

Early Italian Rocket and Propellant Research

LUIGI CROCCO, *Italy*

Introduction

The person invited to present to this symposium a review of our early work in the field of rockets, was my father, General G. Arturo Crocco, a well known personality in the aeronautical world because of his extraordinary contributions to the development of aviation, starting in 1904, and also a pioneer in the field of rocketry. In view of his very advanced age [1] he could not undertake the task, which was then delegated to the son, his closest collaborator during those pioneering efforts.

Considered retrospectively and objectively, this research on solid and liquid propellant rockets (and associated fields) produced rather interesting results, especially considering that when it started in 1927 very little scientific effort had been devoted anywhere in the world to the problem, which had been tackled mostly empirically by more imaginative than scientifically grounded inventors (there were, of course, notable exceptions). Nevertheless, and unfortunately, none of this work was allowed to appear in the press at the time for security reasons. Even more strangely no internal classified reports were ever submitted to the sponsors. The relations with them were limited to verbal expositions of the results. Actually, the very idea of sponsored research at that time was completely extraneous to the military organizations, and there were no rules whatsoever to regulate our exceptional relations with the sponsoring agencies. Hence the records of this research are entirely of a private nature, such as the record books of my father, or my own notes, and in particular an internal report I wrote in 1935, summarizing the research up to that moment. From that report I extracted a few items for a very short exposition which I published in 1950.[2] It may be, then, that this opportunity will help to fill an inexcusable gap in the literature on pioneering work in rocketry.

It all started as follows. My father has always been one of those scientists for whom the practical application of his scientific results counts as much as the scientific effort itself. He intensively applied this double capacity for research and invention in the field of aeronautics for many years, including those of the first world war, as an officer of the Genio Militare Italiano. At the end of World War I, convinced, as were many others, that the time for wars was over, and after resigning from the armed forces, he started an intense civilian activity in connection with industry, which meant, at the time, in non-aeronautical fields. However, his heart always kept him thinking and working, as a hobby, on advanced aeronautical and propulsion concepts, and indeed a number of his publications of the post World War I period show his intense interest in rocketry and supersonic flight.[3]

In 1927 he gave a private lecture to the members of the General Staff, headed then by General Badoglio, on the military possibilities of rockets, theoretically with unlimited terminal velocities, as compared to the fundamentally limited muzzle velocities of artillery. Badoglio, quite impressed, gave him from his secret funds 100,000 lire (5,000 dollars) for research and development in the field of solid propellant rockets.

Having, as a civilian, no laboratory wherein to conduct the research, my father made an agreement with one of the foremost Italian explosive manufacturers, Bombrini-Parodi-Delfino (BPD), whereby the experiments would be carried out in their SEGNI facilities, free of charge, with the collaboration of their Technical Director, Dr. Marenco. My father had to supply the apparatus and also the propellant, unless available at BPD. Shortly there-after, my father was called to a Chair of Aero-nautics at the newly constituted School of Aero-nautical Engineering of the University of Rome.

What Propellant and How Utilized?

The choice of the propellant represented a very important initial step. Of course, an impressive amount of very scientific data was already known to the artillery people; it was, however, limited to ranges of pressure suitable for guns but not for rockets. Very little, if anything, was known, indeed, about the behavior of conventional gun propellants at pressures below 100 atmospheres.

It might have been for this reason, or out of a lack of sufficient background, that so many rocket pioneers derived their concepts from the very empirical formulas of pyrotechnicians rather than from the science of artillery. A notable exception to the rule was provided by an Italian pioneer who proposed the use of dynamite for rockets. Maybe he

was the precursor of project Orion! I would like to add here that, in reality, the intuition of the rocket pioneers may not have been so bad because it is clear today that the greatest present and future achievements of solid propellant boosters follow a line which, conceptually, is more directly derived from pyrotechnics than from gunnery. As a scientist, however, my father was definitely more attracted by the clear background of artillery powders than by the obscure concoctions of fireworks, and his natural choice went immediately to the double-base powders.

The next step was to decide how to utilize these powders so as to obtain the relatively long deflagration times required by rockets, as compared to the extremely short times characteristic of guns. It was immediately clear that the key was to use the largest possible "grain" size, particularly of the "constant burning-area" type. However, the great advantages that might derive from the possibility of "restricted-burning" grains did not escape my father's searching mind, and he decided to work in both directions.

FIGURE 1.—First solid propellant test chamber.

First Tests on Solid Propellants

The first experimental series was conducted in 1927 and 1928 at BPD by my father, with the collaboration of Dr. Marenco. Then 18 and an engineering student in my first years at the university, I was the second collaborator, free of charge. The first chamber designed to test the above concepts is shown in Figures 1 and 2. The propellant in C was ignited by an ignition charge set off via a percussion cap by a mechanical device p-m. The combustion products were exhausted at the opposite end through a nozzle F. The chamber was intended to contain at most 0.1 kg of propellant. With a total volume of 600 cc the maximum combustion pressure was 2000 atm and the thick walls were calculated for 4000 atm at the elastic limit. As an additional safety measure the nozzle end was designed to burst open at 1000 atm. All these safety precautions were, of course, necessary because the tests involved a great amount of uncertainty and were to be conducted on an open test-stand, under our very eyes. Indeed, more than once during the preliminary testing the protective action of the safety features of the nozzle end were called upon. The chamber was free to move axially on rollers and the thrust was converted into oil pressure by a piston P_3. Both chamber pressure and thrust were recorded on a rotating drum by means of a double channel mechanical manograph of the kind used in gas engines.

However, the preliminary tests were carried out without the manograph. The only instrument was a "crusher" (Cr, Figure 2) intended to provide the maximum pressure. Numerous attempts were made to find a reliable binder between the double-base cylindrical charge and the brass case containing the charge, so as to inhibit burning on all but the frontal surface. These attempts failed to attain the necessary reliability, and once in a while resulted in strong overpressures, reaching once the burst limit of the nozzle end, because of the failure of the binder. As a result, my father decided that the inhibition of the burning surface was too unreliable and he decided to concentrate on charges with unrestricted burning.

The propellant chosen for these initial tests was cordite, readily available in appropriate sizes at the Naval Arsenal. The corresponding composition of it is shown below:

Nitroglycerin	25
Nitrocellulose	62
Vaseline	5
Barium Nitrate	8
Total	100

Tubular charges of approximately 21 mm outside diameter and 7 mm inside diameter were used. The charges C were free to move in the brass case B (Figure 3) but held within it by a charge-holder g. The ignition charge c was a mixture of 2 g of ballistite and 1 g of black powder. In order to help the propagation of ignition, because the ignition charge was located downstream of the main propellant, three thin strips of ballistite were inserted into the propellant hole. After the initial test, further to improve the regularity of ignition, which still was not entirely satisfactory, the nozzle was provided with a burst diaphragm. The diaphragm, visible in the details of Figure 2, kept the chamber closed until a preassigned burst pressure was reached. The

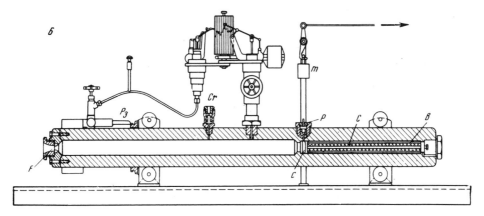

FIGURE 2.—Schematic sketch of first solid propellant test chamber.

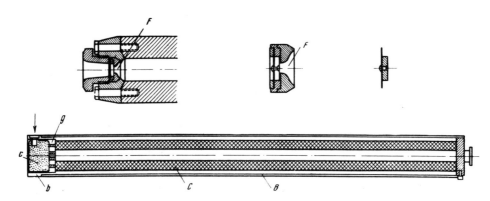

FIGURE 3.—Propellant charge container.

nozzles used in these tests had throat diameters of either 7 or 8 mm.

Samples of three types of pressure records observed are shown in Figure 4: some were quite "normal" (4a); others were rather irregular (4b); and some definitely "abnormal" (4c). The cause of the abnormalities was attributed to poor effectiveness of the charge holder, and indeed a better design of this essential detail resulted in complete suppression of such anomalous tests. However, from the numerous tests it was clearly evident that the equilibrium pressure was not very well defined and could vary substantially from test to test, much more than the small amount shown by Figure 4a, as a result of irregularities in the burst pressure, the nozzle and throat area, and the grain dimensions.

Irregularities in the apparent duration of burning even at equal pressures, such as shown in Figure 4a, were caused by irregularities of the drum revolving speed. This defect was inherent in the instrument and actually prevented accurate determination from individual tests of the burning rate and of the specific impulse. The value of this last quantity oscillated between 150 and 170 seconds.

Based on these results the small rocket stabilized by tail fins (Figure 5) was designed and launched. The corresponding charge was tested in a chamber, as shown in Figure 5, where only the pressure could be recorded. Larger test rockets, also with aerodynamic stabilization, are shown in Figure 6. The corresponding charge was divided into three tubular grains of 300 g total weight and was tested

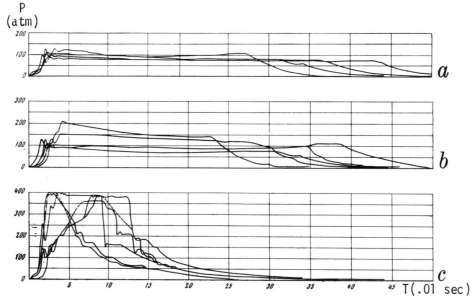

FIGURE 4.—Pressure records (in atm vs. time in sec): a, Normal tests; b, irregular tests; c, abnormal tests.

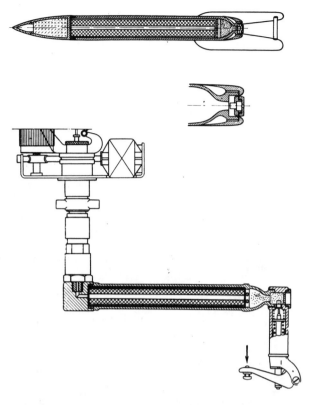

FIGURE 5.—Small fin-stabilized rocket, which used a single tubular grain, and test chamber for it (bottom).

in the chamber shown in Figure 7, where again only the pressure was measured. Figure 8 shows, superimposed, three pressure records from this apparatus, all corresponding to the same burst pressure of 100 atm (nominal). The poor reproducibility of the pressure level is evident, and as a result the rocket wall had to be designed rather thick. However, it was still sufficiently thin to become overheated. In the first rockets launched, the wall reached red heat at the end of the combustion time. To avoid overheating a thin insulating layer of asbestos was inserted between the chamber wall and the propellant.

These rockets were launched with good results and reached velocities of about 1000 fps, which were in agreement with the estimated velocity. The main inconvenience observed in the launching of both types of rockets was the lack of accuracy of their trajectory. It was attributed to the erratic transverse displacement of the center of mass resulting from the fact that there was nothing to prevent the lateral motion of the three tubular charges when their diameter decreased. To restrict

this motion, stabilization by spinning the rocket about its axis was attempted by impressing a fast rotational speed to the rocket holder prior to ignition. This launcher is shown in Figure 9. The whole rocket holder was set in rotation by an electric motor. Moreover, the three tilted exhaust nozzles provided a tangential thrust component after launching. The ignition burst diaphragms were replaced by shear pins (r) which firmly held the exhaust nozzle terminal sections pressed against a terminal plate until a preassigned pressure was reached. In another version of the spinning rocket the initial rotation was obtained through a fast burning charge located in an annual chamber around the single exhaust nozzle. This charge was ignited just prior to the main charge and exhausted through small tangential nozzles. The spinning rockets did not provide any more precise trajectories than the fin stabilized rockets.

Further Research on Solid Propellants

Late in 1928 my father was called from the reserve back to active duty as a general and asked to become Direttore Generale delle Costruzione Aeronautice in the Ministry of Aeronautics, while still continuing his teaching activity as a professor of the School of Aeronautical Engineering. This event had two important effects on our rocket research program. First, the facilities of the Ministry of Aeronautics became available for the continuation of our research; and, second, my father became immediately deeply involved in pressing problems of broader and more immediate interest. The first was a very welcome improvement of the situation, especially in view of the fact that the 100,000 lire of the General Staff were almost exhausted. The second was, on the contrary, a blow to the future dynamic development of the applications, if not to the fundamental aspects of the research. Indeed I was now, practically alone, in charge of our research effort. My father only devoted a little time to it in the evenings, when we discussed our problems at home. Because my mind has always been more attracted by questions solved by basic research, these naturally gained prevalence with respect to questions regarding applied research. I should add that, of course, my studies prevented me from devoting my full attention to the research project. The experiments took place in Rome in an

FIGURE 6.—Large fin-stabilized rockets, which used three tubular propellant grains.

isolated suite of two rooms which was assigned to these tests at the Stabilimento di Costruzione Aeronautiche (SCA), then on Viale Giulio Cesare. There, assisted by Signor Laghi, an excellent technician of the old school, I first carried out a series of tests in the chamber shown in Figure 1, used as a constant volume chamber by closing the nozzle.

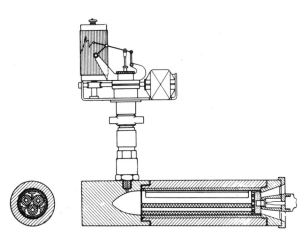

FIGURE 7.—Test chamber for larger rockets.

I compared the performance of tubular charges of the cordite used to that time, with a new double-base powder used by the Navy, the so-called C-powder, the composition of which is as follows:

Nitroglycerin	23.5
Nitrocellulose	70.5
Vaseline	5.0
Sodium Bicarbonate	1.0
Total	100.0

The first advantage I expected from the change in propellant was related to the higher regularity of the grain dimensions, a consequence of the different manufacturing process. The manufacture of cordite requires the evaporation of a solvent which must be added to reach the necessary plasticity. During the drying process the grain shrinks, with resulting roughness of the surface and irregularity of the dimensions. In the case of the C-powder the necessary plasticity is attained by performing the operations at 100°C without solvent; the surface of the finished product remains quite smooth and the dimensions quite regular. The second advantage I

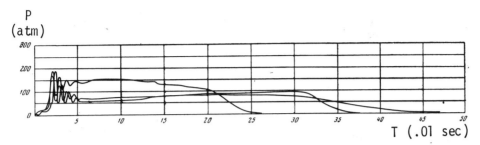

FIGURE 8.—Pressure records (in atm vs. time in sec) of larger rockets, using cordite as propellant.

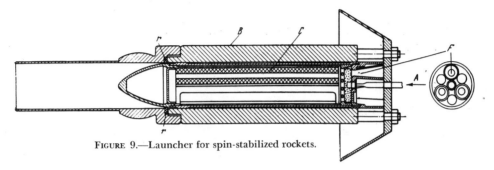

FIGURE 9.—Launcher for spin-stabilized rockets.

hoped from the change was due to the different composition, which led me to expect a smaller sensitivity of burning rate to pressure. I had reached the conclusion that the erratic behavior of the equilibrium pressure was due both to the geometric irregularity of the cordite and to its high pressure sensitivity. This conclusion, subsequently confirmed by the experiments, was based on simple calculations showing that deviations within ± 5 percent of the dimensions of the tubular charges (that is of the order ± 0.5 mm, on the radius, a very realistic deviation for cordite) would result in a range of equilibrium pressures from 30 to 186 atm for a nominal pressure of 100 atm if the burning rate varied with the 0.875 power of the pressure, but only in the range from 82 to 119 atm for an exponent of 0.625.

The results of the constant-volume tests are summarized in Figures 10 and 12. Figure 10 gives the pressure history obtained with different amounts of the two propellants. It was immediately evident from the smaller curvature of the C-powder (Polvere C) records that the pressure sensitivity is decreased. Figure 12, however, shows that where the terminal pressures are plotted against the charge weight, the "effectiveness" of the two powders is very nearly the same. For both powders the pressure sensitivity decrease with decreasing pressure since the pressure/

density ratio appears to follow very closely a $p^{0.25}$ power law within the pressure range of these tests.

Tests conducted next in the chamber shown in Figure 1, with the C-powder and an exhaust orifice of 7 mm, confirmed with their high regularity the superiority of this type of propellant as compared to cordite. For example, Figure 11a shows two representative pressure curves. Figure 11b shows a record obtained in the small test chamber shown in Figure 5. This chamber, of all those employed, allowed the highest charge density of 0.71 kg/dm³. In comparison, the chamber in Figure 1 allowed a loading density of 0.17 kg/dm³ and the chamber shown in Figure 14, a charge density of 0.54 kg/dm³.

The excellent behavior of these tests encouraged construction of the new test chamber (Figure 13) for 300 g of nominal charge. For safety reasons an expansion chamber S was attached to the test chamber to provide additional volume for the gases in case the pressure would rise beyond 500 atm and break the diaphragm R. But this precaution was proved superfluous by the great regularity of the tests. The chamber B was mounted as a pendulum, as indicated in Figure 14, to allow measurement of the thrust.

The values of the burning rates obtained from the tests on the two propellants are summarized in

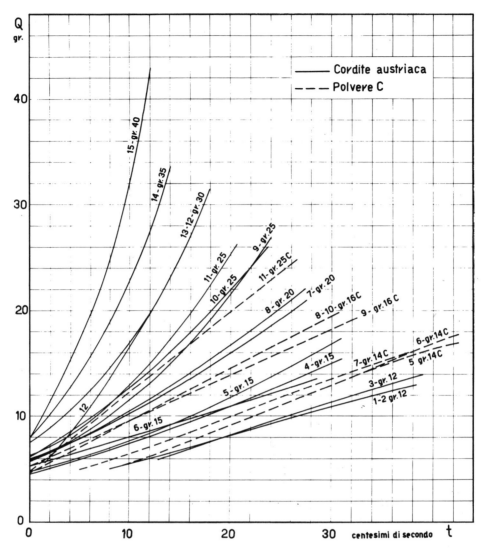

FIGURE 10.—Comparative pressure records in closed chamber for cordite and C-powder.

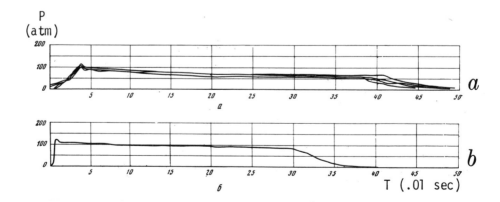

FIGURE 11.—Pressure records (in atm vs. time in sec): *a*, C-powder combustion within test chamber shown in Figure 1; *b*, C-powder combustion within test chamber shown in Figure 5.

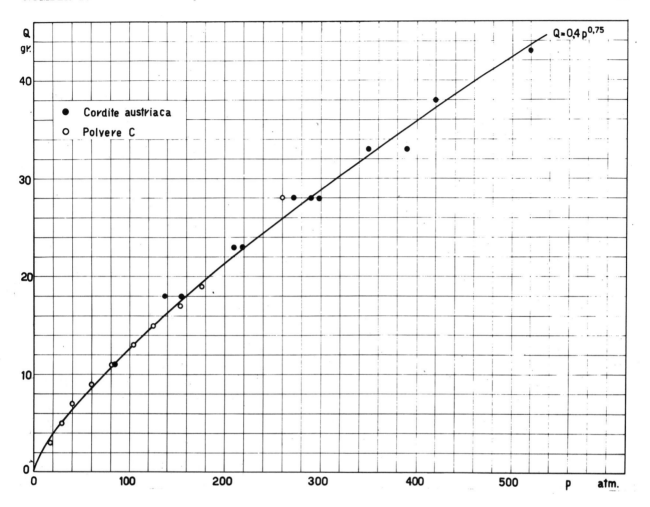

FIGURE 12.—Terminal pressure in closed chamber vs. charge weight for cordite and C-powder.

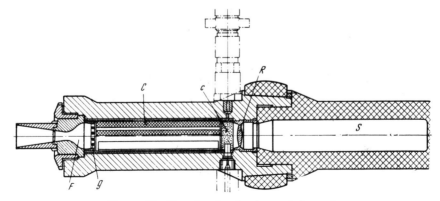

FIGURE 13.—Test chamber for three tubular grains.

Figure 15. The dispersion of the measured values is again due substantially to the poor behavior of the recording drum. The burning rate of the cordite follows more or less a $p^{0.75 \div 0.78}$ law. For the C-powder an exponent of 0.53 best fits the results.

Several theoretical works were also carried out. Figure 16 shows, for instance, the results of a theory developed for the calculation of the pressure distribution within the hole of a tubular charge for a burning rate given by σp^n. The coefficient β is given by

$$\beta = \frac{4\sigma\delta}{r}\left(\frac{2\gamma RT}{\gamma+1}\right)^{\frac{1}{2}}$$

where δ is the propellant density, r the hole radius assumed constant, and T the gas temperature at the burning surface. R and γ have the conventional meanings. The distance from the middle section of the hole is indicated by s. The terminal points on each curve correspond to choked conditions at the two ends of the hole (this way my first contact with the fundamental importance of Mach 1 even in the presence of combustion phenomena). Choking ap-

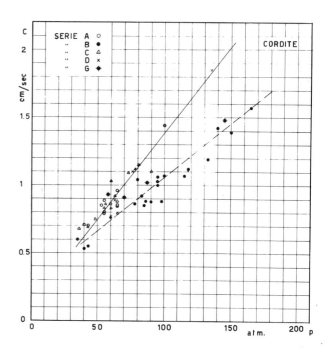

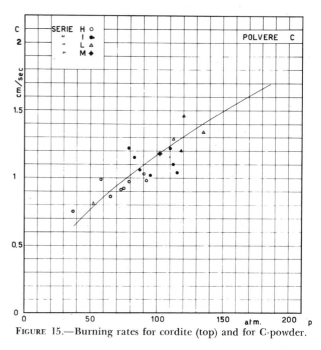

FIGURE 15.—Burning rates for cordite (top) and for C-powder.

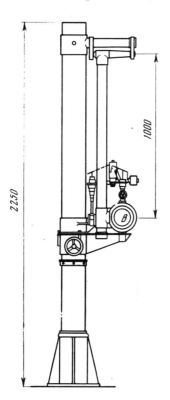

FIGURE 14.—Front view of the pendulum test stand with chamber.

pears for a certain charge length, beyond which no steady solution to the problem exists and the pressure must steadily rise in the hole. It seemed to me at first that this was an important finding, and I was disappointed when I calculated that for the actual charges the maximum value of the abscissa

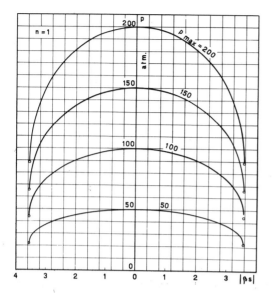

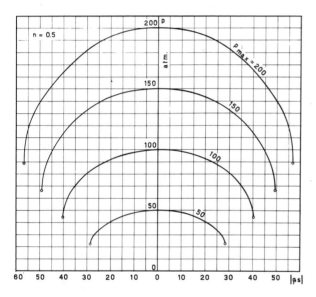

FIGURE 16.—Theoretical internal pressure distribution for tubular charges with burning rate proportional to p (top), and proportional to p$^{\frac{1}{2}}$.

was around 1 for $n=1.00$ and 3 for $n=0.5$ (see Figure 16), indicating that the actual conditions were very much below choking.

By the end of 1929 the Italian General Staff, judging that the dispersion obtained in our tests was too great if compared with the dispersion of guns, and that the velocity was too low, lost its interest in the powder rockets and the research was suspended. However a new phase of our research was started, more suitable for possible future applications to aeronautical problems and supersonic flight.

Research on Biopropellant Rockets

This part of our research was also partially supported by the General Staff through a second allocation of secret funds. My father discussed with Professor Francesco Giordani, an eminent chemist and personality of the Italian scientific world, the choice of the liquid propellants. The preference being, for practical reasons, given to storables, the choice fell on benzene as fuel and nitrogen tetroxide as oxidizer, because of the easy availability and low cost of both. Concentrated nitric acid was also considered, but the problem of the tanks appeared more difficult than for nitrogen tetroxide. It must be realized that stainless steel was only beginning to appear on the horizon, in very limited forms, and its technology was in its infancy.

My father decided that a chemist was needed to help me in the manipulation of the hazardous chemicals, and he hired a Dr. Corrado Landi, with whom, indeed, I collaborated for nearly two years. He was in charge of the propellant supply, while I was myself working on the design of the combustion chamber. My father, of course, gave as much supervision and advice as his very busy time would allow.

A very conventional type of propellant feeding

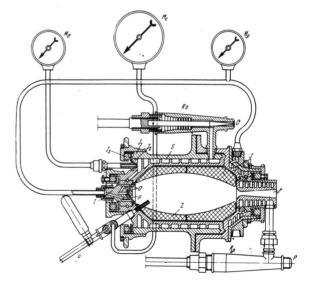

FIGURE 17.—Liquid bipropellant test rocket engine.

system with pressurized propellants was adopted, but special bottles for the nitrogen tetroxide had to be manufactured out of pure aluminum, in view of the corrosiveness which could result from residual traces of water. The chamber is shown schematically in Figure 17. It incorporated several features of present day rockets, such as the regenerative cooling and the impinging jet injector. Credit for the practical design of this chamber as well as of the other equipment described in the rest of this paper goes to Ing. G. Garofoli. The nozzle, including the convergent part of the chamber, was cooled by fuel cooling passages $J;$ the rest of the chamber by the oxidizer cooling passages $S.$ The propellant flow was hand-controlled by means of valves R_p and R_o located at the entrance of the cooling passages. From the cooling ducts the propellants were brought to the injector $I,$ consisting of three concentric annular injector slots, the central one, $p,$ for the fuel; the other two, $O,$ for the oxidizer, resulting in three impinging jets. Shown on the figure is the rather unconventional use of a refractory liner Z to decrease the heat transfer to the chamber wall. The refractory material was zirconia, chosen for its high melting temperature.

The whole chamber was built of stainless steel. For the nozzle I had selected a steel developed in the United States, because it could be welded. Tungsten-arc welding was used, but the welding was porous and gave lots of trouble. The complexity of the chamber design was necessary to make the chamber leakproof without welding. It was manufactured out of a block of stainless steel from COGNE Steelmills; so was the injector unit. Chamber pressure and propellant injection pressures were measured by gauges, as shown in Figure 17, and the whole chamber was mounted on rollers to allow the direct measurement of the thrust, which was designed to be around 1250 g, at 10 atm chamber pressure. The ignition sequence was rather involved. A small gas torch v was first inserted into the appropriate passage in the chamber walls. Gaseous hydrogen and gaseous oxygen, provided by an auxiliary feed system, were then admitted through the propellant valves under very moderate pressures, resulting in nearly atmospheric combustion. The torch was then retracted, the torch passage shut off, and the pressure of the gases gradually increased until a noticeable chamber pressure resulted. The transition to liquid propellants could

then be effected without difficulty.

This chamber was successfully tested late in 1930 by Dr. Landi and myself in a room on the courtyard of the Institute of Chemistry of the University of Rome, then located at via Panisperna. It had been graciously assigned to our research, upon my father's request, by his director, Professor Nicola Parravano. I suppose that this decision of my father of not carrying the tests within the laboratories of the Air Ministry was dictated by the sponsoring General Staff. During the ten-minute run our excitment grew very high, reaching its climax with the successful conclusion of the test. In our enthusiasm we did not realize what an extraordinary noise level we had introduced without warning in that peaceful courtyard, all devoted to basic (and silent) chemical research. What an anti-climax it was when the noise subsided and we heard a loud voice asking what in the h--- was going on there. Dashing to the windows we saw the angry and puzzled faces of Professors Parravano, Malquori, and De Carli at their respective windows. With an evident breach of security we had to provide the technical background for the deafening noise, after which Professor Parravano had a meeting with my father. They agreed that the project had to be transferred to a more suitable location. A few weeks later, while in his laboratory, Dr. Landi was suddenly struck and died without regaining consciousness. I always wondered whether his premature death (he was only 25) could have had something to do with his handling of nitrogen tetroxide and too frequent accidental inhaling of its toxic vapors. In which case, Dr. Landi's name should deservedly be added to the human life toll of rocket development.

With the death of one of the principal collaborators, and the fact that I had to concentrate on the preparation of my theoretical thesis for my forthcoming degree in engineering (which I acquired in July 1931); the research was temporarily stopped. The available funds were exhausted, and despite the promising results obtained, the General Staff did not renew its contract.

Research on Monopropellants

Research was not resumed until the second half of 1932, after I had graduated and satisfied my military obligations. But in the meantime, as a result of long and fruitful discussions between my father and myself, the aim of the research had switched toward the study of monopropellants. Also, the research was now financially supported by a new sponsor, the Italian Air Force. It had new headquarters, the laboratories of the Istituto di Aeronautica Generale of the School of Aeronautical Engineering of the University of Rome. We also welcomed to our program a new, very competent, collaborator, the Doctor of Chemistry Riccardo M. Corelli, later Professor of Aeronautical Technology at the same school.

I remember quite distinctly how the first idea of the monopropellant was born during an evening stroll under the trees of Via Nomentana. My father was wondering about the possibilities of controlling solid propellant burning by introducing it in the combustion chamber as a slurry of fine solid-propellant particles in suspension (but not solution) in a liquid. The discussion centered on the way combustion of such a mixture could take place. I remember how, in what was a sudden illumination for my still unexperienced mind, I realized the meaning of thermochemical calculations which, independently of the burning mechanism, allow a simple prediction of the composition and state of the gases resulting from the combustion of any mixture of chemicals as soon as the temperature is sufficiently high.

In practice, abandoning the not very practical idea of a solid propellant slurry, we chose to work with a liquid explosive, desensitized by dilution with an inert solvent. The most easily available and one of the most effective liquid explosives being trinitroglycerine, we decided to try it despite its bad reputation. However, we also considered other substances, such as dinitroglycerin or dinitroglycol. We performed a limited number of tests with these substances. It was known that a relatively small fraction (30 percent) of an organic solvent such as methanol could practically make trinitroglycerin insensitive to shock. Dr. Corelli carefully checked this and other statements in the literature on the subject, with a small amount of the explosive prepared in our laboratory. After this I felt sufficiently confident to carry personally on a night train from Turin to Rome a few liters of the mixture which had been prepared for us at the powder plants of Avigliana. This was, of course, a flagrant violation to the official regulations concerning the transportation of explosive materials, and I shudder today at the responsibility I was taking. However, it was the only way to avoid the endless red-tape involved in legal shipment.

Gasification tests were conducted in the apparatus shown in Figure 18. The monopropellant m contained in the tank b was pressurized, through the separating piston p by the gas of bottle a. The

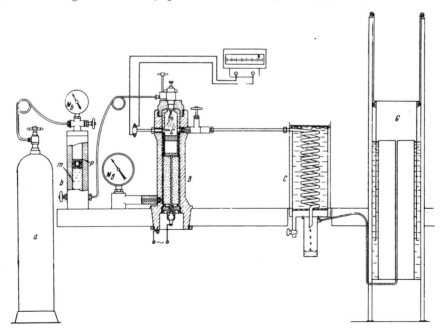

FIGURE 18.—Monopropellant gasification apparatus.

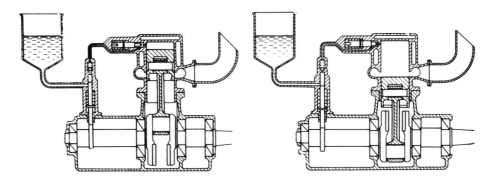

FIGURE 19.—Nitromethane engine.

combustion chamber *C*, all lined with insulating re-fractory material, contained at its bottom a crucible filled with pellets of refractory material. The cru-cible was electrically brought to a deep red tem-perature, after which the current was turned off and the monopropellant injection through the in-jector was started. The resulting gases were evacu-ated through a small nozzle and collected in a gasometer *G*, after cooling and separation of the condensed fraction.

The nitroglycerin mixture responded exactly ac-cording to the predictions of the thermochemical calculations, proving my point (if, indeed, it needed proof!). More important, it provided a hint of the practical possibilities of liquid monopropellants. However, this particular monopropellant was con-sidered to be unsafe because of the possibility of separation, either by evaporation or by water addi-tion, of the two components. Indeed, we had our-selves experienced a delayed explosion in the feed-ing line of Figure 18 which could be attributed to

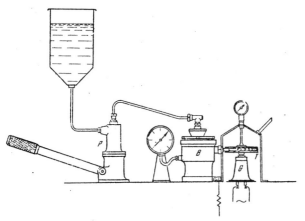

FIGURE 20.—Demonstration turbine for operation with nitromethane.

this reason. Hence Dr. Corelli prepared a list of possible organic solvents, presumably better than methanol with respect to separation, and I started the thermochemical calculations using each of them as a diluent. This was the path that made me acci-dentally stumble on the exceptional properties of mononitromethane.

I was indeed surprised to find that while, ac-cording to my calculations, other solvents provided results comparable to those of methanol, the out-come for nitromethane was well in excess of the others from the point of view of the overall heat of reaction and combustion temperature. Then, performing the calculations for nitromethane alone, I found this compound to be in itself an excellent monopropellant, better than any of the safe nitro-glycerin mixtures. Of course, this was a surprise, since the explosive character of nitromethane had never, to our knowledge, been pointed out.

It is natural that after this find our research con-centrated on nitromethane. Dr. Corelli prepared a good amount of it in our own laboratory because it was not commercially available in Italy, although at about that time it became available in U.S.A. as a solvent of nitrocellulose. To protect secrecy we baptized nitromethane with the name of Ergol. (By a strange coincidence this name was also used a few years later in Germany to indicate any liquid pro-pellant.) We studied carefully its stability against mechanical shocks, which makes it very difficult to detonate, and its resistance to thermal decomposi-tion. We measured its vapor pressure up to 200°C. We determined its thermal stability by dropping into baths of molten metal with increasingly higher temperatures small sealed capsules containing nitro-methane, so designed that they would explode only if thermal decomposition took place. The lower

FIGURE 21.—General Crocco (1), Theodore von Kármán (2), and the General's son (3) at the Fifth
Volta Conference, 1935.

explosion limit was found to be around 400°C. Having, in 1933, reached the conclusion that nitromethane is an easy substance to handle, we tested its gasification in the apparatus of Figure 18, where it behaved according to the theoretical predictions.

Encouraged by these results and by the lack of any adverse indications, my father and I started contemplating other uses for the interesting properties of nitromethane. There was, indeed, very little interest among Air Force officials in the future of rockets. However, Italy had captured some high altitude airplane records, and high altitude flights were fashionable. Consequently we thought of applying nitromethane to the design of an engine which could produce power in the absence of air.

The monocylinder engine, shown schematically in Figure 19, was designed and built. It was intended to work on the two-stroke cycle, whereby the nitromethane was injected in the residual gases of the previous cycle recompressed to a high temperature during the compression stroke.

Fortunately high-pressure fuel injection systems for Diesel engines had become commercially available in those years, thanks to the Bosch Company. For demonstration purposes, a hand-operated Bosch injection system was first tested in the apparatus shown in Figure 20. The gas generator B, similar to, but smaller than, that of Figure 18, was fed by the pump P and discharged its gases on a small turbine

T, connected to an electric generator G. Although the overall efficiency of conversion was certainly well below 1 percent, for the high sponsoring officials this device was more convincing than any scientific chart or presentation.

Next the mechanically driven injection system to be used in the engine of Figure 19 was tested in an apparatus designed to permit the atomization characteristics of nitromethane to be observed. It was unfortunate that the otherwise excellent Bosch injection pumps available at the time were designed for Diesel oil and hence did not require any positive lubrication. During a particularly long run there was an explosion which made the thick pump walls literally disappear under my very eyes. I missed that day my chance of being inscribed on the roll of victims of propellant research, escaping with relatively few injuries; after a month in bed I could walk again. Dr. Corelli, who was standing next to me, was also slightly injured.

The cause of the explosion was attributed to the removal, after a few minutes of operation, of the lubricating oil film from the pump plunger, with resulting seizure of its surface. The corresponding hot spots acted as ignition sources for the closely confined, high-pressure nitromethane. Indeed, it was easy to reproduce the explosion under controlled conditions. Because at the time no injection systems with positive lubrication were available, the high-pressure injection process for nitromethane was judged too hazardous, and was abandoned. A few years later Bosch produced such a positive lubrication system for gasoline engines.

In the following years we designed other monopropellant engines of different types. Let me only mention a compressed-gas engine to be used in underwater propulsion, utilizing the gases produced in a nitro-methane-plus-water gas generator, and a spark-ignition 4-stroke-cycle piston engine to be operated by nitromethane vapor alone. This lead to a series of interesting studies and experiments on the possibility of a decomposition-flame propagation in the vapor itself. But this reseach is too far removed from rockets to allow more than this passing mention.

I also would like to mention our renewed interest, in those years, in bipropellant combinations, and the interesting studies of Dr. Corelli on the properties of tetronitromethane as an oxidizer. The Fifth Volta Conference, of which my father was president (see Figure 21), provided an opportunity

for many of the leaders in the story of high-speed flight to meet. However, generally speaking, the interest of the Italian sponsoring offices in rocketry was at a dead end.

It was only after the war, in 1947, that I became again involved in experiments on the applications of nitromethane to rocket propulsion for the Direction des Études et Fabrication d'Armements of the French Ministry of Defense. It was there that I succeeded in operating a rocket chamber of appreciable dimensions and relatively small L*, using inward radial injectors uniformly distributed on the cylindrical wall of the chamber. After 1949 I continued this work for some time in the United States, with the authorization of the French authorities and the collaboration of the Aerojet-General Corporation, where outward radial injection from a central pylon was also successfully tested. But all this is modern rocket history and not part of my father's pioneering activity in the field of Italian rocketry—the subject of this presentation.[4]

NOTES

Under the title *Rannie issledovaniya v oblasti raket i raketnogo topliva v Italii,* this paper appeared on pages 34–55 of *Iz istorii astronavtiki i raketnoi tekhniki: Materialy XVIII mezhdunarodnogo astronavticheskogo kongressa, Belgrad, 25–29 Sentyavrya 1967* [From the History of Rockets and Astronautics: Materials of the 18th International Astronautical Congress, Belgrade, 25–29 September 1967], Moscow: Nauka, 1970.

1. General Crocco was 90 at the time of this presentation and died the following 19 January 1968. See "Ex mundo astronautico," *Astronautica Acta,* vol. 14, no. 6 (October 1969), p. 689.—Ed.

2. Luigi Crocco, "Instruction and Research in Jet Propulsion," *Journal of the American Rocket Society,* no. 80, March 1950, pp. 32–43.

3. Gaetano Arturo Crocco, "Sulla possibilits della navigazione extra atmosferica, *Rendiconti Accademia nazionale del Lincei* (Rome), ser. 5, vol. 32, part 1, 1923, p. 461; "Possibilita di superaviarione," *Rendiconti Accademia nazionale del Lincei* (Rome), ser. 6, vol. 3, 1926, pp. 241, 363; "Il proiettile a reazione," *Revista aeronautica,* vol. 2, no. 3 (March 1926), pp. 1–4; "La Velocità degli aerei e la superaviarione," *Revista aeronautica,* vol. 2, no. 9 (September 1926), pp. 3–52; "Un paradosso del propulsore a reazione," *Rendiconti Accademia nazionale del Lincei* (Rome), ser. 6, vol. 3, 1926, p. 370.

4. An interesting account by Theodore von Kármán of General Crocco's Presidency of the Fifth Volta Congress of High Speed Flight in 1935 and von Kármán's meeting with General Crocco's son is given in his *The Wind and Beyond,* written with Lee Edson (Boston: Little, Brown and Company, 1967), pp. 216–23.—Ed.

4

My Theoretical and Experimental Work from 1930 to 1939, Which Has Accelerated the Development of Multistage Rockets

Louis Damblanc, *France*

Preamble

Preamble to Mr. Louis Damblanc's paper by L. Blosset, Deputy Director of the National Space Research Center (France).

Mr. Louis Damblanc, who is 78 years old today (26 September 1967)—Chevalier of the Legion of Honor, recipient of the International Astronautics Prize of 1935 and the Gold Medal of the National Research and Inventions Office, and a Laureate of the Society for Encouragement of Progress—may be considered as the father of our present multistage rockets.

Passionately interested in research in fields as different as aeronautics, astronautics, mechanics, and optics, his inventions have aroused the interest of scientific and technical circles, especially in the years before World War II (multistage rocket,[1] rotary-wing airplane,[2] engine with variable stroke and compression[3]).

During the thirties, Louis Damblanc invented, built, and flight-tested the powder-propelled multistage rockets which carry his name: The "Louis Damblanc" two- and three-stage rockets, of which each stage became automatically detached after the end of combustion. This development is the subject of the paper given by him here, and it is in this field that he is the great pioneer, recognized as such by both the French and United States governments.

As a matter of fact, the International Patent Institute of the Hague has confirmed the world priority of the French patent granted to Louis Damblanc on 26 June 1936 for automatically separable multistage rockets: "self-propelled projectiles of which the propellant charge is distributed into several superimposed combustion stages along the longitudinal axis of the rocket." This priority also holds true for his corresponding U.S. patent of 12 April 1938, which covers the marine two-stage Terrier rocket. Another Damblanc United States patent covers the test stands designed by him. During World War II, both patents were sequestrated by the U.S. Alien Property Custodian under the "Trading With the Enemy Act," but as a result of the Franco-American (Blum-Byrnes) agreement concluded after the war, the French Ministry of Finance and Economic Affairs in July 1965 granted Damblanc an indemnity for the use of his two patents by U.S. authorities, thus again confirming the priority of his inventions.

In addition, his research on rockets has been crowned with success in several other areas: he succeeded in "taming" black powder by increasing its combustion time and by obtaining smooth combustion; he increased the strength of rocket bodies by using the most modern materials available at the time (such as the magnesium alloy, called at the time Metal M_1 or "Electron"); he perfected a means of stabilizing rockets in flight; and, above all, he obtained effective separation of stages by means of a process of fuse rings of his own invention, and by this means successfully launched numerous multistage rockets.

Within the context of this Symposium on the History of Astronautics, it is fitting that the Centre National d'Études Spatiales, of France, pay homage to a researcher who has contributed to the early development of space research and who deserves a place of honor among the pioneers of space exploration.[4]

Introduction

On my own initiative and having remained to the very end the only technician working on this great problem—the design, production, laboratory experimentation, static tests and numerous flight tests of rockets of my invention—I was able during the years prior to 1939 to develop a number of rocket prototypes which, at that time, were in the forefront of progress.

From the beginning, I used only solid fuels, in particular, fine-grain slow-burning mine powder. This I succeeded in "taming" by markedly increasing the combustion time and by burning parallel layers at a strictly constant speed. With the help of the Central Pyrotechnics School of Bourges, I was able to obtain blocks of a composite powder, strongly compressed and homogeneous, which always gave the best results. As often as possible, I chose for my tests sunny days without appreciable wind. My theoretical study and an analysis of the combustion process may be found in my first book, *Self-propelled Rockets,* published in April 1935.[5] My second book was published on 11 January 1938.

The use of my compressed powder with internal nozzle enabled me to obtain the specific gravity of 1.48, as compared with 0.83 for uncompressed black powder. Average combustion speeds always proved to be remarkably constant. They varied, depending on the type of Louis Damblanc rocket, between 13 and 20 mm per second. The combustion always took place in successive concentric layers around the internal conical area. During all our tests up to 1939, the combustion of the charge was always constant and stabilized in each stage.

From the very beginning of my research, I was struck by how little care had been given to the construction of the rocket. In my large rockets, we employed ordinary sheet metal from 2 to 3 mm thick, singly-riveted along the whole length. Use of this primitive structure was feasible only because of the very small pressures developed during combusion. The very frequent overpressures, on the order of 10 times ordinary pressure, resulted in immediate failure. The self-propelled rockets designed by me developed pressures 60 times greater in ordinary operation.

The test firing took place at the Bourges Firing Ground (Central Pyrotechnics School). A large number of experiments were made at the test bench and in vertical launches, because angular launching over a very extensive ground did not permit the rockets to be recovered easily.

Development of Test Means for Automatic Axial Pressure Recording

My test stand, shown diagrammatically in Figure 1, was designed to provide the following:

1. Measurement of the maximum thrust value of a rocket by the compression of a previously calibrated spring.

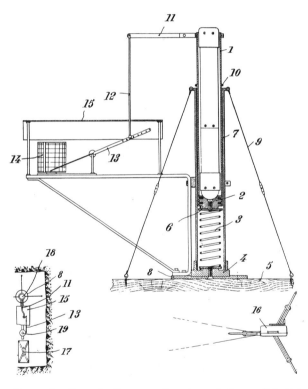

FIGURE 1.—General diagrammatic view of the rocket test stand. Tube (1) constitutes the combustion chamber intended to receive the rocket, open at the upper end to let the combustion products escape and including a bottom (2) intended to receive and transmit the reactive forces resulting from rocket operation. The forces are found by measuring the elastic strains on a coil spring (3). Every stress on the bottom (2) results in depression of spring (3) and in displacement of tube (1), transmitted to a pointer (13) inscribing the corresponding curve on drum (15) driven by a clockwork mechanism.

2. Measurement of thrust at all combustion moments by automatically recording the stress curve as a function of time:

$$\int_0^{t_1} f(t)dt$$

3. Measurement of time by use of a pendulum (Figure 2) which beat the seconds and was clearly visible at a distance. In order to reference pendulum oscillations easily on film, the rod L was extended by another rod L^1 with a large disc D, white and bordered in black, on its top.

For all tests of the experimental rockets, I filmed in slow motion the incandescent jet caused by powder combustion. The sound recording of the "blow" enabled me to observe that the sound intensity remained constant during a very large fraction of the incandescent part of the total combustion time. This coincided remarkably with the long horizontal part of the curve representing the height

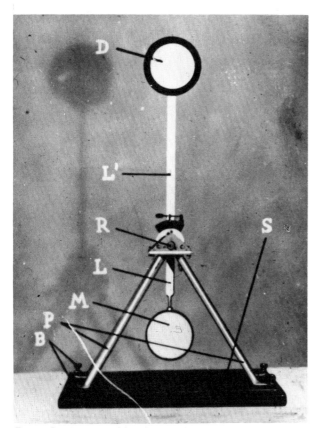

FIGURE 2.—One-second-beating pendulum, serving as metronome, and filmed, together with the test stand, in operation.

FIGURE 3.—Slow-motion recording (left) of the incandescent jet from powder combustion. The band on left side of film shows the amplitude of sound intensity. Right: Filmed combustion recording shows the displacement of the reference rod integral with the movable tube.

FIGURE 4.—Equipment for launching the Damblanc self-propelled variable-inclination rockets (1939), and (right) more compact and simpler launching equipment for smaller diameter rockets (the man in the photo is Damblanc's faithful assistant Maillard).

variations of the incandescent part of the flame. Figure 3 shows frames from the film of a bench test, on which can be seen the amplitude of sound intensity and displacement of the recording pendulum. On film I could observe that the vertical flame progression had a remarkably sharp outline. Our recordings were made by means of a camera provided with a sound-recording device. Two dynamic loudspeakers were interconnected. One, placed near the rocket, served as a microphone while the other, in front of the recorder, was used as the receiver. In this way, I was able to co-ordinate temperature and sound recordings. The receiver-recorder was equipped with a device to translate sound into light beams and to synchronously record it on the photographic film.

The Launching Apparatus

The variable-inclination apparatus shown in Figure 4 (left) I designed, built, and experimented with as early as 1937. Thanks to these experiments I could, in 1939, proceed succesfully to the launching of my largest rockets (133-mm diameter) with several automatically separable stages. For launching smaller rockets, I used the simpler and more compact apparatus shown in Figure 4 (right).

Rockets Tested, 1935–1939

Thanks to my carefully preserved files, the following list may be given:

1. Two-stage 35.5-mm-diameter rockets. The first stage was of steel, the second of magnesium, called Metal M_1 or "Electron," which represented at that time the summit of metallurgical technique. Weight of illuminating flare without parachute, 500 g; firing angle, 90° and altitude as measured by theodolite, 2,150 m, corresponding to a range of 6,325 m.

2. Rocket of the same diameter but, for the first time with both stages made of magnesium. The altitude reached exceeded the one for the previous rocket but could not be measured because of cloudy weather. All these tests were officially certified. This rocket, very light and extremely easy to handle, was tested on 24 October 1939, and was intended to be mass-produced in several thousand units.

The same was true for the rocket of 72 mm diameter tested at the same time. Its first stage was of duralumin and the second, of Metal M_1 (Electron)—a great novelty at the time. This rocket could carry an illuminating flare weighing 10 kg up to an altitude of 500 m. Obviously, on the eve of the Second World War, the practical applications were subordinated to combat requirements.

3. Magnesium-alloy (M_1) rocket of 88-mm diameter and a total length of 2.20 m. It had three stages and triangular stabilization fins. Figure 5 shows this as well as a two-stage, 55-mm-diameter rocket with different stabilization tail planes for each stage. These were successfully launched on

FIGURE 5.—Three-stage rocket of magnesium alloy, 88-mm diameter, 2.20-m long, with triangular stabilization fins. Two-stage rocket, 55-mm diameter, with different stabilization tail planes for each stage. Right: Successful launch of one of these at Bourges in July 1938.

the Bourges firing ground in July 1938, as shown in Figure 5.

4. My 133-mm rockets, the most powerful ones built in France at that time, of which the structure was obtained by cutting off a shell-body. Capable of transporting heavy loads, its drift did not exceed 2 percent. It was built in three stages, each automatically separable, after complete combustion of the lower stage, by means of a device I had invented.

Between 1935 and 1939, I launched 360 rockets of my invention. Listed below are a few of my other special devices from that period:

- Takeoff booster for the Air Ministry.

- "Ballistic wheel" of large diameter, built and successfully experimented in 1938, for the underwater study of self-propelled Damblanc rockets.

- Short-distance postal rocket, of which the launching device is shown in Figure 6.

- Highly successful experiments of vertical support of steel wire ropes by self-propelled systems (antiaircraft).

- "Signal rockets" used in the Sahara in 1938, rising above sand fogs which in this region, may be found at altitudes of 1,200 m and above. In them I used a special color to prevent their being confused with the stars, which are quite bright in tropical countries.

- "Mooring-support" rockets with a range of 500 m.

- Self-propelled supply rocket with the payload recovered by parachute.

My principal invention is indubitably that of multistage rockets whose length was shortened as the propellant was consumed. I applied for my French patent on 7 March 1936, my application in Belgium having taken place earlier—9 March

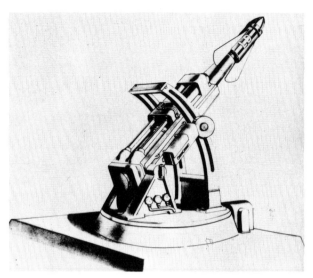

FIGURE 6.—Launching equipment for Damblanc short-distance postal rocket. This drawing apparently prompted the article "Big Guns May Speed Mail Rockets" (*Popular Science*, vol. 128, April 1936, p. 41).—Ed.

1935. My French patent, 803,021, granted on 29 June 1936, protected effectively the following claims:

1. Radial combustion propagation of the powder grain with axial space.
2. Complete combustion before separation of each stage.
3. Separation by fuse ring and stage separation by explosion.
4. Consumable rocket bodies.
5. Multistage rockets.
6. Use of light metals and alloys for the casings of rocket stages.

Figure 7 shows a page from my French patent 803,021. The corresponding patent taken out in the United States, "Self Propelling Projectile," United States Patent 2,114,214, dated 12 April 1938, contains 7 claims and is a literal reproduction of my French patent. Similar patents were also granted me in Germany, the United Kingdom, and Japan. The International Patent Institute, The Hague, the highest court in this matter, in its consultation of 22 December 1960, cites as the first in the world my French patent 803,021 of 29 June 1936, which covers self-propelled projectiles "of which the propellant charge is distributed into several superimposed combustion stages along the longitudinal axis of the rocket."

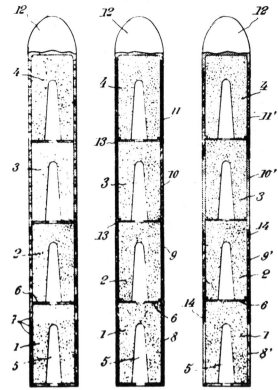

FIGURE 7.—Three cross-sections of rockets as shown in French patent 803,021, 29 June 1936.

In addition, on 11 May 1939, I took out French patent 859,352, covering the replacement of screws by tapped sleeves in order to assemble two adjacent components of a multistage rocket.

A preliminary very important trial of my test stand at the National Office of Research and Inventions succeeded completely, as may be seen on the official test report of 30 May 1936, shown in the appendix.

Another of my French patents that marked an important advance, 802,422, of 26 February 1936, concerned the novel design of the rocket test stand I have described above. The corresponding United States patent 2,111,315, of 15 March 1938, was entitled "Force measuring devices for rockets."

My two United States patents were sequestrated by the Government of the United States during World War II. After the war, as a result of the Franco-American Blum-Byrnes agreement,[6] I requested and obtained in 1965 indemnity for the use of my patents during that period.

In 1935, I received from the Société Astronomique de France the REP-Hirsch Astronautics prize, an international award, in recognition of my role as a pioneer.[7]

NOTES

Under the title *Teoreticheskie i eksperimental'nye raboty vo Frantsii mnogostupenchatym raketam (1930–1939)*, this paper appeared on pages 25–33 of *Iz istorii astronavtiki i raketnoi tekhniki: Materialy XVIII mezhdunarodnogo astronavticheskogo kongressa, Belgrad, 25–29 Sentyavrya 1967* [From the History of Rockets and Astronautics: Materials of the 18th International Astronautical Congress, Belgrade, 25–29 September 1967], Moscow: Nauka, 1970.

1. Louis Damblanc, "Les Fusée autopropulsives à éxplosifs; éssais au point fixé; Application des résultants, éxperimentaux a l'étude du mouvement," *L'Aérophile,* vol. 43, July and August 1935, pp. 205–09 and 241–47; and "I razzi autopropulsive ad esplosivo," *Rivista Aeronautica,* vol. 7, January 1936, pp. 87–100.—Ed.

2. L. Damblanc, "Les Hélicoptères et les laboratoires d'éssais," *l'Aérophile,* vol. 28, 15 October 1920, pp. 314–315; and "The Problem of the Helicopter," *Journal of the Royal Aeronautical Society,* vol. 25, January 1921, pp. 3–19.—Ed.

3. L. Damblanc, "Sur un disposif applicable aux moteurs d'aviation pour réduire les pertes de puissance en altitude," *Comptes Rendus de l'Académie des Sciences,* vol. 180, 14 April 1925, pp. 1161–64; and "Du moteur d'aviation au moteur d'automobile," *l'Aérophile,* vol. 35, 15 March 1927, pp. 67–70.—Ed.

4. Damblanc died in early December 1969. A necrology appeared in the 10 December 1969 issue of *Le Parisien Libéré,* written by Louis Lamarre, "Louis Damblanc, le père des fusées à étages est mort" [Louis Damblanc, The Father of Staged Rockets Is Dead].—Ed.

5. Louis Damblanc, *Les Fusées autopropulsives à éxplosifs* (Paris: Ministère de l'Éducation Nationale, 1935).—Ed.

6. "Memorandum of Understanding Between the Government of the United States of America and the Provisional Government of the French Republic Regarding Settlement For Lend-Lease, Reciprocal Aid, Surplus War Property, and Claims," pp. 4175–78, in *United States Statutes at Large,* vol. 61 (in 6 parts), p. 4, *International Agreements Other Than Treaties* (Washington, D.C.: United States Government Printing Office, 1948).—Ed.

7. "The History of the REP-Hirsch Award," *Astronautics,* No. 34 (June 1936), pp. 6–7 and 13.

Appendix

Official test report, dated 30 May 1936, from the French National Office of Scientific and Industrial Research and of Inventions.

The test was carried out on a body including two metal armatures, with dimensions, diameter and thickness conforming to the actual model, those two armatures being connected by an assembly conforming to the invention.

AUTHENTICATION

1. The total assembly had the rigidity and solidity permitting it to be handled under normal conditions with complete satisfaction.
2. The rocket body was placed in accordance with the experimental conditions (climbing flight). The upper body was restrained; the lower body included a sufficient powder charge for ensuring lining of the rocket up to the connecting assembly level.

This powder charge was ignited and after 7 seconds, the time corresponding exactly to the total combustion duration of the charge, the lower body became detached sharply and fell on the ground, the connecting assembly having melted only when the ignited powder came into contact with it.

The Director of the National Office
of Research and Inventions
(Signed) J. L. Breton
Member of the Institute

5

Robert H. Goddard and the Smithsonian Institution

Frederick C. Durant III, *United States*

Robert Hutchings Goddard, American rocket theorist, inventor, and experimenter was associated with the Smithsonian Institution for nearly thirty years. Throughout this period Charles G. Abbot, fifth Secretary of the Smithsonian Institution, was the prime contact, supporter, mentor and trouble-shooter to whom Goddard unfailingly looked for support and technical assistance in his experimental efforts.

The writer has been privileged since his association with the Smithsonian Institution in 1964 to have access to a remarkable archival collection of Dr. Robert H. Goddard's reports, correspondence, and photographs as well as physical specimens of his rockets. To study these materials is inspiring, for clearly their author was a brilliant, capable, and imaginative man.

The first contact between Goddard and the Smithsonian Institution was by letter, dated 27 September 1916. At that time Goddard was thirty-two years old. Born (5 October 1882) and educated in Worcester, Massachusetts, Goddard received his B.S. degree from Worcester Polytechnic Institute in 1908 and his M.S. and Ph.D. degrees from Clark University in 1910 and 1911, respectively. He conducted research at Princeton University (1912–13) on a post-doctoral fellowship, but for reasons of health returned to Worcester. Majoring in physics throughout his educational training, Goddard (Figure 1) embraced the academic life and taught physics, first as an instructor and soon after as professor, when he was not engaged in research on rockets. In 1916 Charles Greely Abbot (1872–1973) was Assistant Secretary of the Smithsonian under Secretary Charles Doolittle Walcott (1850–1927). As an astrophysicist, Abbot had pioneered in solar measurements and observations. Goddard's letter was lengthy—six and one-half pages. In it he wrote:

For a number of years I have been at work upon a method of raising recording apparatus to altitudes exceeding the limit for sounding balloons; and during the last two years I have tried-out the essential features of the method at the Laboratory of Clark University with very gratifying results. These experiments are now completed, and I feel that I have settled every point upon which there could be reasonable doubt. Incidentally, I have reached the limit of the work I can do single-handed; both because of expense, and also because further work will require more than one man's time.[1]

He mentioned the military potential of his device as a long-range weapon (it will be recalled that Europe was then embroiled in World War I) but added that, "exclusive use of the device for warfare would, I am certain, be a loss to science . . . ." Goddard summarized his theoretical calculations and the results obtained experimentally firing smokeless powder in chambers with a tapered exhaust nozzle. In these tests jet velocities as high as 8,000 feet per second had been achieved. He listed his patent coverage, received in 1914, of multiple rockets powered by both single and repetitive-firing solid propellants as well as by pump-fed liquid propellants. Goddard postulated that a one-pound payload could be fired to an altitude of 200 miles and recovery of apparatus achieved by a parachute. He went on:

I hesitate to give my conclusion regarding the possibility of sending small masses (under what I feel sure are realizable conditions) to very much greater heights than those I have just mentioned.[2]

He asked if the Smithsonian might have his proposed method and techniques reviewed by a scientific committee and, if favorably received, that funds might be found to support further research. Goddard closed by stating:

FIGURE 1.—Robert H. Goddard at blackboard in physics laboratory, Clark University, 1924.

I realize that in sending this communication I have taken a certain liberty; but I feel that it is to the Smithsonian Institution alone that I must look, now that I cannot continue the work unassisted.[3]

When Goddard's letter was received on 29 September, Secretary Walcott was on travel and the letter was brought to Abbot as Acting Secretary. There is no doubt that Abbot was immediately intrigued. For Walcott he wrote a longhand summary of the letter, directing attention to Goddard's specific requests and saying—

I believe there are several meteorological problems . . . of great interest which might be solved by aid of the device, as:
  1. What is the composition of the highest atmosphere?
  2. How does temperature fall at great altitudes?[4]

On 11 October, Secretary Walcott acknowledged receipt of Goddard's letter, indicating interest and inquiring as to the level of funds Goddard was seeking.[5] Goddard responded with a summary of

his approach on a year's program at an estimated cost of 5,000 dollars.[6] More details were requested[7] and Goddard sent copies of his patents and a lengthy manuscript; he also offered to come to Washington to brief a deliberating committee.[8] On 18 December Abbot wrote to Secretary Walcott that he had examined the manuscript carefully as well as the patent specifications, concluding—

I believe the theory is sound, and the experimental work both sound and ingenious. It seems to me that the character of Mr. Goddard's work is so high that he can well be trusted to carry it on to practical operation in any way that seems best to him. I regard the scheme as worth promoting.[9]

An independent assessment of Goddard's concept and technique was solicited from the Bureau of Standards in Washington. Dr. Edgar Buckingham, a theoretical physicist there, agreed with Abbot, albeit more cautiously, and closed by expressing "hope that the Smithsonian Institution will see fit to help Mr. Goddard in developing his invention . . . ." [10]

On the basis of the two favorable opinions, Secretary Walcott wrote Goddard on 5 January 1917 to announce that the Smithsonian Institution had "verified the soundness of your theoretical work and accuracy of the numerical data," that they were "favorably impressed with the ingenuity of your mechanical and experimental dispositions, the clearness of your exposition, and . . . the value of that which is proposed . . . ." Accordingly, a grant of "$5,000 from the Hodgkins Fund" was approved. Reports were to be made "yearly or oftener if notable progress" was made. A part-payment check for 1,000 dollars was enclosed.[11]

Thus began the long relationship between C. G. Abbot of the Smithsonian Institution and the physics professor, Robert H. Goddard. Secretary Walcott asked Dr. Abbot and Dr. Buckingham to serve as a two-man advisory committee regarding Goddard's activity.[12] Thus all correspondence to the Smithsonian was routinely brought to Abbot's attention.

Two months later, on 6 April 1917, the United States entered World War I. On 11 April, Goddard wrote to the Smithsonian and pointed out the possible value of his rocket concept to long-range bombardment because of its lightness of weight, compared with artillery, and its ease of mobility.[13] Abbot wrote to the Secretary that he believed that the proposition had merit and "quite warrants the War Department in spending a sum not exceeding $50,000 under his direction for experiments."[14] On 20 August, Goddard wrote, "if the apparatus has any possibilities as regards warfare . . . it should be ready for the drive by the Allies which will probably take place next spring."[15]

Thus was displayed the strong faith of Abbot and Goddard in the long-range rocket concept. On 22 January 1918 Walcott and S. W. Stratton, Director of the U. S. Bureau of Standards, jointly signed a letter to the Chief Signal Officer, U. S. Army, enclosing a report on Goddard's research activities signed jointly by Abbot and Buckingham [16] and requesting a sum of $10,000 for purposes of development. Based upon Goddard's successive-firing rocket, expectations might be:

Range (miles)	Weight (pounds)			
	Rocket	Propellant	Warhead	Total
7	3	3	3	9
120	4	25	3	32

Since Walcott was Chairman of the Military Committee of the National Research Council in addition to his Smithsonian position, this request carried some weight and Signal Corps support was forthcoming.[17]

The next ten months saw a great increase in tempo. Goddard employed seven men, equipped a shop and laboratory at Clark University, struggled to obtain special powder formulations from the Hercules Powder Company, procured special gun steels, supervised modifications to rocket apparatus design, performed tests, reduced data, and wrote reports.[18]

The Worcester draft board was on the point of drafting a key workman into the Army. Goddard appealed to the Smithsonian for assistance.[19] Abbot, after much effort managed to obtain a draft classification change.[20] Goddard required special powder-testing gauges (crusher blocks).[21] Abbot obtained them.[22] An industrialist attempted to force revelation of Goddard's work in order to produce the military rockets himself. The Smithsonian came to the rescue.[23]

There were other incidents. On relocating test work to Pasadena, California in June 1918 the staff increased, as did Army funds.[24] But now, a new shop had to be equipped and staffed, special steels and tubing obtained, more special formulations of powder, and so on. The Smithsonian Institution monitored all expenditures and Abbot sought to obtain by request or demand each of Goddard's requirements. By 10 July "excellent" results were obtained on a tube-launched rocket.[25] When the Smithsonian received the telegram requesting ordnance and ballistics experts to come and observe progress, Abbot made the arrangements.[26]

One of Goddard's young assistants, Clarence N. Hickman, lost parts of fingers of both hands in an accident while handling explosive detonators.[27] Hospitalization and medical payments required much correspondence but this too, was settled satisfactorily.[28]

By late September 1918, firing tests were requested by the Army Ordnance Corps at Aberdeen Proving Ground, Maryland.[29] On 6 and 7 Novem-

FIGURE 2.—Goddard inserts 3-inch rocket in lightweight tube launcher. Demonstration tests
were made at Aberdeen Proving Grounds, 6–7 November 1918.

ber, one-, two-, and three-inch rockets (launched
from lightweight tubes, see Figure 2), a double-
expansion trench mortar, and a multiple-charge
repeating rocket (Figure 3) were demonstrated.[30]
Witnesses agreed that the weapons systems showed
great promise.[31] However, the war ended two days
later. National reversion to peacetime activities
stopped further development of these wartime applications of Goddard's rockets and interest by
the military.[32]

Returning to Clark University at Worcester,
Goddard attempted to settle his accounts and wind
up the intensive effort of the past few months.

On 7 April 1919 Goddard wrote suggesting that
publication of the concept of his original high
altitude rockets might be desirable as a Smithsonian paper.[33] Some highly sensational and irre-
sponsible newspaper articles on the military work

of Goddard had appeared and it seemed desirable
to set down facts.[34] Abbot replied in the affirma-
tive;[35] Goddard made some modifications to his
manuscript, and it was published by The Smithsonian in December 1919 with the cautious title "A
Method of Reaching Extreme Altitudes."[36] Seven-
teen hundred and fifty copies of this 69-page paper
were printed.

Little notice might have been given to the publication if the Smithsonian had not issued on
11 January 1920 a press release which invited attention to Goddard's speculations on a shot to the
Moon.[37] This portion of the paper was essentially
an extrapolation of the main techniques described,
and in it the concept of a moon shot was under-
played. Typically, however, Goddard had made
experimental tests of the minimum quantity of

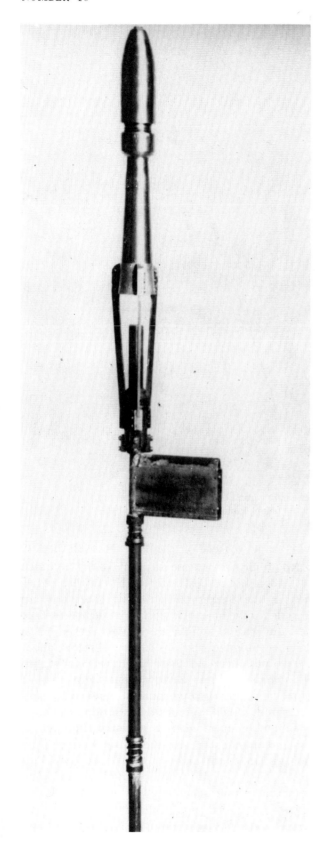

flash powder which might be observed if set off on the dark part of a new moon.[38]

The newspapers leaped on this small element of the report, ignoring the carefully delineated elements of the rocket theory and its promise for upper atmospheric research. Goddard wrote to Walcott on 19 January 1920:

Although there may very likely be ultimate possibilities of even greater interest than the proposed flash powder experiment—for it is difficult to see the limits of application of a perfectly new method—people must realize, nevertheless, that real progress is a succession of logical steps, and not a leap in the dark, and hence it is very important that, for whatever reason interest is taken in the work, adequate support and interest should be given the preliminary investigations.[39]

Shifting from repeating-charge solid propellants to liquid propellants in September 1921, Goddard experimented with liquid oxygen.[40] Striving to handle this cryogenic substance with lightweight apparatus (Figure 4) was an enormous challenge which occupied much of his attention over the next few years. On 16 March 1926, after successful static tests, he achieved his (and the world's) first flight with a liquid propellant rocket.[41] In a report to Abbot on 5 May 1926, he wrote:

In a test made March 16, out of doors, with a model of this lighter type, weighing 5¾ lb empty and 10¼ lb loaded with liquids, the lower part of the nozzle burned through and dropped off, leaving, however, the upper part intact. After about 20 sec the rocket rose without perceptible jar, with no smoke and with no apparent increase in the rather small flame, increased rapidly in speed, and after describing a semicircle, landed 184 feet from the starting point—the curved path being due to the fact that the nozzle had burned through unevenly, and one side was longer than the other. The average speed, from the time of the flight measured by a stopwatch was 60 miles per hour. This test was very significant, as it was the first time that a rocket operated by liquid propellants traveled under its own power.[42]

The necessary lightness of design of Goddard's liquid oxygen and gasoline rocket (Figure 5) was achieved with remarkable skill. The thrust of the motor was about 9 pounds,[43] apparently, because on firing, the rocket remained in the launch stand for some seconds. When the weight became less the rocket lifted slowly on its short historic journey. Although the rocket flew to an altitude of only 41 feet and landed at a distance of 184 feet, it may be considered a bench mark in flight history as

FIGURE 3.—Multiple-firing, solid propellant rocket. Cartridges contained in magazine at center are propelled forward by gas pressure into firing chamber resulting in repeating, intermittent thrust.

FIGURE 4.—Goddard with 1926 design liquid oxygen-gasoline rocket. Rocket motor is at top.
Right, world's first successful liquid propellant rocket before launching on 16 March 1926.

great as that of Orville Wright who in his first
flight achieved a distance of only 120 feet. Mrs.
Goddard was recording this event with a motion
picture camera which held only 7 seconds of film,
and unfortunately the film had run through before
takeoff!

Collecting all the pieces, Goddard reduced the
length of the nozzle, increased the throat diameter,
added some braces to the structure and flew the
apparatus again on 3 April.[44] Two more attempts
were made on 13 and 22 April but the motors
burned through the walls.[45] By 4 May the apparatus
was rearranged (Figure 6), the motor being placed
in its more classic position at the lower end to
eliminate the need (and weight) of the long propellant line tubing in the earlier design.[46] It was
this rocket which Goddard later gave to the Smithsonian Institution and is on display today, together

with large rockets of the later Roswell period.

No public news release was made of the 16 March
1926 success. Goddard realized that further reduction in the weight of his small rocket was not
feasible. In the hope of a spectacular demonstration,
he set at once to build a much larger rocket.[47] The
designed motor thrust was 20 times greater, about
200 pounds, the rocket stood 109 inches tall, weighed
76 pounds dry and carried about 80 pounds of
propellants. Pressurizing gas was obtained by passing liquid oxygen around the combustion chamber.
A spin-table, operated by a 50-pound drop-weight,
was incorporated to give the rocket spin-stabiliza-
tion at launch. In a static test on 20 July 1927
there were problems involving initial pressurization
and combustion chamber failure.[48] An alcohol
burner was added to aid liquid oxygen pressurization at start conditions but in a test on 31 August,

FIGURE 5.—Modification of rocket design in, now classic, configuration: motor at rear, surmounted by liquid oxygen and gasoline propellant tanks. Rocket is on exhibit at Smithsonian Institution.

although a thrust of more than 200 pounds was obtained, the injector head burned through.[49]

To reduce costs and construction effort Goddard now turned to a medium-sized rocket design of thrust equivalent to about 40 pounds. Components were simply designed and easily replaced. Test work on rockets of this general size continued for nearly three years. Two more flights were achieved on 26 December 1928[50] and 17 July 1929.[51] On the latter flight a thermometer and barometer, together with a camera to record data at zenith were carried as payload.[52]

All these flights were conducted on a farm at nearby Auburn, Massachusetts. Because the loud noise resulted in unwelcome publicity[53] and alarmed local authorities,[54] test work was shifted to the U. S. Army artillery range at Camp Devens, Massachusetts.[55] Once again the Smithsonian paved the way with letters to the Army that secured the necessary permission.[56]

At this point substantial financial support became available from Daniel Guggenheim, a wealthy and philanthropic New Yorker who had been supporting development of aeronautics at the request of his son Harry F. Guggenheim. Colonel Charles A. Lindbergh had personally visited Goddard in November 1929 and had been impressed by potential developments of rocket power.[57] At Lindbergh's suggestion,[58] Guggenheim agreed to sponsor Goddard's efforts.[59] Officials of the DuPont Company served as additional technical advisors to Guggenheim. Meanwhile, the Carnegie Institution in Washington in December 1929 advanced $5,000 to the Smithsonian for Goddard's continuing research.[60]

With the Guggenheim support, Goddard was able to increase significantly the size and scope of his work.[61] Moving to Mescalero Ranch at Roswell, New Mexico,[61] privacy and adequate supporting facilities permitted him to devote full effort to developing the many elements of sounding-rocket design which he had conceived. Such items included gyro stabilization, steering-jet vanes in the rocket exhaust as well as aerodynamic flaps, gas generators and turbopumps for propellants, improved injector heads, film cooling of combustion chambers, valving, igniters, launch controls, and parachute recovery.[62] Goddard recognized that although Abbot would continue as a member of the Guggenheim advisory committee his work would no longer be under the direct support of the Smithsonian Institution. To Abbot he wrote:

I am deeply appreciative of the support of the Smithsonian has given this rocket work, from its start as a bare idea with little experimental verification, in 1917. I am so particularly grateful for your interest, encouragement, and far-sightedness. I feel that I cannot overestimate the value of your backing, at times when hardly anyone else in the world could see anything of importance in the undertaking.[63]

As it turned out, however, Abbot continued his close and friendly relationship until Goddard's untimely death on 10 August 1945. For example, when Goddard's basic 1914 patents were about to expire in 1931,[64] Abbot obtained sponsorship for a special bill in Congress.[65] Military support of such a bill was necessary. However, the Army Ordnance Corps declared that "no immediate or near future use of rockets for ordnance purposes seems probable."[66] The Navy, just as shortsightedly, declared that if rocket development were more public greater progress in national defense could be expected. Thus Abbot reluctantly wrote a half-dozen letters acknowledging the viewpoints of the military, requesting withdrawal of the bill from committee action and to Goddard informing him of the lack of interest in his work.[67]

In 1932, at the depth of the world financial depression, Guggenheim funds became unavailable.[68] Goddard returned to Worcester and resumed teaching at Clark University.[69] He wrote to Abbot asking if the Smithsonian might find 250 dollars for specific tests aimed at reducing weight of rocket designs.[70] Abbot found the money[71] and next year on 2 September, Goddard wrote:

It made possible work which will save much time when the development is continued later on a larger scale, and without it things would have been stopped completely.[72]

If Abbot occasionally expressed impatience with Goddard's penchant for becoming fascinated and diverted by compelling and burgeoning new technical concepts, his interest was obviously sincere and in the hope of successful demonstration of high-altitude rocket flight. When Goddard wrote to Abbot on 4 September 1934[73] that major funds had been resumed from the Daniel and Florence Guggenheim Foundation, Abbot replied:

May I urge you to bend every effort to a directed high flight? That alone will convince those interested that this project is worth supporting. Let no side lines, however promising, divert you from this indispensable aim . . . .[74]

On 1 April 1935 Goddard mentioned in a letter to Abbot:

You may be interested to know that I followed your advice last fall, and am glad I did so. I had planned on new controls, stabilization, and a large light model all at once. It seemed necessary to do this, as the time was so short. I see now that I might have worked the whole year without having much in the way of flights to show for it.[75]

When special problems of technical logistics arose, such as supply of liquid oxygen and importing special equipment from abroad, it was to Abbot and the Smithsonian that Goddard turned for help. It was in recognition of this relationship and fully appreciating the historical importance of his work that on 2 November 1935 Goddard,[76] on the strong urging of Guggenheim and Lindbergh,[77]

sent a complete 1934 Series A rocket to the Smithsonian. Goddard asked that it not be placed on exhibition until requested by him, or in the event of his death, by Mr. Harry F. Guggenheim and Colonel Charles A. Lindbergh.[78] Goddard's wishes were respected. When it arrived, the box containing the rocket was bricked inside a false wall in the basement of the Smithsonian to be exhumed and placed on display after World War II.

On 16 March 1936 the Smithsonian published the second of Goddard's papers, entitled "Liquid-Propellant Rocket Development," covering his research at Roswell from July 1930 to July 1932 and from December 1934 to September 1935.[79] Whereas the 1919 paper had concerned itself with the theory of rocketry and its potential, the 1936 paper described progress made, established priority on the world's first liquid propellant rocket flight, work on gyro-stabilization, static firings and flight tests to 7500 feet, and future plans to reduce weights to a minimum.

There was one further relationship between Goddard and the Smithsonian which is revelatory both of the man and his view of the Smithsonian Institution. During the period 1920–1929 Goddard wrote four unsolicited reports dated March 1920, August 1923, March 1924, and August 1929.

In these reports, which he asked the Smithsonian not to make public, Goddard revealed his dreams of interplanetary flight and how it could be accomplished by rocket power. He also displayed his trust and confidence in the Institution knowing that the reports would be safeguarded and preserved. Never publicly released until published in *The Papers of Robert H. Goddard*, they set forth the principles of lunar and interplanetary flight, and they document Goddard's interest in and appreciation of the potential of rocket power as well as his fertile, creative imagination.

His March 1920 report, of 23 typewritten pages, is entitled "Report on Further Developments of the Rocket Method of Investigating Space."[80] Part I, "Investigation Conducted without an Operator," we would today entitle "Scientific Satellites and Space Probes." In this section Goddard suggests the value of photographing the Moon and

FIGURE 6.—*a*, Larger rocket, developing about 200-lb thrust, tested 20 July 1927; *b*, "Hoop Skirt" rocket, flown 26 December 1928; *c*, payload-carrying rocket, flown 19 July 1929; *d*, barometer and camera to photograph atmospheric pressure at zenith (rocket also carried alcohol thermometer).

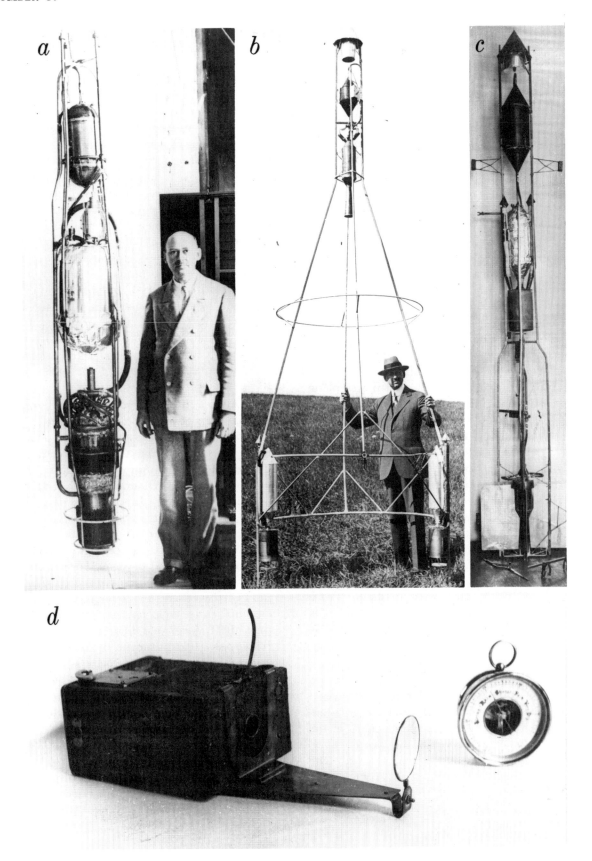

planets, the use of gyros and flight-path correction by small rocket motors, an ablating reentry heat shield, tracking of vehicle on reentry, communication with planetary extra-terrestrials, and sets forth the advantages of liquid hydrogen and liquid oxygen as ideal propellants. In Part II, "Investigations Conducted with an Operator" (today we would say "Manned Space Flight"), Goddard considers man essential for landing upon and taking off from planets. The use of retro-rockets on lunar landings and tangential atmospheric drag on return to Earth are mentioned as well as a launch vehicle with a desirable mass ratio of 0.93.

Launch takeoff weights of 100 to 250 tons for lunar landings are given. A section is devoted to the advantages of producing liquid hydrogen and liquid oxygen on a planet if water of crystallization were available from the soil. Solar energy would be used "except possibly on Venus." Goddard states, "The best location on the Moon would be at the north or south pole with the liquefier in a crater, from which the water of crystallization may not have evaporated, and with the [solar] power plant on a summit constantly exposed to the Sun. Adequate protection should, of course, be made against meteors, by covering the essential parts of the apparatus with rock." Goddard goes on to discuss the advantages of shortening the time of journey by the use of electric propulsion. A solar powered turbogenerator with a mirror collector 500 feet square is discussed, as are methods of producing an ionized jet of gas, and accelerating it electrostatically. Both positive and negative ions would be produced to prevent space charge effect. Techniques of producing ions are discussed and experiments performed at Clark University in 1916–17 are cited. Goddard concludes in his report that "it is believed that an appeal for public support is justifiable."

The August 1923 report to the Trustees, Clark University, "Principles and Possibilities of Rocket Developed by R. H. Goddard," is eight pages long.[81] The first four pages contain a documentary summary of his work to that date and elements of the March 1920 report. The remaining pages are devoted to a discussion of Herman Oberth's *Die Rakete zu den Planetenräumen* (Munich and Berlin: R. Oldenbourg, 1923) and of the many design elements which Goddard had suggested previously and had treated experimentally.

In March 1924 Goddard sent to the Smithsonian a nine-page "Supplementary Report on Ultimate Developments." [82] It represents, in the main, the results of further thought and study on the various aspects of interplanetary flight he had speculated about four years earlier in the March 1920 paper. In it he treats of propellant mixture ratio with excess hydrogen to reduce combustion chamber temperature and discusses suggestions for hydrogen and oxygen tank arrangements, the rotation of tanks (for stability), considerations of temperature and stress in tank design, a 1200-pound manned "observation compartment," selection of the "most economical acceleration" (about 4.8 g), atmospheric retardation, further considerations and calculations on soft landing on the Moon, low-density lithium as a construction material, and production of hydrogen and oxygen by solar energy on the Moon and planets (with the exception of cloud-shrouded Venus). "In the case of Venus," Goddard suggests, "it is very likely that the wind could be used as motive power, as there appears to be good evidence of strong winds . . . ."

The August 1929 "Report on Conditions for Minimum Mass of Propellant" [83] contains 13 pages, plus a 2-page Appendix and 4 pages of supplemental notes referencing the March 1920 report and reflecting further study and new data. The first 8 pages propose a space-launch vehicle consisting of an airplane with transparent wings or a lighter-than-air ship with a transparent envelope within which is contained solar collectors and power plant. Goddard conceives of the possibility of accelerating air mixed with charged particles. Both electrostatic and electromagnetic repulsion are discussed. Acceleration of the vehicle about the Earth would continue until escape velocity had been achieved. To depress the trajectory at increasing velocity, Goddard suggests that it might fly inverted to give negative lift. Once escape velocity is achieved the vehicle would continue to accelerate at characteristically low-g ion-propulsion rates "for half the journey, decelerating for the second half, in order to reduce the time of transit to a practicable amount." Different techniques of ion accelerators are discussed. "In space,' writes Goddard, "the best method of propulsion, and the one involving least mass of ejected material, is undoubtedly the repulsion of low speed electrons, and positive metallic ions, the latter by means of an electrode, an application for a U.S. patent on which has been filed by the writer." Three possible methods are suggested for "reaction against the air" electrostatically and electromagnetically. The next five pages list several dozen notes on rocket and space propulsion techniques contained in Goddard's notebooks, together with the dates recorded. The period covered is 1906–1912.

Abbot's reaction to these four remarkable reports was not encouraging. In acknowledging the August 1923 report, Abbot wrote, ". . . very interesting reading. I am, however, consumed with impatience, and hope that you will be able to actually send a rocket up into the air some time soon. Interplanetary space would look much nearer to me after I had seen one of your rockets go up five or six miles in our own atmosphere." [84] The March 1924 and August 1929 reports were each acknowledged with a single sentence stating that the material had been filed with the other papers relating to his experiments. One has the feeling that Abbot may have shaken his head gently while doing so.

In summing up this review of the relationship between Goddard and the Smithsonian, the following points are clear:

1. The Smithsonian Institution, primarily through the efforts of Charles Greely Abbot, enjoyed 29 years of friendly association with Robert Hutchings Goddard and continually supported his work.

2. Professor Goddard was a man of great creativity and inventiveness. A practical physicist, he displayed remarkable patience and persistence in his efforts to achieve successful sounding rockets for upper-atmosphere research.

3. Goddard's unpublished papers show that he dreamed of flight to the Moon and planets, and was caught up in the excitement of exploring the unknown. In a letter written in 1932 to H. G. Wells (Goddard, then 50 years old, had been strongly influenced by Wells' *War of the Worlds*) he revealed his inner drive by saying:

How many more years I shall be able to work on the problem, I do not know; I hope, as long as I live. There can be no thought of finishing, for "aiming at the stars," both literally and figuratively, is a problem to occupy generations, so that no matter how much progress one makes, there is always the thrill of just beginning . . . .[85]

A special note of appreciation is given Mrs. Robert H. Goddard for her kindness in supplying detailed information not easily located, answering questions, and otherwise generously assisting the writer in understanding this remarkable man.

NOTES

1. Robert H. Goddard to President, Smithsonian Institution, 27 September 1916, in *The Papers of Robert H. Goddard,* edited by Esther C. Goddard and G. Edward Pendray (New York: McGraw-Hill Book Company, 1970), 3 vols., vol. 1, p. 170. (Hereafter cited as "*Papers*").

2. *Papers,* 1:174.

3. *Papers,* 1:175.

4. Abbot to Walcott, 2 October 1916, *Papers,* 1:175.

5. Walcott to Goddard, 11 October 1916, *Papers,* 1:176.

6. Goddard to Secretary, Smithsonian Institution (C. D. Walcott), 19 October 1916, *Papers,* 1:177–78.

7. Walcott to Goddard, 29 November 1916, *Papers,* 1:179–80.

8. Goddard to Walcott, 4 December 1916, *Papers,* 1:180.

9. Abbot to Walcott, 18 December 1916, *Papers,* 1:181.

10. Buckingham to Walcott, 26 December 1916, *Papers,* 1:181.

11. Walcott to Goddard, 5 January 1917, and Goddard to Walcott, 9 January 1917, *Papers,* 1:190–91.

12. Walcott to R. S. Woodward, President, Carnegie Institution of Washington, 1 June 1918, *Papers,* 1:232–33.

13. Goddard to Walcott, 11 April 1917, *Papers,* 1:194.

14. Abbot to Walcott, 14 April 1917, and Walcott to Goddard, 20 April 1917, *Papers,* 1:195–96.

15. Goddard to Walcott, 20 August 1917, *Papers,* 1:199.

16. Walcott and Stratton to Major General George O. Squier, U.S. War Department, 22 January 1918, and report on Dr. Goddard's device by Abbot and Buckingham, 22 January 1918, *Papers,* 1:210–12.

17. *Papers,* see footnote, 1:213.

18. These activities are described in great detail in *Papers,* 1:213–95.

19. Abbot to Walcott, "Report on Trip to Schenectady and Worcester," 19 March 1918. Robert H. Goddard-Smithsonian Institution Correspondence in the Archives of the Smithsonian Institution (hereafter cited as "S I Archives").

20. Walcott to Squier, 19 March 1918; Abbot to Walcott, 29 March 1918; Walcott to Maj. Gen. E. H. Crowder, 1 April 1918; Abbot to Goddard, 2 April 1918; SI Archives.

21. Goddard to Walcott, 1 May 1918, SI Archives.

22. Walcott to Squier, 3 May 1918; Capt. J. R. Hoover, Office of Chief of Ordnance, U.S. Army, to Walcott, 10 May 1918; SI Archives.

23. "Statement of C. G. Abbot," 31 May 1918, SI Archives. Goddard to George I. Rockwood, 24 January 1918, *Papers,* 1:212. Colonel E. M. Shinkle, Army Ordnance Department, to Rockwood, 27 May 1918; Memorandum by Brigadier General C. McK. Saltzman, Signal Corps, for Acting Chief of Ordnance, 27 May 1918; Goddard to Walcott, 29 May 1918; Walcott to Squier, 31 May 1918; *Papers,* 1:228–32.

24. See note 12. Also Woodward to Walcott, 3 June 1918; Walcott to Goddard, 3 June 1918; Goddard to Abbot, 4 June

1918; telegram, Abbot to Goddard, 5 June 1918; *Papers*, 1: 233–34.

25. Telegram George E. Hale to Abbot, 10 July 1918; Goddard to Walcott, 15 July 1918; *Papers*, 1:246–48.

26. Goddard to Edmund C. Sanford, 15 July 1918; telegram, Abbot to Hale, 17 July 1917; Squier to Chief of Ordnance, 19 July 1918; Abbot to Goddard, 22 July 1918; telegram, Goddard to Abbot, 1 August 1918; *Papers*, 1:248–49.

27. Goddard to Walcott, 8 August 1918, *Papers*, 1:253.

28. Memorandum, Abbot to Walcott, 14 October 1918; Chairman, U.S. Employees' Compensation Commission, to C. N. Hickman, 10 October 1918; SI Archives.

29. Telegram, Abbot to Goddard, 23 September 1918, *Papers*, 1:288–89.

30. Program for Tests at Aberdeen Proving Ground, *Papers*, 1:296–99.

31. Goddard to Walcott, 15 November 1918, *Papers*, 1:300-301.

32. Lieutenant Colonel Herbert O'Leary, Army Ordnance Department, to Secretary, Smithsonian Institution, 19 November 1918; Abbot to Goddard 26 March 1919; *Papers*, 1:302–3, 315–16.

33. Goddard to Abbot, 7 April, 1919, *Papers*, 1:320.

34. "Invents Rocket with Altitude Range 70 Miles; Terrible Engine of War Developed in Worcester by Dr. Robert H. Goddard, Professor of Physics at Clark in Laboratory of Worcester Tech, under Patronage of U.S. War Department," *Worcester Evening Gazette* (Massachusetts), 28 March 1919, *Papers*, 1:316.

35. Abbot to Goddard, 10 April 1919; Goddard to Abbot, 15 April 1919; Abbot to Goddard, 18 April 1919; *Papers* 1:322–23.

36. *Smithsonian Miscellaneous Collections*, vol. 71, no. 2, 69 pp., 10 pls.; reprinted in *Papers*, 1:337–406.

37. "New Rocket Devised by Prof. Goddard May Hit Face of the Moon; Clark College Professor Has Perfected Invention for Exploring Space—Smithsonian Society Backs It," *Boston Herald*, 12 January 1920, reprinted in *Papers*, 1:406.

38. *Papers*, 1:393–95.

39. Goddard to Walcott, 19 January 1920, *Papers*, 1:410.

40. Goddard's Diary (hereafter cited as Diary), 11 July-13 September 1921, *Papers*, 1:474.

41. Diary, 16–17 March 1926, *Papers*, 2:580–82.

42. Goddard to Abbot, 5 May 1926, *Papers*, 2:587–90.

43. *Papers*, 2:588.

44. Diary, 1–11 April 1926; *Papers*, 2:584–85.

45. Diary, 13 April-5 May 1926; *Papers*, 2:586–87.

46. Diary, Papers, 2:585.

47. Goddard to Abbot, 29 June 1926, *Papers*, 2:597–98.

48. Diary, 20 July 1927, *Papers*, 1:620.

49. Diary, 31 August 1927, *Papers*, 2:621.

50. Diary, 24–26 December 1928, *Papers*, 2:651–53; Goddard to Abbot, 3 January 1929, *Papers* 2:654–55.

51. Diary, 3–17 July 1929, *Papers*, 2:667–68; Description of Flight of 17 July 1929, Goddard's Notebook on Experiments, *Papers*, 2:668–73.

52. Goddard to Abbot, 18 July 1929, *Papers*, 2:674–76; Abbot to Goddard, 20 July 1929, *Papers*, 2:678. Memorandum to Associated Press by Smithsonian Institution, 20 July 1929, *Papers*, 2:679–81.

53. "Goddard Experimental Rocket Explodes in Air; Clark Professor Making Tests on Auburn Farm," *Worcester Evening Gazette*, 17 July 1929, reprinted in *Papers*, 2:673; "Moon Rocket-Man's Test Alarms Whole Countryside—Blast as Metal Projectile Is Fired Through Auburn Tower Echoes For Miles Around, Starts Hunt for Fallen Plane, and Finally Reveals Goddard Experiment Station," *Boston Globe*, 18 July 1929, reprinted (along with other newspaper clippings) in *Papers*, 2:674.

54. Robert E. Molt, State Fire Inspector, to George C. Neal, State Fire Marshal, Boston, 25 July 1929, *Papers*, 2:682.

55. Goddard to Abbot, 26 July 1929, *Papers*, 2:682–84. A summary of Dr. Goddard's experimental notes for the test at Camp Devens is presented in Goddard, *Rocket Development: Liquid Fuel Rocket Research 1929–1941* (hereafter cited as *Rocket Development*), Esther C. Goddard and G. Edward Pendray, editors (Englewood Cliffs, New Jersey: Prentice-Hall, Inc., 1961), pp. 1–14.

56. The efforts which lead to the issuance of a license by the War Department for use of the Camp Devens Reservation for rocket experimentation are detailed in *Papers*, 2: 685–710.

57. C. Fayette Taylor, Department of Aeronautical Engineering, Massachusetts Institute of Technology, to Goddard, 22 November 1929, *Papers*, 2:713; and Diary, 23–27 November 1929, *Papers*, 2:713.

58. The events of the eight months between Charles A. Lindbergh's initial meeting with Dr. Goddard and the subsequent financial support by Daniel Guggenheim are described in *Papers*, 2:713–44.

59. Guggenheim to Wallace W. Atwood, 12 June 1930, and Atwood to Guggenheim, 13 June 1930, *Papers*, 2:744–45.

60. John C. Merriam to Goddard, 19 December 1929, and Goddard to Merriam, 26 December 1929, *Papers*, 2:726–28.

61. Atwood and Goddard to Abbot and other members of the Advisory Committee, 14 June 1930, *Papers*, 2:746; and statement released by Clark University "for publication in newspapers of Thursday, July 10, 1930," 9 July 1930, *Papers*, 2:752–54.

62. A summary of Goddard's experimental notes for the tests conducted in New Mexico is presented in *Rocket Development*, pp. 15–46 and 57–215.

63. Goddard to Abbot, 28 May 1930, *Papers*, 2:742.

64. Goddard to John A. Fleming, 22 January 1931, and statement regarding the desirability of a reissue of U.S. Patents 1,102,653 and 1,103,503 from the standpoint of national defense, 22 January 1931, *Papers*, 2:782–84.

65. H.R. 16451, House of Representatives, 21 January 1931, and H.R. 7174, House of Representatives, 8 January 1926, SI Archives.

66. W. H. Tschappat to Abbot, 6 February 1931, SI Archives.

67. Abbot to Goddard, to W. W. Gilbert, to J. T. Robinson, to R. Luce, and to Goddard, all 1 February 1931, SI Archives.

68. Telegram from Goddard to Atwood, 2 June 1932; Atwood to the members of the Advisory Committee on the Goddard Rocket Project, 14 June 1932; and Colonel Henry Breckinridge to Goddard, 16 June 1932; *Papers*, 2:830–32.

69. Diary, 28 June-21 July 1932, *Papers*, 2:833–34.

70. Goddard to Abbot, 5 August 1932, *Papers,* 2:837.

71. Abbot to Goddard, 25 August 1932, and Goddard to Abbot, 12 September 1932, *Papers,* 2:838–39.

72. Goddard to Abbot 2 September 1933, *Papers,* 2:865. Summaries of Dr. Goddard's experimental notes for the test conducted at Clark University, 1932–34, appear in *Papers,* 2:866–67 and 878–84. See also *Rocket Development,* pp. 47–56. These activities were assisted by a grant from the Guggenheim family of $2500 on 15 July 1933, *Papers,* 2:850–51 and 860.

73. Goddard to Abbot, 4 September 1934, *Papers,* 2:878.

74. Abbot to Goddard, 17 September 1934, *Papers,* 2:887–88.

75. Goddard to Abbot, 1 April 1935, *Papers,* 2:910–11.

76. Goddard to Abbot, 2 November 1935, *Papers,* 2:945.

77. Abbot to Goddard, 2 October 1935, *Papers,* 2:938-39.

78. See note 76.

79. *Smithsonian Miscellaneous Collections,* vol. 95, no. 3, 16 March 1936, 10 pp., 11 pls., 1 fig.; reprinted in *Papers,* 2:968–84.

80. *Papers,* 1:413–30.

81. *Papers,* 1:509–17.

82. *Papers,* 1:531–40.

83. *Papers,* 2:688–98.

84. Abbot to Goddard, 3 November 1923, *Papers,* 1:519.

85. Goddard to H. G. Wells, London, England, 20 April 1932, and Wells to Goddard, 3 May 1932, *Papers,* 2:821–23, 825.

6

Giulio Costanzi: Italian Space Pioneer

ANTONIO EULA, *Italy*

Giulio Costanzi was born in 1875. Originally an officer of artillery of the Royal Italian Army he joined in 1911 the Battaglione Specialisti del Genio. This military corps, with its free and captive balloons, airships, and hydrogliders, was the nucleus of the Italian Air Force. Part of its facilities included a laboratory with wind tunnels and a towing tank. Costanzi, who had a university degree as a civil engineer, was in charge of this laboratory, which had been created by the well-known air and space pioneer Gaetano Arturo Crocco (1877–1968), who died on January 19 of this year [1968].[1]

During World War I Costanzi was commander of a reconnaissance airplane squadron of the Italian Air Force. At the end of the war, as a lieutenant colonel, he headed the Experimental Station of the Air Force. In 1923, as a colonel, he joined the newly established independent Royal Air Force and was assigned various technical tasks. Later, he was technical assistant to the Air Force Minister and Professor at the Royal Air Force Academy in Caserta.

In 1928, he resigned from the Air Force as a General and was appointed member of the Consiglio di Stato. In 1938 he became President of the Registro Aeronautico Italiano, the Italian counterpart of the U.S.A. Federal Aviation Agency, and kept this official position until 1945. The author of several technical papers, he died at the age of ninety, in 1965.

In 1914 Costanzi published in the Italian magazine *AER*,[2] a paper which can be considered the first Italian contribution to the study of space flight. Costanzi anticipated in a poetic and prophetic way some features and problems of space flight and also, though in a particular sense, the possibility of using nuclear forces for propelling spacecraft.

Such a clear intuition of what was to happen more than forty years later is astonishing, and because the paper is rather short, it is translated in its entirety in the following paragraphs.

It seems now that the heroic period of conquest of the air is near its end. When, in the not too distant future, men seeking great achievements, having flown the Atlantic Ocean and made round-the-world flights, look for new obstacles to overcome, the Promethean age of the conquest of the sky will begin.

Is it really the time to consider escape from the Earth and to seek new colonies in space? As a matter of fact, it seems that the Earth has already become too narrow an area to contain such immense boldnesses, and that thoughtful audacious spirits can indeed seriously consider an undertaking born in the imagination of poets and novelists. These spirits wonder whether the barriers that forbid the undertaking of such a flight are really impenetrable, and whether the bonds that hold mankind on the narrow surface of our planet will be perennial. The planet's low, dense atmosphere ceases to be attractive. It is so dense that monstrous ships filled with hydrogen can float in it and heavy-winged machines can support themselves as on invisible rails. It is so impenetrable that only with enormous power consumption is it possible to reach a speed of a few hundred kilometers per hour. Yet only a short distance from us, just a few kilometers from our homes, it is possible to enter into free space that is endless, boundaryless, dragless, and nightless—where limitations to velocity do not exist and the sunlight flashes in a cloudless sky.

Some men endowed with faith and energy, and belonging to the heroic generation which attained the previous goal, are preparing themselves for the new attempt. From Russia Riabouchinsky announces that he is going to begin some preliminary experiments in his laboratory at Koutchino. In France Esnault-Pelterie,[3] one of the first conquerors of the air, has demonstrated on the basis of sound and thoughful calculations, that the present barriers, though severe and insuperable to-day, are of a mechanical and structural character, which is to say that the possibility of a practical realization does exist.

Which kind of machines will prove capable of departing from the atmosphere into space, where no air exists to give

71

lift and life? Has there yet been conceived by human genius, or does it yet exist in embryo, an engine capable of thrusting a vehicle into the vacuum of space.?

For many years it has been recognized that such an engine does exist. One need only to think of a machine-gun free to recoil on its own carriage while launching shells at great velocity in order to concieve of a propelling unit which would operate better in a vacuum. In any case, the principle of the so-called reaction engine is well known. The problem is to determine whether the energy required to attain this goal does exist, or whether we here face an insuperable natural barrier.

It is known that the energy necessary to transfer a body from the surface of a star to infinity is given by

$$L = K \frac{mM}{R}$$

where K is the universal gravitation constant, m the mass of body, M that of the star, and R the radius of the star.

From this formula, it follows that a body on the Earth's surface, launched with a velocity equal to or larger than 11,280 m/sec, will not fall back but will continue traveling indefinitely. For a 1-kg body on the Earth, the energy to attain this velocity would be 6,371,103 kgm, equivalent to 14,970 cal. Now 1 kg of hydrogen-oxygen mixture contains a much smaller amount of energy, i.e. 1,420 cal[4]; therefore 1 kg of such a mixture has not within itself the capability of transfering even a single gram of its own substance to infinity.

On the other hand, 1 kg of radium, which contains 2,900,000,000 cal, would have an energy 194,000 times greater than the amount required of it.

Esnault-Pelterie has shown that a body on the Earth subjected to a constant force greater than its weight and directed outwards would attain a velocity sufficient to make its propulsion superflous at an altitude approximately equal to an Earth radius.

Let us analyze the order of magnitude of the energy involved if one were to transfer, for example, a body from the Earth to the Moon and bring it back again to Earth. Three phases are to be considered:

First phase: the body accelerates up to an altitude of 5,780 km; then its velocity will be 8,180 m/s and the time spent 24 minutes and 9 seconds;

Second phase: the engine is cut off; the body continues to move on account of inertia; at the moment where the attraction of both Earth and Moon become equal, the velocity will be reduced to 2,030 m/sec and the time spent will be 48 hours and 30 minutes;

Third phase: the engine is accelerated in the opposite direction for descent onto the Moon; the time spent during this phase is 3 minutes and 46 seconds. The total elapsed time from departure will be 48 hours and 58 minutes, and that for return will be the same. During this return trip the engine will operate only 28 minutes, the time being the same both going and returning.

Now let us assume that the vehicle weight is 1000 kg, of which 300 are consumable (this ratio is customary for present-day airplanes). A short calculation shows that the engine power should be 414,000 hp. Such a vehicle at the speed of 10 km/sec would spend 47 days and 20 hours to reach Venus and 90 days and 15 hours to reach Mars.

The analysis of probable sensations of a space traveller during the trip deserves particular attention. Aside from difficulties arising from the temperature and space radiations, there exists a probably serious one of a physiological character. At a distance of 5,780 km from the Earth the traveller will feel as though his weight was eleven tenths of his normal weight; this feeling, though unpleasant, will not be prejudicial to his organism. But, when, during the second phase, weightlessness occurs, he will have the feeling of falling with the vehicle which contains him. Then it would be necessary to replace the force of gravity by a constant acceleration of the engine so controlled as to provide an acceleration that will at every moment replace the loss of gravitational pull.

This method would eliminate the above mentioned inconvenient, but would cause a progressive increase of velocity to 61,700 m/sec in the case of a lunar trip, with the advantage of reducing the required time to 3 hours and 5 minutes; but the required power would be 4,760,000 hp. Then, even though the above assumed 300 kg of propellant were dynamite, it would amount to $\frac{1}{47,300}$ of the propellant necessary; but if radium were used it would still be 433 times that required. Travelling at a constant acceleration, Venus could be reached in 35 hours and 4 minutes with a maximum speed of 643 km/sec and Mars in 49 hours and 20 minutes with a maximum speed of 883 km/sec.

The order of magnitude of such velocities is that of the celestial bodies, and in order to obtain the necessary energy concentration at the start it would be necessary to seek them among atomic forces.

If a 1000-kg vehicle had on board 400 kg of radium and we were able to extract from it the required energy, we would have available the amount of propellant sufficient to a round-trip to Venus; but this amount would be hardly sufficient for an analogous trip to Mars, always assuming a flight with constant acceleration.

Thus the difficulties that prevent us from achieving this ultimate human dream are not beyond human reason, but are dependent only on the possibility of a practical realization of the necessary means. Having observed the prodigiously accelerated development of findings in the field of mechanics, we can therefore doubt but cannot deny such a possibility.

On the other hand argument and speculation are useless and unfruitful. The world advances, driven by tenacious willpower rather than by words and formulae. Perhaps scientists will still be arguing when the first auto-meteor penetrates interplanetary space.

Some comments on Costanzi's text seen appropriate.

His clear intuition as to the advantage, from an economical point of view, of flying at high altitudes, of the need for jet engines, and of the enormous propellant consumption required by space flight, is remarkable.

As far as his considerations on Moon flights are concerned, it is to be noted that the escape velocity would not be reached, because the Moon is an Earth satellite and therefore is always subject to the Earth's attraction. Nevertheless, as is well known, the velocity necessary to fly to the Moon is very near, although less than, the escape velocity. The considerations on the second phase of the lunar trip seem not to be completely clear.

The restarting of the engine during the third phase is probably intended to decelerate for descent onto the Moon, but Mr. Constanzi does not say this explicitly.

The ratio of propellant to total weight in present-day spacecraft is much higher than that assumed by the author but was valid for the airplanes of his day.

What is astonishing are the author's very clear conception of the physiological sensations that space travellers have experienced during the coasting flight, and his concept of creating artificial gravity by means of acceleration to eliminate it. In order to obtain this result, which the author considered necessary, flights without acceleration are not taken into consideration by him. Walter Hohmann (in 1925) had not yet shown the advantages of following cotangential trajectories.[5]

It is not clear how the figure of 4,760,000 hp [6] for the required power was calculated. It would undoubtedly have been better to have spoken in terms of thrust, which is well known, than in terms of power, or to have considered energy instead of power, as the author did at the start of his paper.

The author's intuition of the advantages offered by the use of atomic forces to make space flight easier is extraordinary indeed.

In conclusion, though some inexactness is apparent, Costanzi's paper is a most interesting, valuable, and ingenious anticipation of the many space events which have now taken place, more than forty years later.

NOTES

1. See Luigi Crocco, "Gaetano Arturo Crocco, 1877–1968," *Astronautica Acta,* vol. 14, no. 6 (October 1969), p. 689.—Ed.

2. Giulio Constanzi, "To Escape from The Planet," *AER,* no. 5, 1914.

3. Robert Esnault-Pelterie, "Considerations sur les résultats d'un allégement indéfini des moteurs" [Considerations on the Results of Indefinite Decrease in Weight of Engines], *Journal de Physique Théoretique et Appliquée,* ser. 5, vol. 3, March 1913, pp. 218–30.

4. Apparently Costanzi, basing his calculations on those of Robert Esnault-Pelterie, made a copying error in his original article, where he is paraphrasing Esnault-Pelterie. The correct value should be 3,860 calories. See page 222 of note 3, above, or page 296 of Andrew G. Haley, *Rocketry and Space Exploration* (Princeton, New Jersey: D. Van Nostrand Company, Inc., 1958), which contains a complete English translation of Esnault-Pelterie's 1913 article (this is reprinted as an appendix to Paper 2 of this series).—Ed.

5. Walter Hohmann, *Die Erreichbarkeit Der Himmelskörper* [The Attainability of Heavenly Bodies], Munich-Berlin: R. Oldenbourg, 1925. An English translation has been published by the National Aeronautics and Space Administration, Washington, D.C., November 1960, as Technical Translation NASA TT F-44.—Ed.

6. An explanation of this figure appears on page 230 of Esnault-Pelterie (see note 3), and on page 301 of the English translation thereof (see note 4), wherein Esnault-Pelterie explains the need for 4,760,000 hp as follows:

The time used to reach the moon would be

$$t = 3 \text{ hr } 5 \text{ min.}$$

But in this new case, the work to be furnished, using the assumption of a 1,000 kg vehicle of which 300 kg are consumable, would reach 67.2×10^6 cal/kg of fuel, i.e., 131 times more than in the first case.

Dynamite would be 47,300 times too weak, but radium would still be 433 times too powerful.

As to the necessary power, it would be

$$\frac{857 \times 10^{10}}{24,000 \times 75} = 4.76 \times 10^6 \text{ hp.}$$

If we now assume that this method of constant propulsion is used for voyages to the closest planets and investigate what the times and velocities would be, we find the maximum velocity

for Venus	643 km/sec
for Mars	883 km/sec

and the corresponding times

for Venus	35 hr 4 min
for Mars	49 hr 20 min

7

Recollections of Early Biomedical Moon-Mice Investigations

Constantine D. J. Generales, Jr., *United States*

The year was 1931. The place was Zurich. The protagonists were two students, one aspiring to become an engineer, the other, a physician.

It was in the beginning of March when I decided to have my first lunch at the student cafeteria open to matriculants of the University of Zurich and of the Eidgenossische Technische Hochschule. I had just arrived from an intersemester vacation in Athens after having spent my sixth semester (third year) at the University of Berlin, and I had found quarters at 34 Scheuchzerstrasse overlooking the beautiful lake of Zurich. My decision to continue my medical studies at various university centers such as Athens, Heidelberg, Zurich, Paris and Berlin was not a random one but based on a pre-conceived plan to combine study and travel with attendance at lectures by professors of note in the various fields of medicine, e.g., Menge, Naegeli, Gougerot, Sauerbruch, His.

As I was waiting in line at the cafeteria, I happened to overhear a brief conversation in English behind me. At that time this was unusual since German and Schweizer Deutsch and some French were the most frequently spoken languages in that part of the country. Curious and eager to speak English again, I turned around and faced a tall blond chap who informed me that he had just arrived from Berlin. We lunched together. After the usual exchange of amenities, he unexpectedly turned the conversation to rockets, and of all things, of using them to get to the moon. He mentioned Herman Oberth, the German genius of rocketry, and Goddard, the immortalized American rocket pioneer. This German lad was quite serious about space travel and especially, of getting to the moon. I professed ignorance about the subject, even barely recollecting the distance between Earth and

the lunar satellite. My field was medicine and all my subjects and efforts were directed toward obtaining a medical degree. I just could not see, as a young student, how rockets and getting to the moon were going to help me in taking care of sick people!

The first conversation was quite brief, we finished our lunch and parted. Approximately two weeks later we met again by chance and the topic again reverted to the construction of rockets to get to the moon. To me, this whole thing, as I recall, seemed rather ridiculous, and I began making fun of my friend with "a one-track mind" until he reached into his pocket and pulled out a letter and asked me to read it. The envelope was postmarked Berlin. I remember staring at the indecipherable equations pertaining to mathematical problems and solutions in rocket design and propulsion. I was dumbfounded and deeply impressed when I recognized the signature to be that of Professor Albert Einstein. The recipient of the letter that I held in my hand was my newly found friend, Wernher Freiherr von Braun.

As I read the letter and listened to Wernher I became aware of the possibility of future space travel and realized that it was not as absurd as it had seemed at first. Remember, the year was 1931, two years before the founding of the famous British Interplanetary Society. The question immediately arose in my mind: what about man, can he withstand all these unknown forces and new experiences while being propelled by a sheet of flame into the vastness of space with the contemplated rocket? Right then and there I realized the inescapable necessity for the interdependence of medicine and technology in this great venture and I became a convert to the idea of exploration of space and space travel. I remember clearly my verbal reaction as I handed the letter back to Wernher with the caution, "Wenn Du zum Mond gehen willst ist es besser zuerst mit Mausen zu versuchen!" [1]

While Wernher was thinking in terms of linear propulsion and linear acceleration, I suggested that we might experiment with some mice and simulate the accelerative force by rotating them. The g factor would be the same. The laboratory centrifuge, second in popularity to the microscope, was standard equipment in bacteriology. However, its basic construction and its short radius would not do. We needed a larger contraption. What was wrong with a wheel from my bicycle? Nothing! It was no problem to attach the pedal to the dismantled front wheel, which had a tachometer.

A dozen white mice were easily "borrowed" from the animal caretaker in the biology lab with no promise of return. At this time, we had no funds other than our monthly allowance. It was decided to use Wernher's room (Figure 1), as it was larger than mine, and so within a week's time, we were spinning mice arranged in four little hammock-like bags attached, 90° apart, to the perimeter of the

FIGURE 1.—In a corner room of this house in Zurich, Switzerland, biomedical space-oriented experiments were conducted in 1931 by students Constantine Generales and Wernher von Braun.

bicycle wheel that was mounted on a stand. Thus, the centrifugal effect expressed in g's would be analogous to that experienced in rocket launchings.

Years later, I discovered that a number of people had used the centrifuge principle experimentally. For example, Erasmus Darwin, a physician and grandfather of Charles, had reported the first observation on the effects of centrifugal force on man. [2] And a crude centrifuge had been used by a Dr. Horn from 1814–1818 at the Charite Hospital of Berlin [3] in an attempt to improve the state of mentally deranged patients. Also, I learned many years after our early experiments, the Wright brothers had used the lowly bicycle wheel to acquire aerodynamic data necessary for the construction of their first airplane.

We had no idea what the tolerance of the mice might be. In the beginning, after a few turns of the wheel, the poor mice, whose hearts you could feel pounding in the palm of your hand, were placed upon the table. They would not move. Were they frightened? But frightened mice ordinarily tend to run away! I nudged them and still they would not move. Their eyes were open and as they were lying on their side I noticed a very rapid lateral nystagmus. Only when the nystagmus began to subside did the little creatures start to move in ever widening spirals. Many of the mice succumbed to the very high "acceleration" forces (to 220 g's). [4] Autopsies that I performed showed a displacement of the heart and lungs (Figure 2). There was bleeding from the intrathoracic, intraabdominal, and intracranial areas. All the organs in the chest and abdominal cavities, as well as the brain, were displaced and torn in varying degrees from the surrounding tissues. It was obvious that the force which we had achieved was far greater than the mice could tolerate. I noticed that in some cases, the entire cardiovascular system was disrupted. Were some of the milder effects transitory? Could they be prevented? Would permanent damage result? A new area of investigation was opening up, that of g forces, whose limits had to be defined before man was to attempt to reach the moon. The investigations were proving very exciting.

Right at the height of our activities, a dramatic incident occurred. A mouse accidentally slipped out of its cradle and was dashed against the wall leaving bloody stains at the point of impact. The next day (I believe it was the third day of our experiments),

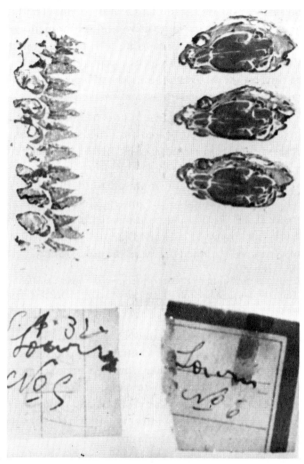

FIGURE 2.—First biomedical documentation of space-travel-oriented studies. Photograph illustrates various degrees of damage in the paraffin-blocked histopathological stained slides of skull, brain, heart, and lungs of mice.

we were not too surprised that the landlady who was not accustomed to the odor of small laboratory animals, noticed "the blood on the wall"; became infuriated; seized my notes as evidence of nonsensical cruelty and torture; and threatened to evict us and notify the police unless we immediately ceased these crazy experiments.

A long time ago, about a century and a half, before our space-minded experiments, there had been another landlady in Avignon. She was more cooperative and indeed showed some courage. Her boarder, a Joseph Michel Montgolfier, had been gazing before a burning fireplace at an engraving depicting the siege of British-held Gibraltar by the allied French and Spanish land and sea forces. His eyes next wandered over to the fireplace and,

as countless generations had before him, watched the smoke rise from the fire in the hearth. Now, why couldn't the besieged English leave by air, he mused. If clouds float in the sky, why not capture a cloud of smoke in a bag? He obtained an oblong bag of fine silk from his landlady and held the open end over some burning paper. The bag swelled into an awkward sphere and immediately sailed to the ceiling much to his satisfaction and her very great surprise.[5] Thus, the first unmanned balloon ascension was conceived and aeronautical science was born in the western world.

Now back to the two police-threatened chagrined students. We had no choice but comply with our nonscientific but meticulous landlady. And, at the same time, we were very sad about our first casualty, which was, to the best of my knowledge, the first fatality of biomedical research conducted under admittedly crude but nevertheless effective simulated space-flight conditions. As a redeeming measure and to relieve our burdened conscience, we let loose the remaining lucky four mice in the fields to a happier life away from an institutional environment. Thus ended the Zurich portion of our experiments.

After continuing my studies in Paris in the autumn of 1931, at the Sorbonne, I resumed my experiments with a large centrifuge (50 cm.) and with the help of Helene, laboratory technician to Professor Milian, Chief of the Dermatology Clinic of the Hospital St. Louis, who prepared parafin sections for microscopic slides of the succumbed mice, I was able to show, for the first time, histopathologically, the effects of high g forces.[6] Unfortunately, my notes have not survived the usual ravages of time, but I still possess some of those original slides.

During summer 1931, Wernher and I traveled to Greece in my Opel roadster (Figure 3), and after we returned in October I visited with Wernher at the Raketenflugplatz in the outskirts of Berlin and met Rudolf Nebel and Klaus Riedel who were engineering liquid-propelled rockets. There I had the opportunity of seeing one of the launchings of Mirak I which rose to over 1000 feet. It was a spectacular sight as the pencil-shaped rocket descended, a small parachute attached to its tail. I shall never forget how the four of us, Wernher, Nebel, Riedel, and I raced to the landing spot, crowded into my Opel.

It was that little Opel again that helped make history, for as Wernher wrote in the British Interplanetary Society *Journal*:

Early one beautiful July morning in 1932 we loaded our two available motor cars and set out for Kummersdorf which lay some 60 miles south of Berlin. As the clock struck five, our leading car with a launching rack containing the silver-painted Mirak II atop and followed by its companion vehicle [the Opel] bearing liquid oxygen, petrol and tools, encountered Captain Dornberger at the rendezvous in the forests south of Berlin.[7]

The successful launching of Mirak II convinced the German Ordnance Department of the feasibility of the rocket as a missile as well as progenitor for space travel.

Although our early experiments were unrefined in the face of today's sophisticated methods, the very high g's over the many minutes of exposure produced for the first time scientific evidence as to what damage one might expect to unprotected living organisms. I noted cases of cerebral hemor-

FIGURE 3.—Wernher von Braun and Constantine Generales, on a pleasure trip to Greece in 1931, photographed in the Saint Gotthard Pass, where the author's Opel became overheated and chunks of snow and ice had to be used to cool the motor. Upon our return, because I was to be in Paris, the car was left in Wernher's care for the use of the Raketenflugplatz experts—to further the cause of rocket research. Shortly after my return from Paris I painted the Opel red. Subsequently it was stolen while I was visiting my parents in the United States.

rhage, pulmonary stelectasis, hemothorax, avulsion or dislocation of the eyeballs, and so on. To the green mind of this inquisitive and experimenting student, thoughts of presenting a paper disclosing these pathological findings, so completely unrelated to any orthodox discipline in the accepted medical curriculum of those days, never occurred.

Finally, in June 1960, the results of these original investigations first appeared in a medical journal.[8] Indeed, according to Dr. von Braun, it took 20 years for researchers in this and other countries to verify these results, and it wasn't until 1958 that I had an opportunity to present to Wernher several tissue slides of the mice as a memento of our early work (see Figure 4). Edward Diamond, senior editor of *Newsweek*, quoted Dr. von Braun as follows:

This was probably the first experiment in space medicine. The Air Force has probably spent $7 million to find out what we learned.[9]

In 1959 I proposed to the NASA, and in 1962 to the U.S. Air Force, a centrifugal space-vehicle simulator or Biocyclothanathron (Figure 5), to simulate, on the ground, the many unique properties of space flight.[10] Many of today's centrifugal facilities have subsequently incorporated certain features of the Biocyclothanathron.

It is of interest to note that in 1931, the same year our space-minded biomedical experiments were being performed, Karl Jansky was studying peculiar static noises from outer-space which gave birth to the new science of radio astronomy; Wiley Post was successfully completing the first round-the-world flight in his monoplane "Winnie Mae"; and an enthusiastic crowd, including von Braun and the author, was greeting Auguste Piccard in front of the Baur au Lac Hotel at Zurich, following his first stratospheric flight, on 27 May with Charles Knipfer, to 51,753 feet (15,786.5 m.), from Augsburg, Germany, to Glazier, Austria.

Incidentally, the Zurich-Paris research antedated my first flight experience in an airplane by two years. Thinking of this always reminds me of the quotation of Dr. M. P. Lansberg of Holland:

Space flight is indeed many centuries the senior of aviation, consequently, it was space medicine that preceded aviation medicine and not vice-versa.[11]

FIGURE 4.—Presentation by Dr. Constantine Generales to Dr. Wernher von Braun of the first biomedical-histopathological tissue slides from the mice used in their early experiments. Presentation took place during a testimonial dinner honoring Edward Teller and Wernher von Braun, 15 May 1958, New York City.

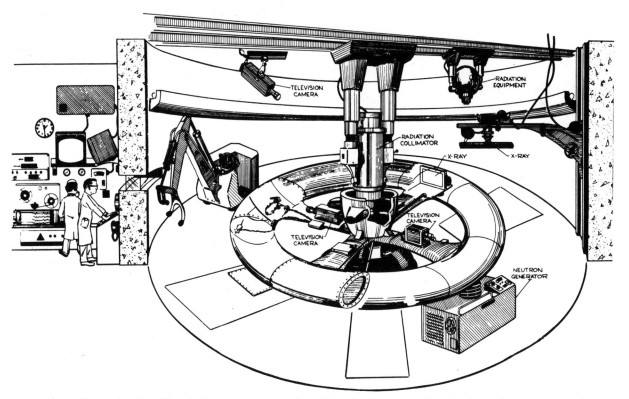

FIGURE 5.—The Biocyclothanathron, or cosmic vehicle simulator, conceived by the author and designed for him by the consulting engineering firm of McKiernan and Terry Corporation, Dover, New Jersey.

NOTES

1. "If you want to get to the moon, it is better to try with mice first!" Parenthetically, I would like to mention the Moonbeam Mouse Project that was the realization, thirty years later, of the foregoing statement. This project was presented before the 155th Annual Convention of the Medical Society of New York at Rochester, New York, 12 May 1961. Its aim was to acquire as much physiopathologic data as possible from the moon for medical evaluation before the advent of man. The purpose was threefold: (1) to investigate the behavior and effects of transplanted terrestrial life under physical lunar conditions, (2) to detect possible lunar microbial life, and (3) to study the effects of such captive hosts on the terrestrial germ-free rodent guests. It represented a refined inter-disciplinary study with multiple-channel telemetry of exquisite biomedical data for a predetermined length of time for recording respiration rate, body temperature, blood pressure, blood flow, red and white corpuscle count, also, determination of the gamma-globulin. Gamma-globulin itself is almost completely absent in absolutely germ-free bred mice. The mice themselves were to be contained in a special vehicle that would bore itself mechanically into the ground up to ten meters. The lunar soil was to be drawn into the specially designed capsule where the mice would be exposed to the radiation-free and temperature-constant subsurface lunar soil. The mouse-carrying capsule was to be thoroughly sterilized with ethylene oxide and to have a self-supporting ecology for a two-week life supporting period under the surface of the moon.

Since mice do not catch colds, they would be spared the discomfort of Astronauts Walter M. Schirra, Donn F. Eisele, and Walter Cunningham. Coryza was noticed first by Schirra within the first 24 hours; later the other astronauts became infected during the 11-day orbital flight of the Apollo 7 capsule, 11–27 October 1968, using 100-percent oxygen at about 5 pounds pressure. Isolation of a period of 2–3 weeks would be medically sound before extended space flights.

What happened to the "Moonbeam Mouse Project"? It died prematurely at the hands of a high NASA executive in the life sciences (1960). He could not foresee "how mice could survive in the moon's environment which does not have an appreciable atmosphere," even though the major details of propulsion, landing, life-support, telemetry, etc., were workable. It received, however, recognition by two world-renowned scientists: a NASA rocket engineer who commented that "this project could be of value for future manned lunar landings"; and a microbiologist of the Rockefeller Institute, who stated that it "presents a great interest from both the biological and medical points of view. In brief, I would be inclined to regard your project as a necessary first step in the analysis of the ecological problems that will arise when terrestrial organisms enter into contact with the various aspects of the lunar environment." The project was not pursued further.

See also C. D. J. Generales, "Selected Events Leading to the Development of Space Medicine," *New York State Journal of Medicine*, vol. 63, no. 9 (May 1963), p. 1310.

2. In his *Zoonomia* (1795), saying:

Another way of procuring sleep mechanically was related to me by Mr. Brindley, the famous canal engineer, who was brought up to the business of a mill-wright: he told me that he had more than once seen the experiment of a man extending himself across the large stone of a corn mill, and that by gradually letting the stone whirl, the man fell asleep, before the stone had gained its full velocity, and he supposed would have died without pain by the continuance or increase of the motion. In this case the centrifugal motion of the head and feet must accumulate the blood in both extremities of the body, and thus compress the brain.

3. William J. White, *A History of the Centrifuge in Aerospace Medicine* (Douglas Aircraft Company, Inc., Santa Monica, California, 1964).

4. Generales, "Space Medicine and the Physician," *New York State Journal of Medicine*, vol. 60, no. 11 (1 June 1960), p. 1745.

5. Peter Lyon, "When Man First Left the Earth," *Horizons*, vol. 1, September 1958, pp. 114–28.

6. Erik Bergaust, *Reaching for the Stars* (New York City: Doubleday & Company, Inc., 1960), p. 59; and *Project Satellite* (New York City: British Book Center, Inc., 1958), p. 23; Wernher von Braun, "Reminiscences of German Rocketry," *Journal of the British Interplanetary Society*, vol. 15, no. 3 (May-June 1956), p. 128; "Constantine D. J. Generales, Jr.," *Twenty-Fifth Anniversary Report, Harvard College—1954* (Cambridge, Massachusetts: Harvard University Printing Office), p. 429; "Space Medicine," in History of Medicine "An International Bibliography," *The Welcome Historical Medical Library*, vol. 27, no. 177 (April-May 1960); "Die Traene Der Ruehrung Quilt," *Weltbild*, Munich, June 2, 1958, p. 4; "Constantine D. J. Generales, Jr.," *Explorers Journal*, vol. 37, no. 4 (December 1959) p. 10; and "Mars-och Venus-skott at vänta när som helst" (from page 1 of Stockholms-Tidningen, 16 August 1960), *Explorers Journal*, vol. 38, no. 4 (December 1960), p. 18.

7. "Reminiscences of German Rocketry," *Journal of the British Interplanetary Society*, vol. 15, no. 3 (May-June 1956), p. 129.

8. See note 4.

9. "His Eyes Are on the Stars," *Saga*, February 1961.

10. Generales. "The Dynamics of Cosmic Medicine," *New York State Journal of Medicine*, vol. 64, no. 2 (15 January 1964), p. 231.

11. Martin Lansberg, *A Primer in Space Medicine* (New York City: Elsevier Publishing Company, 1960).

8

The Foundations of Astrodynamics

Samuel Herrick, *United States*

Astrodynamics is defined in terms of celestial mechanics and of space navigation in its broadest sense: pre-Sputnik, including orbit determination and correction, as well as post-Sputnik, which adds control and optimization.

Basically there are three areas of celestial mechanics:

1. *Mathematical celestial mechanics* is concerned with the existence of solutions to defined and restricted problems in celestial mechanics. It prefers methods that have generality in the sense that they are applicable to other fields of mechanics as well as to a range of problems in celestial mechanics. But these methods tend to be restricted to a given type of problem: e.g., the elegant potential and Hamiltonian methods are limited to conservative and quasi-conservative forces.

2. *Physical celestial mechanics* is concerned primarily with the use of celestial mechanics in the determination of physical constants that are of interest to other areas of physics, especially geophysics and astrophysics.

3. *Astrodynamics,* as we term the third area of celestial mechanics, is greatly interested in physical constants, but also in all other factors that contribute to accurate space navigation, such as integration constants, integration procedures, singularities, and indeterminacies. Astrodynamics makes fundamental use of the general methods of mathematical celestial mechanics, and also of special methods that fit particular real problems. But whereas mathematical celestial mechanics tends to pursue one solution to a conclusion, with maximum use of a particular class of elegant mathematical tools, astrodynamics seeks to develop all possible solutions for purposes of comparison and selection. Mathematical celestial mechanics is concerned with ideal problems involving motion in a theoretically simple framework; astrodynamics is concerned with fitting a theory to observation and to the coordinate systems of the real world, and so is concerned with precession, nutation, aberration, parallax, the reduction of observations (electronic as well as optical), and with all the force fields that are encountered in real problems. General methods and tools (e.g., the method of least squares and Bessel's functions) have often come out of the particular solutions of these real problems.

No "celestial mechanic" devotes himself exclusively to one of these areas, but his heart is likely to be in one of them, and his judgement less than clairvoyant in the others. I shall indicate some of the differences between the areas and their methods in the following discussions of the historical development of astrodynamics before 1940.

My own serious concern with astrodynamics and space navigation began when I was an undergraduate student at Williams College. Four letters from Dr. Robert H. Goddard survive to attest to my plan for graduate study in the area, to Dr. Goddard's encouragement, and to his kindliness in taking time to give it even when his own prospects were bleak. I quote from two paragraphs of one of his letters, dated 15 June 1932:

. . . owing to the depression, the rocket project is being discontinued July first, and the matter of its being resumed later is an uncertain one.

I cannot help feeling that a theoretical investigation such as you mention has advantages over experimentation during such times as these . . . .

These letters encouraged me to proceed to graduate study under Armin Otto Leuschner, Russell Tracy Crawford, and C. Donald Shane, at Berkeley, where I developed a thoroughgoing devotion to celestial mechanics as well as to space navigation.

Early History Illuminates the Character of Astrodynamics

Physical celestial mechanics may be said to have begun with Galileo Galilei, Isaac Newton, and the laws of force and gravitation. Astrodynamics and mathematical celestial mechanics, on the other hand, date back at least to Heracleides of Pontus in the fourth century B.C. The Greek invention of epicycles and eccentrics was developed into a system by Apollonius of Perga in the third century and Hipparchus of Alexandria in the second century B.C. It was refined and published by Ptolemy of Alexandria in the second century A.D., and came to be known as the Ptolemaic system. It is generally assumed that the epicycle was discredited by Johannes Kepler some 1500 years later, but in point of fact epicycles have persisted in astrodynamics down to the present day, and have extended their domain into other areas of science under the guise of Fourier series!

Hindsight is a valuable tool in the history of science and serves to illuminate on the one hand the contemporary understanding and acceptance of an idea, and, on the other, its clarity and persistence. The historian of science is likely to emphasize the former; the scientist himself is understandably more interested in the latter.

My own hindsight theory has been presented to my students over the past 20 years, and by them conveyed to others, but for the most part it has remained unpublished in the conventional sense (except in preprints of my reference work *Astrodynamics* [1]). Basically it asserts that history has been unjust to epicycles, and even to Nicolaus Copernicus. (Some historians have gone so far as to say that the system of Copernicus was just as cumbersome as the Ptolemaic system, and that Kepler was the real author of our modern heliocentric theory.)

With hindsight we can see that there are in a planet's motion three kinds of deviation from uniformity that confronted the Greeks and their successors, and required explanation by a "system" such as the Ptolemaic or the Copernican:

1. The annual or Copernican or retrograde deviation, caused by the motion of the Earth around the Sun.

2. The elliptic or Keplerian deviation, explained in simple two-body motion by the discovery that

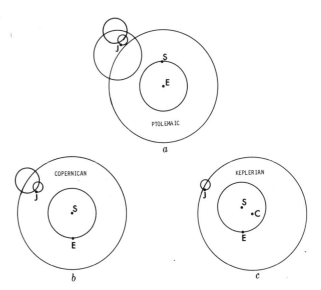

FIGURE 1.—*a*, Ptolemaic, *b*, Copernican, and *c*, Keplerian systems.

the relative orbit of the two bodies is an ellipse or other conic section.

3. The perturbed or Newtonian deviations, caused by the attractions of the planets and their satellites for one another.

The Ptolemaic system explained all of these deviations by geocentric deferents surmounted by epicycles piled upon epicycles (see Figure 1, in which the largest epicycle is the annual one, the second represents the elliptic ones, and the smallest represents the perturbed-deviation epicycles).

Aristarchus of Samos, and later Copernicus, eliminated the first deviation by shifting the center of the system from the Earth to the Sun, but the remaining deviations of the Copernican system still had to be accounted for by epicycles. It is this fact that led to the dictum that the Copernican system is "just about as complicated as the Ptolemaic system." It may have appeared so to contemporary eyes, but in retrospect it is clear that the elimination of the five annual planetary epicycles—that is, one epicycle for each of the five known planets, the total "population" as of that time—was a major simplification of the mechanics of the system, so that Copernicus unquestionably deserves the popular recognition accorded his name.

Kepler accounted for the second class of deviation by his perspicuous laws of planetary motion. It is this fact that has generally been credited with the destruction of the epicycle as a mechanical device.

But it should be recognized that there were perturbed deviations still unaccounted for in the Keplerian system. These deviations are most conspicuous in the motion of the Moon around the Earth, but the observations of Kepler's time were sufficiently accurate to show evidence also of the mutual perturbations of Jupiter and Saturn. When Newton's development of the law of gravitation made it possible to explain these perturbed deviations by mechanical means, the epicycles that had survived Kepler's onslaught were adopted into Newtonian mechanics. As a matter of fact, the basic epicyclic theory re-expanded to include even the elliptic deviations, thus rejecting the Keplerian system in favor of the Copernican system, whose handling of the elliptic terms by systems of epicycles (rechristened "Fourier series") proves to be simpler than the use of expressions in terms of Keplerian ellipses. In a sense this development may be noted as realistic astrodynamic replacement for a theoretical mathematical formulation.

We may note that Fourier series, with arguments that are multiples of a single angle, are less flexible than the original "astrodynamic" concept of epicycles, in which noncommensurate arguments are used: consider, for example, the representation of the geocentric motion of Venus, assuming that Venus and Earth are both travelling in circular heliocentric orbits. The Ptolemaic development would require only one epicycle; the Fourier development would require a theoretically infinite number of terms or epicycles. In modern perturbation theory we actually take account of the original epicyclic concept by combining several Fourier series that have arguments based upon different angular variables.

Astrodynamics Illuminated by Modern Treatment of Parallax

Recent developments in the treatment of geocentric parallax illustrate the importance to astrodynamics of physically real reference systems, and of the reduction of observations, as contrasted with developments in mathematical celestial mechanics, in which the reference system is idealized and observations are only theoretically taken into account.

Figure 2 shows how geocentric parallax enters into the observations. The position of the Sun is designated by S, that of the observed object by the

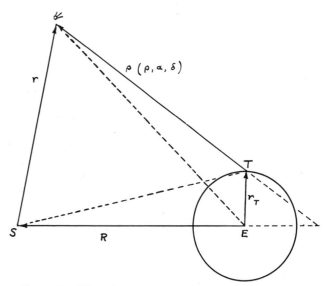

FIGURE 2.—Effect of geocentric parallax on observations.

cometary symbol "☄", the center of the Earth by E, and the observer by T (for Greek *topos*, place, and for the adjective topocentric). The dynamical position of ☄ is defined by the vector r (i.e., the line segment of S☄). The position of the Sun referred to the center of the Earth is specified conventionally by the "solar coordinates" that are given in astronomical almanacs, i.e., by the vector R (in the figure, ES). The geocentric position of the observer is specified by r_T (ET). Finally the topocentric position of the comet is specified by the vector ρ, which represents the topocentric distance (today the "range") ρ, right ascension α, and declination δ.

Classically the topocentric right ascension and declination are corrected for geocentric parallax to what they would have been had the observation been made from the center of the Earth, so that we have a single triangle relating E, S, and ☄. In some problems there is still justification for such a procedure, but in preliminary orbit calculations based upon observations of α and δ the parallax can be calculated only after a first approximation has given a value of ρ. Successive approximations of this character were standard practice in orbit determination for a great many years more than should have been the case! There were clumsy experiments with the "locus fictus" which is shown in Figure 2 as the intersection of the line of T☄ with the line ES. When Gibbs became interested in the orbit problem (1889),[2] largely in connection with his development of vector analysis, he was fortunately ignorant of astronomical practice. Consequently he decided very simply to correct the solar coordinates or the vector R from the center of the earth to the observer, at the start of the problem, by subtracting the known vector r_T, thus replacing the triangle $ES\angle$ by the triangle $TS\angle$. We find in the literature that this thought had occurred previously to Challis (1848),[3] and possibly to Leverrier (1855),[4] but had not taken hold. In fact astronomers were slow to adopt Gibbs' simple solution to the parallax problem until the much more recent contributions of Bower (1922, 1932),[5] Merton (1925),[6] Rasmusen (1951),[7] and others.

My own contribution to revised thinking in this area is associated with my work on my thesis [8] in 1935 and 1936 and with a mathematically oriented contribution of Poincaré (1906).[9]

Poincaré had suggested a "second approximation" for the Laplacian method of determining orbits. In the Laplacian method three observations of α and δ are numerically differentiated in order to produce velocities and accelerations in these angular coordinates (see Figure 3). The numerical differentiation ignores the higher derivatives in the first approximation, and it was these that Poincaré aimed to restore in his "second approximation." The Laplacian solution usually involves an assumption that the observer is travelling in a two-body orbit, and this assumption was uncritically accepted by Poincaré. But it is not the observer (T in Figure 3) who travels in a two-body orbit, nor is it even the center of the Earth (E in Figure 3) but (to a high degree of approximation) it is the barycenter of the Earth-

Moon system (B in Figure 3). Williams (1934) [10] attempted to make the Poincaré method work by correcting for geocentric parallax, but found that barycentric parallax ultimately prevented the process from converging. He did not attempt to apply Leuschner's (1913) [11] technique for complete elimination of parallax. William's work came to my attention when I was writing my thesis.

In reviewing the matter I became aware that the "motion of the observer" has nothing whatsoever to do with the problem, but is only a mathematical fiction: the "observer" may actually be three different observers at three different observatories. Consequently I decided to assume that this fictitious motion is determined by the real motion of the object and by the further assumption that the higher derivatives of the observed angular coordinates were zero. These assumptions made it possible to carry the "second approximation of Poincaré" to a successful "real" conclusion.

These assumptions also made it possible to relate the basic first approximation of the Laplacian methods exactly to the first approximation in the methods of Gauss,[12] Lagrange,[13] and Gibbs,[14] a relationship that is necessary to the development of criteria for the selection of method in "real" problems of orbit determination.

Linearization in Astrodynamics

One of the issues in astrodynamics that is still unresolved nearly three decades after 1939 is the use of linear methods in astrodynamics. Many linear methods based upon the work of Poincaré have been brought back into celestial mechanics without realization on the part of Poincaré or his successors that non-linear solutions to the problems considered not only exist, but have been in constant use! Nevertheless some of the ideas have been provocative, and newer uses may be found for them.

It seems clear at present that linear methods may be used *after* a basic non-linear integration is complete, especially to obtain partial derivatives, but that their use in the basic integration is suspect, and may be either erroneous or unnecessary or both.

The basic geometrical equation used in the comparison of a theory with observations is certainly in a category for which linearization is allowable, and I find that Stumpff (1931) [15] and I (1940) [16]

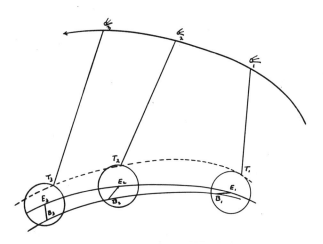

FIGURE 3.—Illustration of real problems of orbit determination.

were experimenting in the use linear combinations of the residuals before 1940. The equation is

$$\rho L = \rho = r + R \qquad L = \begin{Bmatrix} \cos \delta \cos \alpha \\ \cos \delta \sin \alpha \\ \sin \delta \end{Bmatrix}$$

where r is *SE* in Figure 2 and R has been corrected from *ES* to *TS* as discussed above.

Stumpff had already proposed the use of residuals in two of the ratios between the three components of L, selected according to size, when I, having proposed residuals in the interdependent components themselves, realized the equivalence of the two proposals. Essentially their aim was the avoidance of successive trigonometric recalculations of α and δ in comparisons of successive theories with the observations.

The basic Stumpff concept, I found, could be extended to residuals in ρ or r or even to the "ratios of the triangles" used in preliminary orbit determinations by the methods of Lagrange, Gauss, and Gibbs.

Series Expansions

Preliminary orbit determination, perturbation theory, correction theory, all make effective use of series expansions of many kinds. The use of Fourier series (or epicycles) has been remarked upon in the foregoing. Power series now almost universally called the "f and g series" were developed by Lagrange (1783) [17] for the equations

$$r_j = f_j r_0 + g_j \dot{r}_0$$

and from the series for $j=1, 3$ (with 0 replaced by 2) were developed the series for the "ratios of the triangles" referred to above. Gibbs (1889) [18] reexamined these expansions with his usual clear-sightedness and contributed new expressions for the "ratios" that have been the most generally recognized of his contributions to orbit theory. Happily, he left for me (1940) the extension of his developments to companion expressions, even simpler, for the determination of velocity components from three sets of position components.[19] These expressions have made the Lagrangian method for determining a preliminary orbit as effective as the Gaussian, but simpler. They enter also into orbit determinations that involve modern electronic observations of "range-rate."

In Conclusion

The foregoing remarks have been designed to give not a complete history of the pre-1940 foundations of astrodynamics, but rather samplings of these foundations that reveal the character of the subject, as it may be partially distinguished from the more purely mathematical developments of celestial mechanics. These samples nevertheless demonstrate again that universal principles and ideas tend to crop up independently in more than one time or place, that their excellence depends upon provability, and that they will be used when the time is ripe if they are continuous from sound antecedents.

Subsequent decades were to build enormously on the pre-1940 foundations, and to expand them, in conjunction with new instrumentation, with new vehicles, and with searches for previously inaccessible physical constants or for greater accuracy in relativity constants, the solar parallax, and other basic data of value both to physics and to precision space navigation.

NOTES

On 21 March 1974 Dr. Samuel Herrick Jr. died. His obituary was carried in *The Washington Post* of 25 March 1974. —Ed.

1. Samuel Herrick, *Astrodynamics* (London, New York: Van Nostrand Reinhold, 1971), vol. 1.
2. Josiah Willard Gibbs, "On the Determination of Elliptic Orbits from Three Complete Observations," *Memoirs of the National Academy of Science*, vol. 4, 1889, pp. 81–104; Ernst Friedrich Wilhelm Klinkerfues, *Theoretische Astronomie*, ed., edited by Hugo Buchholz (Braunschweig: Vieweg, 1912), pp. 413–18; and *The Collected Works of J. Willard Gibbs* (New York: Longmans Green, 1928), vol. 2, pt. 2, pp. 118–48.
3. James C. Challis, "A Method of Calculating the Orbit of a Planet or Comet from Three Observed Places," *Memoirs of the Royal Astronomical Society*, vol. 14, 1848, pp. 59–77.
4. Urbain Jean Joseph Leverrier's anticipation of the correlation of solar coordinates to the observer was once shown to the author by Ernest C. Bower, but he has not been able to find it for reference in this paper.
5. Ernest C. Bower, "On Aberration and Parallax in Orbit Computation," *Astronomical Journal*, vol. 34, 1922, pp. 20–30; and "Some Formulas and Tables Relating to Orbit Computation and Numeric Integration," *Lick Observatory Bulletin*, no. 445, vol. 16, 1932, pp. 34–45.
6. Gerald Merton, "A Modification of Gauss's Method for the Determination of Orbits," *Monthly Notes* (of the Royal Astronomical Society), vol. 85, 1925, pp. 693–731; ibid., vol. 86, 1926, pp. 150–51; ibid., vol. 89, 1929, pp. 451–53. Also

see Russell Tracy Crawford, *Determination of Orbits of Comets and Asteroids* (New York: McGraw-Hill, 1930), pp. 103–35.

7. Hans Qvade Rasmusen, "Tables for the Computation of Parallax Corrections for Comets and Planets," *Publikationer og mindre Meddelelser fra Københavns Observatorium,* no. 155, 1951, pp. 3–7.

8. Herrick, "The Laplacian and Gaussian Orbit Methods," *University of California Publication, Contributions of Los Angeles Astronomical Department,* vol. 1, 1940, pp. 1–56.

9. Jules Henri Poincaré, "Sur la détermination des orbites par la méthode de Laplace" [On the Determination of Orbits by the Method of Laplace], *Bulletin Astronomique,* vol. 23, 1906, pp. 161–87.

10. Kenneth P. Williams, *The Calculation of the Orbits of Asteroids and Comets* (Bloomington: Principia, 1934).

11. Armin Otto Leuschner, "Short Methods of Determining Orbits" (Second and third papers), *Publication of the Lick Observatory, University of California,* vol. 7, 1913, pp. 217–376 and 455–83.

12. Carl Friedrich Gauss, *Theoria motus corporum coelestium in sectionibus conicis solem ambientium* [Theory of the Motion of the Heavenly Bodies Moving about the Sun in Conic Sections] (Hamburg, 1809); translated by Charles Henry Davis (Boston: Little, Brown, 1857).

13. Joseph Louis Lagrange (1736–1813), "Sur le problème de la détermination des orbites des comètes, d'après trois observations" [On the Problem of the Determination of the Orbits of Comets from Three Observations], *Nouvelle Mémoire de l'Academy Royale des Sciences et Belles-Lettres de Berlin; Oeuvres* (Paris: Gauthier-Villars, 1869), vol. 4, pp. 439–532.

14. See note 2.

15. Karl Stumpff, "Uber eine kurze Methode der Bahnbestimmung aus drie oder mehr Beobachtungen" [On a Short Method of Orbit Determination from Three or More Observations), *Astronomischer Nachrichten,* vol. 243, 1931, pp. 317–36, and vol. 244, 1932, pp. 433–64.

16. See note 8.

17. See note 13.

18. See note 2.

19. See note 8.

9

Vladimír Mandl: Founding Writer on Space Law

DR. VLADIMÍR KOPAL, *Czechoslovakia*

In the industrial city of western Czechoslovakia, Pilsen (Plzeň), famous for its Škoda engineering enterprise and large breweries producing the famous Pilsner beer, Dr. Vladimír Mandl (Figure 1) was born on 20 March 1899 and there lived the major part of his life. He became a pioneer in astronautics in Czechoslovakia and, in particular, author of the first monograph on legal problems of outer space flights.

The family Mandl had lived in Pilsen for gener-

FIGURE 1.—Dr. Vladimír Mandl (1899–1941).

ations. Vladimír's father, Dr. Matouš Mandl, was an attorney and his son, though an engineering enthusiast since his youth, decided to follow his father's career. After studies at the Pilsner high school Vladimír entered the Czech Faculty of Law, Charles University of Prague, where he graduated on 21 November 1921. Following graduation, he first practiced for a short time at a district court in Prague and later in an attorney's office. In March 1927 he opened his own office in Pilsen.

While still a student Vladimír Mandl developed a deep interest in legal theory, especially in private law. Between 1921 and 1926 he was a member of the seminar on civil law procedure directed by the distinguished Czech scholar Professor Václav Hora. In 1925 Mandl submitted an interesting report on problems of evidence to the first Congress of Czechoslovak Lawyers. Later (1926), he wrote a monograph on Czechoslovak civil law regarding marriage. Finally, Mandl completed his specialization in civil law procedure by postgradual studies at the University of Erlangen, in Germany, where he obtained a doctorate by his dissertation on the law of damages.

Having qualified for the bar with such excellent scholarship, Vladimír Mandl was free to dedicate his energy to actual legal problems created by industrial and technological developments of the 1920s and 1930s. First, he published a series of essays on the legal aspects of motor vehicles. These he amplified, in 1929, into a monograph on the subject.

Simultaneously Mandl studied legal problems of aviation which was developing rapidly in the years following World War I. His enthusiasm was so great that he became a pilot. The result of Mandl's intensive work in this field was his study on air law,[1] the first systematic treatise on this new subject writ-

ten in Czechoslovakia. Following a historical introduction, the author dealt first with the Czechoslovak
air regulations. In the second part he considered
some general problems of air law, such as liability
arising from international air transport contracts,
conflicts of law concerning aviation, customs, and
insurance against damage caused by aircraft. The
final chapter dealt with air warfare.

Dr. Mandl submitted his book on air law as his
advanced work in residence, hoping to gain a pro-
fessorship at the Faculty of Mechanical and Electrical Engineering, Czech Technical University of
Prague. Documents deposited in the Archives of the
University of Prague demonstrate that Mandl fulfilled admirably all the conditions required and that
his scholarly work and knowledge were highly respected by the accreditation commission.[2] On 20
September 1932 the Czechoslovak Minister of Education confirmed the decision of the Board of Professors of the Faculty concerning the granting of
venia docendi to Dr. Vladimír Mandl for the subject, Law of Industrial Enterprises.[3] Although appointed for a different course, air law remained his
concern, as witnessed by his study of the Paris
Convention on the Regulation of Aerial Navigation
and by the substantial article on parachutes which
he published in 1935 in French.[4] Beginning with
the academic year, 1933–34, the course given by
Professor Vladimír Mandl on industrial law appears
in the university curriculum, as it did in the year
1938–39. As is known, German troops occupied the
whole of Czechoslovakia in March 1939, and in
autumn of that year the Nazis closed all Czech
universities. That also meant the end of Mandl's
University teaching.

During the last few years before the occupation
Professor Mandl participated in the search of documents and objects for the aeronautical collection of
the National Technical Museum in Prague.[5] For
this purpose he visited the foremost foreign mu-
seums and reported on them in Czech journals.
For example, in 1937 he visited the Frunze Air
Museum in Moscow and in summer 1938 the aviation collection of the Smithsonian Institution in
Washington.[6] He was also familiar with the aeronautical collections in Paris and Munich.

The loss of independence in 1939 interrupted
the successful development of Czechoslovak aviation. Shortly before those events, Mandl concluded
his article about the Smithsonian's Museum by

saying: "The glorious past and the promising present of Czechoslovak aviation will certainly be reflected in one of the best collections of the Czechoslovak Technical Museum."

Mandl thought about the Museum also during
his "involuntary holidays in the sanatorium in
Pleš" when his illness was added to the tragedy of
his nation.[7]

His keen interest in aeronautics led Vladimír
Mandl to think about the more advanced means of
space transport. While the pioneers of astronautics
tested their modest rockets, Mandl thought of them
as instruments of navigation in space which would
some day require new rules of law—space law. It
was in this new field that he was able to apply crea-
tively his broad knowledge, which went well beyond
the usual limits of legal scholarship and which
made it possible for him to contribute to the technical aspects of rocketry as well. The results of his
studies and thoughts in astronautics fall into two
categories.

The first is found in his book, "The Problem of
Interplanetary Transport," which appeared in 1932
in Prague.[8] His treatise opened with a brief survey
of developments in astronautics, in which he described the work of Konstantin Tsiolkovskiy, Dr.
Robert H. Goddard, Dr. Franz von Hoefft, Professor Hermann Oberth, and others. In the second
part he explained the basic principles of rocketry.
The book concluded by his own drawing of a high
altitude rocket (Figure 2) for which he applied, on
14 April 1932, for a Czechoslovak patent.[9] Mandl's
rocket would have consisted of three cylinders, one
inserted into the other. The payload would have
been placed in the head of the interior rocket
("automatic instruments for measurements of pressure, compositions of atmosphere, temperature,
radiation, etc. in the stratosphere and beyond").
Nozzles in the form of ring slots around the circumference of the rocket would be near the top of
rockets which should be fired successively. Both
solid and liquid propellants would have been used.

In the second category, however, without any
doubt falls the important work by which the name
of Professor Vladimír Mandl is recorded forever in
the history of astronautics. It is continued in his
monograph on "The Law of Outer Space, a Problem of Spaceflight," for which he finally found a
publisher in 1932 in Germany.[10] In this concise
book Mandl placed before the reader many

PATENTNÍ ÚŘAD

REPUBLIKY   ČESKOSLOVENSKÉ

Třída 44 d.   Vydáno 25. září 1931.

PATENTOVÝ SPIS č. 52236.

JUDr. VLADIMÍR MANDL, PLZEŇ.

Vysoko stoupající raketa.

Přihlášeno 14. dubna 1932.   Chráněno od 15. května 1935.

Předmětem vynálezu jest vysoko stoupající raketa, složená z několika válcovitých raket do sebe zasunutých, postupně vypalovaných, při čemž po vypálení jedné rakety její prázdný obal jest odmrštěn výbuchem rakety další, čímž dociluje se výhodnějšího pohonu. Zasunutím válcových raket stejné podoby do sebe se umožňuje spojení libovolného počtu raket, bez újmy aerodynamických vlastností a rovnováhy celku. Rovnováha je podporována tím, že výfuk výbušných plynů děje se vpředu každé jednotlivé rakety. Vhodný pohon docilen spojením třaskavin dvojího druhu, totiž pevných a kapalných.

Na výkresu jest znázorněn schematicky příklad provedení vynálezu.

Přístroj jest sestaven ze tří válcovitých raket I—III, vsunutých do sebe (vnější raketa č. I vyznačena jest silnějšími čarami, ostatní rakety jsou postupně menší a menší, avšak zařízení jejich jest podobné). Užitečná váha A (samočinné přístroje k měření tlaku a složení vzduchu, teploty, záření atd. ve výši stratosférické a i další) umístěna jest v hlavě vnitřní rakety č. III. Výbušné plyny náboje rakety vyfukují tryskou B ve tvaru prstencové štěrbiny kol celého obvodu rakety; trysce předchází rovněž prstencová spalovací komora C. Tryska je umístěna blíže vrcholu rakety, čímž má býti dosaženo rovnováhy letu, neboť působiště reakčního účinku jest posunuto do výše, před těžiště rakety, takže nastává zde táž výslednice sil, jakoby raketa byla reakcí tažena, nikoli tlačena jako u raket jiných; vedle toho má každá raketa směrové tyčky F. Štěrbina trysky, jdouc kolem celého obvodu rakety, jest značně dlouhá, čímž dociluje se rychlého, účinného vyprázdnění třaskavinové nádrže; při dalších raketách jest délka trysky vždy menší a menší. Vnitřní rakety mají též menší zásobu třaskavin a nesou menší náklad (též odporu vzduchu ubývá do výše).

Počínaje č. I. zapalují se rakety jedna po druhé. Každá raketa má dvojí třaskavinový náboj: pevný D (střelný prach) a tekutý E (zkapalněné plyny nebo hořlavé tekutiny, alkoholy atd.). Nejprve vybuchne náboj prachu, který jest nacpán v trysce a spalovací komoře, a vyžene raketu do výše. Plameny vybuchujícího prachu, sršící z trysky, ohřívají těleso rakety a kapaliny E. které tamže se nalézají, roztahují se teplem, a proudí

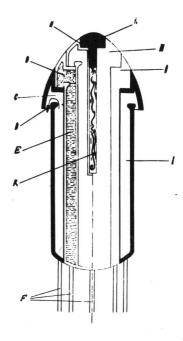

Příloha k patentovému spisu čís. 52236.

FIGURE 2.—First page of Dr. Mandl's patent and the design of his high-altitude rocket.

thoughts which have not lost their relevance despite the passage of time.

Attention should first be drawn to his concept of the law of outer space as an independent legal branch, based on specific instruments of space flight and governed by different principles than is the law of the sea or the law of the air. Although the writer did not underestimate the examples of the other legal branches for analogies in special cases, he stressed the need for specific regulation of the legal problems of astronautics. From this point of view he considered in the first part of his monograph selected problems of civil law, criminal law, and international law concerning outer space.

Still more interesting is the second part of the study, "The Future." It was not science-fiction, but a number of serious predictions which have become reality in our age. For example, Mandl opposed the then usual idea of sovereignty as applied to space without limits and asserted that sovereignty of States governs only the adjacent atmospheric space. Beyond the "territorial spaces" a vast area begins which is "independent on any terrestrial State power and is *coelum liberum*." [11]

It is worth recalling, in this connection, that thirty years later the United Nations General Assembly recommended in its resolution 1721/XVI of 20 December 1961 such a principle as a starting point of any space legislation, saying: "Outer space and celestial bodies are free for exploration and use by all States in conformity with international law and are not subject to national appropriation." Furthermore, this principle has been developed and inserted in Articles I–III of the Space Treaty of 27 January 1967.

The concluding part of Mandl's analysis is preceded by his prediction of a surprising new progress in physics, chemistry, and engineering that would correspond to a similar epoch of the 19th century—in fact, a vision of the scientific and technical revolution of our times. Moreover, as a consequence of the penetration by men into outer space, Mandl predicted a substantial change in relations between the State and its nationals which would not be based on State domination, so that both State and its nationals would become equal subjects. According to Mandl, territory would lose its importance as one of the basic dimensions of each State, and new communities based exclusively on personal adherence would emerge. People would retain such new nationality when going to outer space and other planets.

Finally, according to Mandl's conclusion, space law would become a new set of norms which will be "quite a different phenomenon than is the present law of jurists." [12]

Vladimír Mandl died on 8 January 1941 at the age of 41 and was buried on 13 January 1941 at the Central Cemetery in Pilsen.

Professor Mandl, who is recognized by the community of space lawyers as the founding writer in this new branch of law embodied some of the characteristic features of the people from a small country in the heart of Europe, Czechoslovakia. Its best creative men, whether scientists, philosophers, or artists, always blended into their ideas the particular interests of their own nation in progress and freedom with the dreams and concerns of the whole of mankind.

NOTES

1. Mandl, *Letecké právo* [Air Law] (Pilsen, 1928).

2. In a report of the Accreditation Commission on Dr. Vladimír Mandl, dated 6 February 1930, the "significant juridical erudition of the author, great knowledge of literature, unusual diligence and devotion to scientific work" was stressed. In his accreditation colloquium, Dr. Mandl received the unanimous approval of the seven examiners, on 20 April 1930. On 30 April 1930 he delivered a test lecture before the Board of Professors on "Liability of Contractors for Damage"; and at a meeting of the Board, when a vote in regard to his appointment was taken among the 24 voting members, 23 votes were cast for and only 1 against Dr. Mandl.

3. Decree of the Minister of Education 89212/31–IV/3, of 30 September 1932.

4. Mandl, "Mezinárodní úmluva o úpravě lectectví ze dne 13.října 1919" (Praha, 1932); "Le Parachute," *La révue générale de droit aérien*, nos. 2, 3, 4, 1935 (reprint, Paris: Les Éditions Internationales, 1935).

5. In a letter dated on 28 February 1939 and addressed to one of the main organizers of that collection, Ing. Karmazín, Mandl wrote with characteristic modesty: "I have followed the history of aviation since its beginning during my childhood, of course, only as an amateur, not a scientist. It will be a great pleasure for me to discuss with you on this subject of our common concern." In a series of letters Mandl offered original suggestions concerning the organization of the collection.

6. "Aero-muzej im. M.V.Frunze v Moskvě," *Letectvi* [Aviation], Praha, August 1937, p. 365; and "Aircraft Building ve Washingtoně, U.S.A.," *Letec* [Aviator], October–November 1938, p. 165.

7. "Let us hope to see as soon as possible the accomplishment of your life work—the Air Museum," wrote Dr. Mandl in a brief, handwritten letter to Ing. Karmazín dated 22 September 1940, only a few months before his death.

8. *"Problém Mezihvězdné Dopravy"* (Prague, 1932), 100 pp.

9. High Altitude Rocket, Patent 52236, Class 46d, granted on 25 September 1933. The patent provided protection from 15 May 1935. Mandl also described his rocket in his book published in Germany: *Die Rakete zur Höhenforschung, Ein Beitrag zum Raumfahrt problem* (Leipzig and Berlin: Hachmeister & Thal, 1934), 16 pp.

10. *Das Weltraum-Recht: Ein Problem der Raumfahrt* (Mannheim, Berlin, Leipzig: J. Bensheimer, 1932), 48 pp.

11. Ibid., p. 33.

12. Ibid., p. 48. In the 1930s Mandl was also interested in some more general problems of economics, science and philosophy. He explained his economic views in the following studies: *Technokracie, hospodářský systém budoucnosti?* [Technocracy—Economic System of the Future?] (Prague, 1934); *Přírodovědní národohospodářská teorie* [Scientific Economic Theory] (Prague, 1936); *Stát a vědecká organizace práce* [State and Scientific Management] (Pilsen, 1937). From among his other writings the following studies should be mentioned: "Vědecká metoda Einsteinova relativismu" [Scientific Method of Einstein's Relativisme] in *Česká mysl, časpois filosofický* [Czech Thought, a Philosophical Journal] (Prague, 1935), vol. 31, no. 3–4; *Příčinná teorie právní* [Causal Theory of Law] (Prague, 1938); and *Válka a mír* [War and Peace] (Prague, 1938).

10

Developments in Rocket Engineering Achieved by the Gas Dynamics Laboratory in Leningrad

I. I. Kulagin, *Soviet Union*

The first rocket research and development body in the Soviet Union began its activities in Moscow in March 1921.

Its foundation was proposed by Nikolay Ivanovich Tikhomirov (1860–1930), a chemical engineer, the aim being to develop his invention in the field of self-propelled (rocket) mortars. This organization was originally named the Laboratory for Development of Engineer Tikhomirov's Invention. N.I. Tikhomirov's assistant and test superviser was Vladimir Andreyevich Artem'yev (1885–1962), who was appointed to the Laboratory in May 1921.

The key problem encountered by the organizers of the Laboratory in the development of rocket mortars was the problem of propellant powder. The joint effort of the Laboratory and specialists from the Artillery Academy resulted in the development of granular smokeless powder with a thick web (slow-burning), based on a non-volatile trotyl-pyroxiline solvent.

Along with research in powders, the structural design of missiles was developed and improved, thus modifying the original version of N.I. Tikhomirov's rocket mortar. For example, ground-firing of powder rockets was begun in 1924 near Leningrad. In 1928, after successful development of engines burning smokeless powder, significant advances were made by powder rockets. However, a great deal of experimental work on powders had to be done in Leningrad proper. This caused unnecessary inconveniences and difficulties. Consequently in 1927, the entire Laboratory was transferred to Leningrad, where it acquired its final name, the Gas Dynamics Laboratory (GDL).

During 1928 and 1933, various caliber rockets burning granular smokeless powder were developed at the GDL, and underwent official tests. These rockets were intended for firing from ground and aircraft. They were used during combat operations on the Khalkhin-Gol River and, in a somewhat modified form known as the "Katyusha," they were extensively employed in the Great Patriotic War of 1941–45.

The principal authors of all these developments were staff members of the GDL: N.I. Tikhomirov, V.A. Artem'yev, B.S. Petropavlovskiy, G.E. Langemak, and I.T. Kleymenov.

In 1927, the GDL began to develop rocket-assisted takeoff for aircraft, the aim being to shorten the takeoff. Successfully completed during and after 1932–1933 were tests of rocket-assisted takeoff units for light and heavy aircraft (types I-4, TB-1, TB-3, and others).

Beginning with 1929, the GDL broadened its work program. In April 1929, organizational work was begun to establish a GDL subdivision (later becoming Department II of GDL) for developing electrical and liquid-propellant rocket engines. Experimental work in this area started on 15 May 1929.

Department II of the GDL was the first state-sponsored body in the USSR charged with practical implementation of the ideas conceived by K.E. Tsiolkovskiy, the founder of contemporary cosmonautics and rocket engineering.

Before Department II of the GDL inaugurated its activities, there were in the Soviet Union public bodies that engaged in investigation and popularization of the problems of rocket engineering and interplanetary travel. Thus, in May 1924 the Interplanetary Travel Study Group at the Military-Research Society at the N.E. Zhukovskiy Air Force

Academy in Moscow was reorganized into the Society for the Study of Interplanetary Communication, with G.M. Kramorov acting as chairman. Participating in the work of the newly organized society were K.E. Tsiolkovskiy, F.A. Tsander, V.P. Vetchinkin, and others.

Among the personnel of the Department II of GDL who took part in development of electrical and liquid-propellant rocket engines were such talented engineers and technicians as A.L. Malyy, V.I. Serov, Ye.N. Kuz'min, Ye.S. Petrov, N.G. Chernyshev, P.I. Minayev, B.A. Kutkin, V.P. Yukov, V.A. Timofeyev, N.M. Mukhin, I.M. Pankin, and others.

The work of Department II was put on a scientific basis from the very beginning: first, a theoretical study was made of the problem, and then the theoretical principles were checked by experiment.

To accomplish the principal task of developing electrical and liquid-propellant rocket engines, a number of engineering problems had to be solved in Department II of the GDL, among which were the following:

1. Working out a functional diagram of the electrical rocket engine;
2. selection of the working fluid (from among solid and liquid conductors) for the electrical rocket engine;
3. development of feeding devices to supply the working fluid to the thrust chamber of the electrical rocket engine;
4. selection of the method for feeding propellant into the thrust chamber of the liquid-propellant engine;
5. development of the most expedient forms for mixing chambers and for injectors;
6. solution of the problem of pump-feeding propellant components;
7. investigation of the behavior of prepared propellant mixtures during combustion in an open vessel and in a semienclosed volume (detonation in rocket engine);
8. development of methods for igniting propellant mixtures (pyrotechnical, electrical, and chemical ignition);
9. development of methods for cooling the thrust chamber and selection of heat-insulating material for the chamber;
10. selection and investigation of various types of liquid propellants and special additives, with the aim of increasing the specific weight of fuel and enhancing its calorific value, including (a) use of colloidal propellant for rocket engines and (b) production of nitrogen tetroxide;
11. investigation of the influence that the design elements of the engine nozzle and combustion chamber exert upon the value of the reaction force, and development of the exponential-contour nozzle;
12. design of vehicles powered by liquid-propellant motors with nominal ceiling of up to 100 km (RLA-1, RLA-2, RLA-3, and RLA-100); [1]
13. development of means for measuring pressure in the combustion chamber, the thrust of the rocket engine, propellant consumption, and other parameters.

In 1929 and 1930, Department II first proved theoretically and experimentally the general ability of an electrical rocket engine to function, using as a working fluid liquid or solid conductors (continuously fed metal wires or liquid jets), exploded at a predetermined frequency by high-power electric sparks in a thrust chamber. The injector and the chamber body, separated by an insulator, were connected to wires running from an electric pulse generator facility of high power, whose principal elements were a high-voltage transformer, four rectifiers, and 4-mfd oil-filled capacitors charged to 40 kv. Subjected to firing were carbon filaments, wires of aluminium, nickel, tungsten, lead and other metals, as well as such liquids as mercury and electrolytes.

The working fluid was fed into the engine's com-

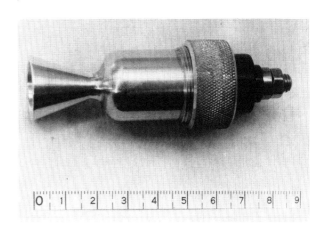

FIGURE 1.—The first electric rocket engine, 1929–1933.

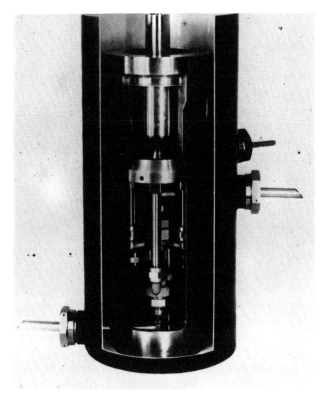

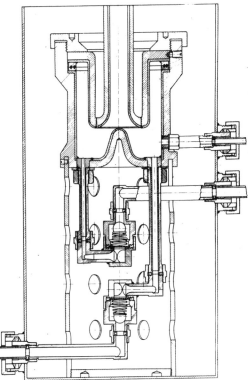

FIGURE 2.—The first experimental liquid-fuel rocket engine in the USSR, the ORM–1, was designed in 1930 and built in 1930–31 at GDL.

bustion chamber by means of special devices known as carburetors of the wire, liquid, or mercury type.

During 1932 and 1933, the electric rocket engine was tested on a ballistic (gun) pendulum (see Figure 1).

In 1930, Department II of GDL was the first to propose the following substances to be used as oxidizers in liquid-propellant engines: nitric acid and its nitrogen tetroxide solutions, hydrogen peroxide, perchloric acid, tetranitromethane, and mixtures of these, while beryllium and other substances were proposed as fuel. Exponential-contour nozzles and combustion-chamber heat-insulation coatings made of zirconium dioxide and other substances were developed and tested in engines as far back as 1930.

During 1930 and 1931, for the first time in the USSR, three experimental liquid-propellant engines (ORM, ORM-1, and ORM-2) [2] were designed and manufactured at Department II of GDL. In 1931, some 50 static firings of liquid-propellant rocket engines were conducted with the engines firing nitrogen tetroxide in association with toluene and gasoline. In that same year there were proposed for the first time a hypergolic propellant and method of chemical ignition, as well as a gimbaled engine with pump assemblies (see Figure 2).

Of particular interest from the historical and technical points of view is the ORM-1 engine, the first Soviet experimental liquid-propellant engine designed in 1930 and manufactured in 1930–31 (see Figure 3).

The ORM-1 engine was intended for short-term operation; it burned nitrogen tetroxide with toluene, or liquid oxygen with gasoline. When firing liquid oxygen with gasoline, the engine developed a thrust of up to 20 kg.

The inner surfaces of the steel thrust chamber were copper-plated. The copper surfaces of the 6-jet injectors were gold-plated to ensure resistance to the corrosive effect of propellant components. Spring-loaded non-return valves with filters were installed at the oxidizer and fuel inlets of the injector. The combustion chamber was provided with a set of nozzles having internal diameters of 10, 15, and 20 mm. The engine was cooled with water poured into the jacket.

Ignition was effected by means of a piece of cotton soaked in fuel and fired with the help of Bickford fuse.

SMITHSONIAN ANNALS OF FLIGHT — page 94

The propellant components were pressure-fed from the tanks by compressed nitrogen. The engine was tested with the nozzle directed upwards.

The ORM-1 had 93 parts.

Experimental piston-type propellant pumps driven by gases bled from the combustion chamber were designed and tested in 1931–32.

In 1932, Department II of the GDL designed and tested experimental engines from ORM-4 through ORM-22 to find the best type of ignition, methods of start-up, and mixing systems for various propellant components. When these engines underwent static tests in 1932, the oxidizers used were liquid oxygen, nitrogen tetroxide, nitric acid, and nitrogen tetroxide dissolved in nitric acid; the fuels were gasoline, benzene, toluene, and kerosene.

The ORM-4, ORM-5, ORM-8, ORM-9, and ORM-12 engines underwent several score of firing tests. With the pressure in the combustion chamber up to 50 atm (gauge), the engines were run for up to one minute. Spark plugs and pyrotechnical ignition were used. The internal diameter of the cylindrical steel combustion chambers of the ORM-4 through ORM-8 engines was 40 mm. The combustion chamber of the ORM-9 engine had an internal diameter and height of 90 mm and a thermal ceramic lining 10 mm thick (zirconium dioxide or magnesium oxide with soluble glass). Its nozzle, 15 mm in diameter, was plated with an 8-mm layer of red copper. The combustion chamber and nozzle in the ORM-12, of the same dimensions as those in the ORM-9, were copper-plated.

So that the best method for supplying propellant components could be selected, various types of injectors were tested in the engines: the ORM-4 engine was provided with spray injectors, the ORM-5 with spray-split type, and the ORM-8 with split injectors.

In the ORM-9 engine the split injector was located in the combustion chamber head opposite the nozzle (see Figure 4). In the ORM-11, it was placed on the wall of the cylindrical combustion chamber.

The ORM-12 engine already featured two separate swirl injectors, one for oxidizer and the other for fuel. The injectors, provided with non-return valves, were arranged opposite each other on the wall of the cylindrical combustion chamber (see Figure 5).

The ORM-16 engine had swirl injectors of a more advanced design.

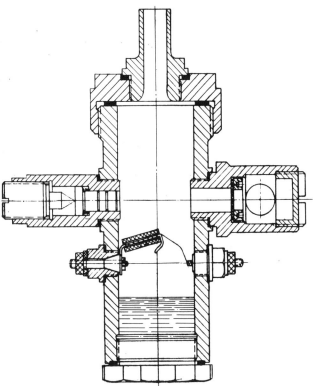

FIGURE 3.—The ORM rocket engine was designed and tested on the stand in 1931.

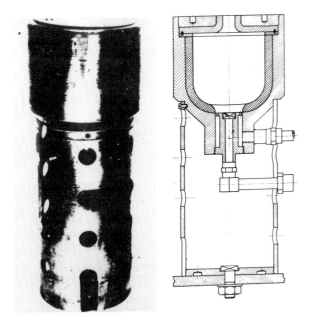

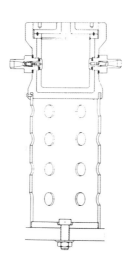

FIGURE 4.—The ORM–9 engine, designed and tested in 1932, used liquid oxygen with gasoline.

FIGURE 5.—ORM–12 engine, designed and tested in 1932. It operated on lox with gasoline and nitric acid or nitrogen tetroxide solutions in nitric acid with kerosene. For fuel injection, use was made of centrifugal nozzles with non-return valves.

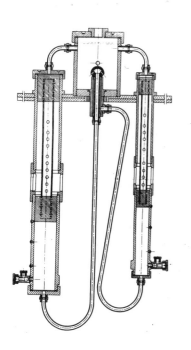

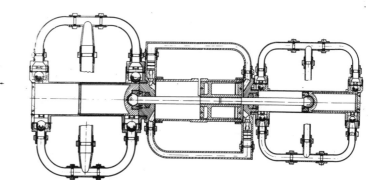

FIGURE 6.—Piston pump assemblies ORM-A, NA, and TNA.

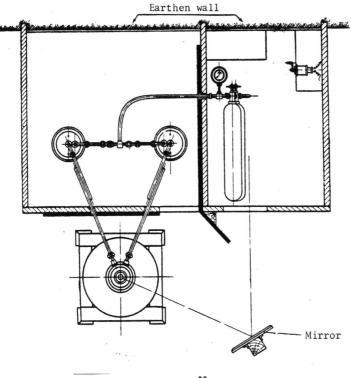

FIGURE 7.—Diagram of a rocket engine
static test installation, 1930–32.

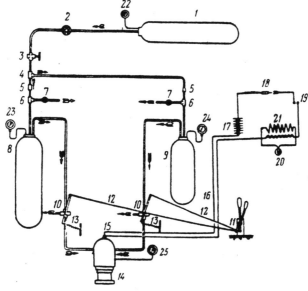

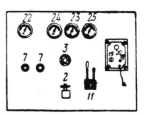

FIGURE 8.—Diagram of the rocket engine static test installation, 1933–38.

1. Air cylinder	11. Starting lever	21. Resistor
2. Air valve	12. Cable	22. Manometer for air
3. Reduction valve	13. Spring	cylinder
4. T-connection	14. Engine	23. Manometer for the
5. Reverse valve (non-	15. Spark plug (current	oxidizer cylinder
return valve)	collector)	24. Manometer for fuel
6. T-connection	16. Wire	cylinder
7. Drain valve	17. Storage battery	25. Manometer for measur-
8. Oxidizer tank	18. Plug	ing the compression in
9. Fuel tank	19. Shut-off switch	the engine
10. Starting valve	20. Control bulb	

FIGURE 9.—ORM–50 engine on the test stand.

The experimental short-run ORM-23 engine was specially developed and manufactured to work out the method of initial ignition by means of an air-gas flame (gasoline and air mixture). Satisfactory results were obtained for the single as well as for the repeated ignition.

The numerous tests of various types of experimental rocket engines made by that time showed that uncooled nozzles deteriorated rapidly; therefore, to increase the permissible rocket-firing duration, air-cooling of the nozzle was applied in the ORM-24 and ORM-26 engines. The cooling was effected by means of shaped adapters attached on the outside (in the ORM-24) and shaped fins on the nozzle (in the ORM-26).

The test runs indicated that air cooling was inadequate. Therefore, the design of the ORM-27 engine provided for a complete fluid-flow system to cool the combustion chamber and the finned nozzle. Temperature compensation of the nozzle expansion was also provided in this engine.

Some other methods, in addition to those mentioned above, were suggested to protect the nozzle against failure. For example, in the ORM-28 engine, use was made of an uncooled thick-walled nozzle, whereas in the ORM-30 engine, the nozzle was protected by a fuel curtain produced by additional injectors. Neither of these produced satisfactory results.

In later designs (beginning with the ORM-34 engine), the problem of nozzle cooling was solved more comprehensively: the nozzles began to be designed with complete flow-cooling.

The most advanced engines developed at the Department II of GDL were ORM-50 and ORM-52.

The 150-kg-thrust ORM-50 engine burned a nitric acid plus kerosene propellant ignited chemically; it was developed at the request of the Moscow Group for Study of Jet Propulsion (MosGIRD), and was intended for the O5 rocket. It passed the static acceptance tests in 1933. The engine could undergo repeated tests. The steel cylindrical combustion chamber, with an inside diameter of 120 mm, had a regeneratively acid-cooled cover and a conical nozzle with spiral fins. The diameter of the nozzle throat section was 23 mm. The chamber was furnished with four swirl injectors having nonreturn valves (see Figure 9).

The 300-kg thrust ORM-52 engine, using nitric acid plus kerosene propellant with chemical igni-

Along with development of engine design, methods of propellant feeding were investigated, and as early as 1930 it was found that pressure-feeding was more efficient for small rockets, and pump-feeding for large rockets.

Proposed and tested in 1931–32 were a number of piston-pump assemblies, such as the ORM-A engine with a pump assembly (see Figure 6) capable of feeding nitrogen tetroxide plus toluene propellant into the 300-kg thrust engine.

In 1933, the ORM-23 through ORM-52 engines, burning a nitric acid plus kerosene propellant and provided with pyrotechnical and chemical ignition systems, were developed and statically tested. The ORM-50 experimental engines with a thrust of 150 kg and the ORM-52 engines with a thrust of 300 kg passed official static tests in 1933 (see Figures 7 and 8).

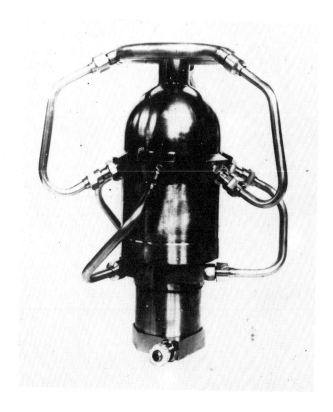

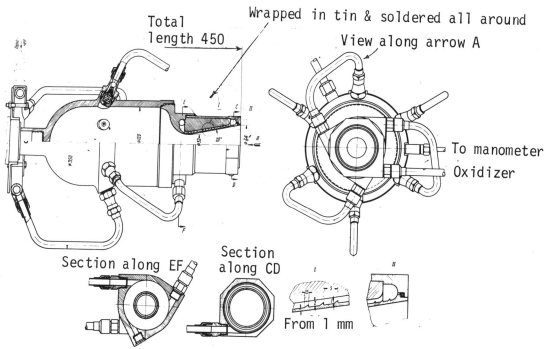

FIGURE 10.—The ORM–52 engine was designed in 1933 and passed static acceptance tests in that year. Designated for experimental rockets and naval torpedoes, it used nitric acid and kerosene as propellants. Engine data were as follows: Thrust at ground level 250–310 kg; specific thrust 210 sec; chamber pressure 20–25 atm; excess oxidant ratio 1.08; fuel feed pressure 40 atm; ignition, hypergolic; combustion chamber volume 2.25 l; engine weight 14.5 kg.

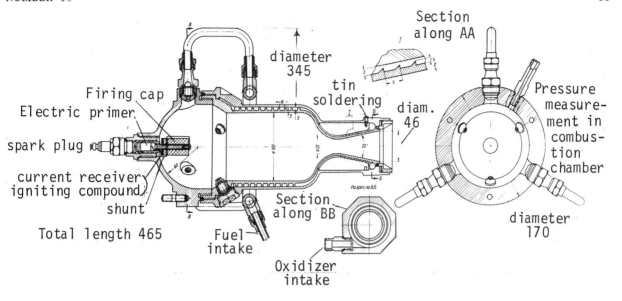

Certificate to liquid fuel rocket engine ORM-65, No. 1

Certificate to liquid fuel rocket engine ORM-65, No. 2

FIGURE 11.—The ORM–65 engine, which passed the official tests in 1936, was designed for the use in the RP–318 rocket glider and the KR–212 winged rocket. Its fuel and oxidant were kerosene, OST 6460, and nitric acid, OST 5375; ignition was pyrotechnic, with electric starter; and engine weight was 14.26 kg. Other engine data:

	Maximum	Normal	Minimum
Thrust at ground level (kg)	175	155	50
Specific thrust (sec)	195	210	. . .
Chamber pressure (atm)	25	23	8
Fuel feed pressure (atm)	35	30	8

Winged missile 212 on catapult

FIGURE 12.—Winged rocket 212, constructed in 1936 by S. P. Korolyev, was powered with an ORM–65 engine and was equipped with an automatic launching system containing an automatic, stabilized guidance system. The rocket engine was installed on the air frame in the tail section of the missile and covered with a streamlined metallic shield to separate and protect the tail surfaces from the exhaust flame. Propellants were fed by displacement. Before the summer test firing of the 212 rocket, engines ORM–65–1 and 3, were ground-tested 8 times. Basic data were as follows: Wing spread 3060 mm, length 3160 mm, diameter 300 mm, area of wing 1.7 m², flying weight 210 kg, fuel weight 30 kg, weight of useful load 30 kg, length of flight 50 km.

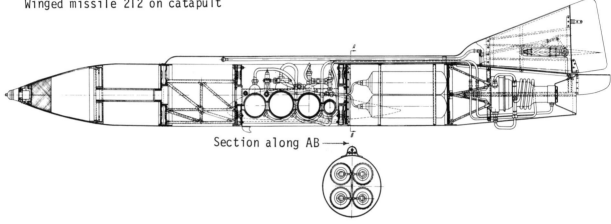

Section along AB →

tion, was for rockets and naval torpedoes. This engine was also intended to power the experimental rockets RLA-1, RLA-2 and RLA-3. It passed static acceptance tests in 1933. The ORM-52 engine had a specific impulse of 210 seconds and a combustion chamber pressure of 25 atm (absolute). The 120-mm steel cylindrical combustion chamber, featuring a spherical head, was provided with internal cooling, whereas the chamber cover and spirally finned nozzle were regeneratively acid-cooled. The nozzle was conical (20°) with a throat section diameter of 32 mm. There were six injectors provided with non-return valves. The weight of the engine was 14.5 kg (see Figure 10).

In 1933, development of propellant-feed systems for rocket engines progressed. Also developed in that year was the design of a turbo-pump assembly

comprised of centrifugal pumps for feeding the liquid propellant components into a 300-kg thrust engine.

It should be noted that the engines developed and continuously modified in those years at the GDL were the most advanced engines of the time and invariably met the approval of experts.

Professor V.P. Vetchinkin of the Central Aero-Hydrodynamics Institute (TsAGI) visited the GDL in December 1932 and witnessed the static tests of the ORM-9 liquid-propellant engine. He expressed his impressions as follows: "The GDL has done the major part of the work in the creation of the rocket, i.e., the liquid-propellant rocket motor . . . In this aspect the GDL's achievements may be considered brilliant."

In late 1933, the personnel of the GDL and

→

FIGURE 14.—Gas generator, designed in 1935–36 successfully passed the official stand tests in 1937. After 1 hour and 46 minutes of work it showed no defects and was useful in the further studies. Basic data were as follows: Gas output 40–70 1/sec, gas pressure 20–25 atm (abs), gas temperature 450–580°C, fuel use 0.15–0.17 kg/sec, water use 0.2 kg/sec, fuel feed pressure 30 atm, weight of gas generator 20 kg.

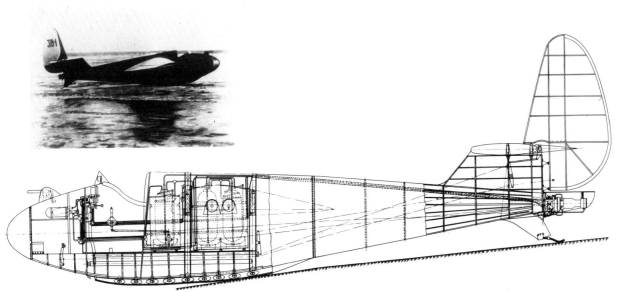

FIGURE 13.—The experimental RP–318–1 rocket-propelled aircraft designed by S.P. Korolyev was created by modifying the two-seater SK–9 airframe with installation of ORM–65 engine containing a fuel system. The fuel supply on the RPA provided 100 sec of continuous engine operation with thrust of 150 kg. Fuel was delivered to the engine with compressed air, having entered from tanks, via a pressure-reducing valve. The engine, mounted on a frame in the tail of the fuselage, was covered with a metal jacket to protect the tail unit from flame. During firing tests, maximal duration of continuous engine operation reached 230 sec.

Specifications of the rocket-propelled aircraft were: Wing span 17.0 m, length 7.44 m, midsection of fuselage 0.75 m², supporting area of wing 7.85 m², initial flight weight 700 kg, fuel weight 75 kg. Flight tests of the RPA were run in 1940 by Pilot Fedorov; a modified ORM–65 (RDL–150–1) engine was mounted in the airframe.

The ground-based firing tests of the RPA with the ORM–65–1 and ORM–65–2 were conducted from December 1937 to April 1938; after this the engines were transferred to the 212 winged rocket. Twenty-one launchings were made with the ORM–65–1 engine (total running time 18 min 43 sec); with the ORM–65 No. 2, 9 launchings lasting for 13 min 37 sec were made. With the ORM–65–1 engine 21 launchings were made (total running time 18 min 43 sec) and with the ORM–65–2, 9 launchings (running time 13 min 37 sec).

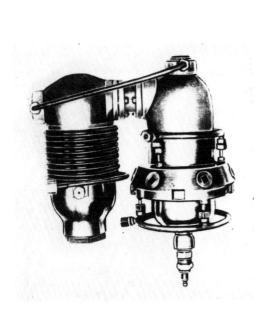

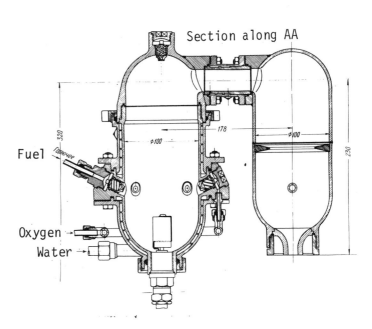

GIRD were merged into the Jet Propulsion Research Institute (RNII). Within the walls of this Institute was formed and tempered the creative body of Soviet rocket engineers; also developed here were a number of experimental ballistic and winged missiles and the engines for them.

At the above Institute, the body of specialists in liquid-propellant engines, which stemmed from the GDL, between 1934 and 1938 developed the series of experimental engines ORM-53 through ORM-102 using nitric acid and tetranitromethane as oxidizers. They also designed the first Soviet gas generator, the GG-1,[3] that could operate for hours using nitric acid with kerosene and water.

The ORM-65 engine, which passed official tests in 1936, was the best engine of its time. Burning a propellant of nitric acid plus kerosene, it had a controlled thrust of 50 to 175 kg, and a specific impulse of 210 sec; it could be started both manually and automatically (see Figure 11). The ORM-65 engine successfully withstood repeated starts. Engine ORM-65-1 was started 50 times on the ground, this being adequate for 30.7 minutes of operation, including 20 stand firings, 8 firing in a KR-212 winged rocket[4] and 21 firings in an RP-318 rocket glider.[5] Engine ORM-65-2 had 16 starts, including

5 starts in a KR-212 winged rocket and 9 starts in an RP-318 rocket glider (see Figures 12, 13 and 14).

The research work carried out by the GDL, GIRD, and RNII was a valuable contribution to the history of Soviet rocket science and engineering.

It was the GDL, the first Soviet establishment for the development of rocket engines, that in 1929–1933 created and successfully tested in operation the world's first experimental electric rocket engines and the first Soviet liquid-propellant rocket engines ORM, ORM-1 through ORM-52 using liquid oxygen, nitrogen tetroxide, nitric acid and toluene, gasoline, and kerosene. The body of the research workers stemming from the GDL, which later at the RNII and after RNII continued to work on development of liquid-propellant rocket engines operating on various fuels, has created many other, more powerful engines which have found widest application.

NOTES

1. RLA (Reaktivnyy Letatel'nyy Apparat) rocket vehicle.
2. ORM (Opytnyy Raketnyy Motor) experimental rocket engine.
3. GG (Gazo-Generator) gas generator.
4. KR (Krylataya Raketa) winged rocket.
5. RP (Raketoplaner) rocket glider.

11

A Historical Review of Developments in Propellants and Materials for Rocket Engines

O. Lutz, *German Federal Republic* [1]

In the early days of rocket propulsion the interest of scientists and engineers centered on the right choice of propellants because these are of vital importance for quick and successful development. My collaborator at that time, Dr. Noeggerath, in his doctoral thesis compiled, from the thermodynamic standpoint, all practically applicable reactions. What is known generally today would have been most surprising in those days, i.e., that no combination of chemical propellants could be discovered which were exceptionally better in output of energy than others.

Starting in 1935 at Stuttgart and from October 1936 at Brunswick, our work was oriented towards increasing the output of energy and simplifying the design of rockets by cooperation between chemists and design engineers, because to carry out this task required not only the right engineering methods but also the right choice of propellant mixtures. By this means we succeeded in discovering propellants and processes reducing the difficulties of rocket engineering and improving the performance of missiles and airplanes.

As you know, the simplest rocket possible can be manufactured with powder, because both reacting components of the propellant are already mixed in the right proportion in the reaction chamber. However, even if one neglects other disadvantages, maintaining a continuous flow of powder into the reaction chamber raises unique design problems. These problems can be avoided by using liquid propellants. So one of our first steps led us to the monergoles—liquids containing fuel and oxidizer either mixed or dissolved, or even in the same molecule. (By the way, I should like to mention here that all propellant names ending in "ergol" were created by

us at Brunswick—monergole, lithergole, propergole, hypergole—although some other types of monergoles have been developed, for example, gel-propellants and thixotropic propellants.)

The requirements for such a system were numerous. Our special interest concerned instant ignition and complete reaction in the chamber. Many accidents showed us how difficult it is to avoid an ignition delay that results in a flashback of the combustants into the propellant tank, and to maintain a controllable pressure distribution (Figure 1). In close cooperation with I. G. Farben we experimented with the so-called "Divers' Liquid," a solution of ammonium nitrate in ammonia, named monergole H. This solution could easily be controled, from the point of view of safety, yet its corrosiveness and the fact that the mixture tended to separate brought up new difficulties. Another trouble was that the ammonium nitrate, when atomized, caused deposits on the injector elements, constricting their cross section, while a strong vaporization of nitrous oxide was observed. We could not eliminate this phenomenon. With monergole A, a solution of nitrous oxide in ammonia, we overcame most of the difficulties. We even succeeded in making the engine explosion proof by installing high-heat-absorbing material in the piping system, but could not achieve absolute safety from shock waves caused by detonations. These results brought about suspension of further experiments, although we believed that, due to the extraordinary simplicity of this type of engine, the monergoles would remain useful in certain special applications.

After the war, when we again began our research on rocket propellants and rocket engines in my institute, the Deutsche Forschungsanstalt für Luft-

103

FIGURE 1.—Interruption of a monergol explosion by safety device.

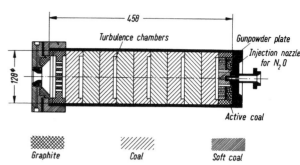

FIGURE 2.—Lithergol engine combustion chamber. Maximum thrust was attained in 12 seconds.

FIGURE 3.—Simplified coal charges.

fahrt [German Aeronautical Research Institute] in Trauen, we worked very successfully with a thixotropic monergole based on ammonium perchlorate suspended with higher alcohols and certain soaps in nitromethane. We could control this system and overcome all the difficulties which had troubled us in the 1930s.

Another possibility in our effort to find an engine system as simple as possible was to place one propellant component as a solid in the reaction chamber and to inject the other as a liquid, gas or vapor. We called such a system a "lithergole." It was necessary to find a suitable arrangement in the chamber to obtain reaction everywhere on the surface of the solid. It was Andrussow who proposed putting the fuel in the reaction chamber in the form of coal and injecting the oxidizer in the form of nitrous oxide. The cross section through an experimental engine in Figure 2 shows the coal charge consisting of single discs with holes drilled axially. As coal has a very low thermal conductivity, the outer shell did not need heat protection, and only the area nearest to the circumference was left unperforated. We ignited the system (see Figures 3–5) by means of a

FIGURE 4.—Partly burned coal charge of a lithergol engine.

FIGURE 5.—Lithergol combustion chamber.

small charge of gunpowder. The problem was to cause a simultaneous reaction over the full length of the intake so that the charge would burn off not from one end to the other but radially. We solved it by a lining of celluloid inside each hole, which instantly heated the entire inside surface to ignition temperature. In our experiments on the test stand, full thrust could be reached within one second and thrust oscillations could be reduced to less than 5 percent. At that time we thought these simple systems could be used for long burning times, although we realized that the necessary diameter sets a limit on the overall impulse.

At this point it is pertinent to remark on the application of the oxidizer used in the lithergole engine to increase the high-altitude output of piston engines and pulse jets. Figure 6 shows an arrange-

ment to inject the liquid nitrous oxide into the air intake of the supercharger. In the graph is plotted the temperature of the air for different oxidizers and for injection before and behind the supercharger. The cooling of the air results in a greater mass flow into the cylinder. Figure 7 illustrates the increase of the cylinder pressure due to the injection of N_2O and to varying the point of ignition. The thermodynamic and physical properties of nitrous oxide suit the requirements of a piston engine in such a fortunate manner that the high altitude out-

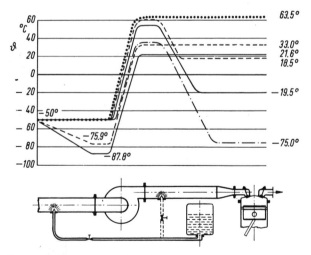

FIGURE 6.—Temperature distribution in the air intake to the supercharger.

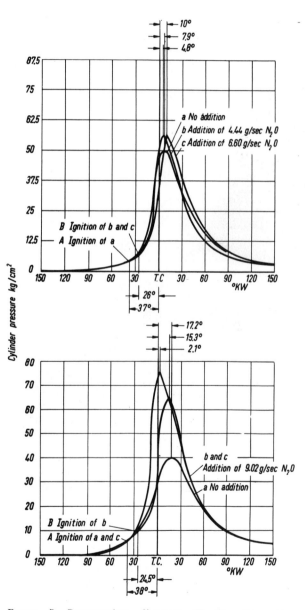

FIGURE 7.—Pressure-time diagrams (T. C. = top center, °KW = crankshaft angle).

put of the aero engines of that time could be increased by about 100 percent without any need for additional accessories for cooling or fuel injection. Figure 8 represents a booster unit for twin-engined reconnaissance planes which carried the nitrous oxide aboard as a non-pressurized liquid at about −90°C.

As described above, with the monergole and the lithergole systems we tried to simplify the entire powerplant by the selection of a specially favourable process. The next step was to shift the emphasis from construction to the propellants, considering particularly the ignition process. This led to the hypergolic principles, i.e., propellant combinations which, due to chemical affinity, ignite without noticeable ignition delay. By use of this principle we solved a lot of ignition problems, because explosive mixtures could not arise. It might not have been of great merit to have proposed this idea, but I had the good fortune to have colleagues who—after I had mentioned this principle in 1935—worked for years with intuition and unfailing energy towards the realization of this idea. I should

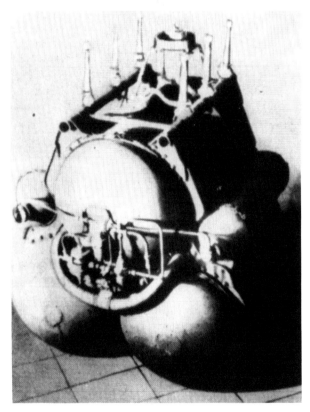

FIGURE 8.—Booster unit for increase in performance.

like to mention here Dr. Haussmann, Dr. Noeggerath, and Dipl.-Ing. Egelhaaf.

The first hypergole—this term was coined by Noeggerath—was a combination of hydrogen peroxide and hydrazine hydrate, for which we applied in Germany for a patent on 18 July 1936 under the number L 90798 IV d/46a6.

We experimented first with copper as a catalyst and got ignition in less than .01 second with mixtures of hydrazine hydrate and methanol 1:1 and 50 percent hydrogen peroxide at room temperature. At that time we found this hypergole very interesting because of the low carbon content (it burns practically without residue). This combination, however, could not be used below −25°C. The very small contents of catalyst could not be brought into the hydrazine hydrate in the form of salts without being reduced to metallic copper. So we introduced colloidal copper in solution, using first gum arabic as a protection colloid, and later, cellulose ether of alkyls. We succeeded in getting solutions of very fine dispersed copper, stable for years, with very good catalytic properties. Even at −20°C the ignition had proved acceptable. Of course, this material had to be stored under an air seal. For this purpose we covered the solution with a thin layer of wax and used nitrogen as the pressure gas. Of course, it is possible to introduce the catalyst either into the fuel or into the oxidizer, or it can be injected separately. But the separate injection would complicate the design. As we could not handle concentrated hydrogen peroxide at that time we thought it even dangerous to put the catalyst into the oxidizer. Difficulties in supplying the hydrazine hydrate compelled us to lower its content from 50 to 30 percent. As this propellant combination was to be used for our rocket-propelled fighter Me 163 and we were not allowed to exceed a temperature of 1750°C we mixed 13 percent water with 30 percent hydrazine hydrate and 57 percent methanol. But with this mixture we did not get a stable solution. The Walter Works at Kiel tried rather successfully to use copper as catalyst bound to cyanogen.

I will not list here all the different ways we tried to find out the right substance, all the discussions about it, and the multiplicity of experiments and theoretical considerations about the catalytic process; but I must mention the difficulty, at that time, of obtaining the necessary substances in the proper quantities and sometimes, even, quality. This meant that the possibility of application in our research and development was sometimes limited. For example the proposed nitroprussid natrium at that time was the only proved iron salt with catalytic effect that together with the described mixture of hydrazine hydrate and methanol and water gave a stable solution. But the application was limited because the hydrazine hydrate we got contained zinc which gave with the nitroprussid natrium insoluble hydrazo- and nitroso-groups in zinc-iron-pentacyanides.

In order to get instant ignition at even lower temperature we experimented with a group of substances called "optoles" (that means catechole). By the way, the optoles proved to be important hypergol initiators, not only with hydrogen peroxide but also with nitric acid. In addition to the optoles, several aldehydes were proposed as initiators with hydrogen peroxide. Further research was done with cyclopentadiene, butynediol, and furfuryl alcohol. But they never were used in action because those substances could not be obtained in sufficient quantities. At last we managed to develop substitutes for the hydrazine component substances on the basis of optole and aldehydes for a propellant system using hydrogen peroxide as oxidizer. You may imagine that it was not easy to find for this oxidizer the most favorable hypergolic partner, one which would function even at low temperature. As already mentioned, a temperature limit had been set in connection with its use in our Me 163. Additional requirements were: burning without residues, no blocking of the chamber or nozzle, harmlessness of the exhaust gases, stability, no corrosion, and so on. Sometimes those requirements were contradictory, so that we had to make an optimal compromise.

As for hypergoles for hydrogen peroxide, here is a short summary of the groups discussed:

1. For low-percentage hydrogen peroxide: 50% $N_2H_4 \cdot H_2O$, 47% methanol, 3% water plus 0.3% colloidal copper.

2. For high-percentage hydrogen peroxide: 30% $N_2H_4 \cdot H_2O$, 57% methanol (called "C-stoff"), 13% water, and traces of cupro-potassium-cyanide or colorless dissolved copper oxide.

3. Other hypergoles for H_2O_2: Hydrazine hydrate substituted by aliphatic amino compounds: Diethylene-triamine, ethylene-diamine, and tri-ethylene-tetramine with a copper sulphate catalyst show good ignition properties, and the most

important one of their physical properties is a high viscosity; however, their behavior in the cold was found to be unfavorable. Aldehydes (with vanadium or iron as catalyst), also show good ignition properties but are not as good as hydrazine hydrate. Liquids normally used as developers, such as hydroquinone and pryocatechol in a methanolic solution and with iron as catalyst, gained importance as chemical byproducts and were taken into consideration to ensure a broader fuel basis for the Me 163 fighter plane. There were good results (Egelhaaf).

In summing up, it can be said that "T-stoffs" could not, even after intensive study, yield results as good as those obtained with hydrazine hydrate.

Another oxidizer we tested at that time for use in hypergolic systems was concentrated nitric acid. Besides the favorable thermal properties and the high specific density the acid could be supplied in any quantity. Mainly, three groups of initiators determined the new development of the new ergoles based on nitric acid: organic amines, catecholes, and furans. In the choice of the other components to be mixed with nitric acid, it was of importance that there was no need to be careful of the solubilities of metalsalts with a catalytic effect, nor was there any temperature limit for the reaction in the chamber; therefore, the substances for the blend could be chosen freely. Typical components had been vinyl ether, benzene, and tetrahydro-furan.

It was remarkably difficult to obtain good properties at low temperatures. As nitric acid solidifies at $-40°C$, we used 98 percent nitric acid with 6 percent iron trichloride. As for the ergoles (the fuel portion in a hypergole) used, a mixture of catecholes and tetrahydro-furan with 8 percent furfuryl alcohol gave the best properties down to $-50°C$, with acceptable viscosity and very good ignition behavior.

The following list indicates the diverse groups of hypergolic systems with nitric acid as oxidizer that we worked with:

1. Aliphatic amino compounds: e.g., Diethylene-triamine, poly-alkyl-polyamines, triethylamine, methylamine; these reacted very well with ordinary nitric acid, as well as with nitric acid to which iron or vanadium catalysts were added, or with mixed acid (MS 10).

2. Aromatic amino compounds: Starting with cyclo-hexylamine, the following amines proved

to be especially suitable: aniline and its mixtures with other aliphatic or aromatic compounds (triethylene-amine, cyclo-hexylamine, methylaniline, pyridine, ethylaniline, xylidine, piperidine, pyrrole). Certain mixtures show a "eutectic hypergolity." The hypergolity of the above mentioned compounds is so good that dilutions with inert fuels have been possible. The group of hypergoles mentioned was called by BMW "Tonka," and at Brunswick, "Gola." The BMW research staff conducted studies themselves in this field of hypergoles with excellent results (Figure 9).

3. Unsaturated compounds: Substances belonging to the acetylene group (Dr. Reppe) as, for instance, di-acetylene. Vinyl-ethers: vinyl-ethyl-ether, vinyl-isobutyl-ether, butane-diol-divinyl-ether, divinyl-acetylene, diketenes, cyclo-pentadine. The hypergoles of the vinyl-ether group were called "Visoles" and were mostly used in combination with amino compounds.

4. Developers: Pyrocatechol, hydroquinone, pyrogallol, and, in addition, "Optoles." The components suitable for hydrogen peroxide proved to be suitable also for nitric acid.

5. Others: Furan and derivates, in particular furfuryl alcohol, called "Fantol" (Egelhaaf). They have particularly good hypergolity, especially with mixed acid, even when diluted to a high degree with xylol (up to 70 percent). Hydrazine also reacts hypergolically with nitric acid.

Almost all proposed hypergolous propellants consisted of mixtures of different compounds. This results, of course, in a complication of the individual effects, yet mixing offers the possibility of intensifying one or the other of the desired properties, for instance, the chemical affinity of a mixture of two substances is in some way analogous to the solidification diagram of a system. Figure 10 shows this affinity expressed as a limit concentration, i.e., the acid concentration at which ignition takes place without perceptible delay. It can easily be understood that mixtures may have a considerably higher affinity than the single components, an effect which has also been proved true with numerous other substances. The same diagram shows the lowest admissible temperature, the so-called "cold point." This cold point is given at both ends of the diagram by the solidification point, in the middle by the highest admissible viscosity, which was assumed to be 40 centi-strokes for a particular case. In this special case the optimum in regard to cold point as well as that to ignition delay are almost identical. There are, however, combinations of substances showing

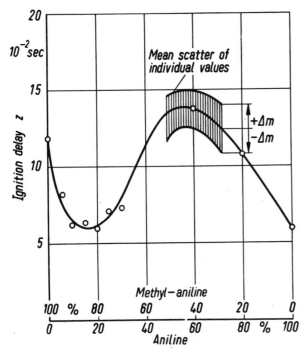

FIGURE 9.—Ignition delays of the hypergolic fuel "Gola," showing mean scatter of ten individual values.

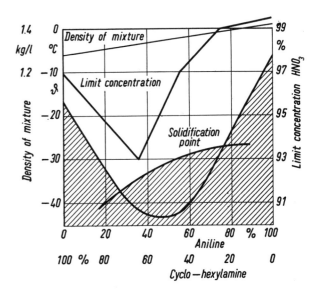

FIGURE 10.—Characteristic values of the hypergolic fuel system with aniline and cyclo-hexylamine, showing limit concentration (i.e., acid concentration up to which no delay is noticed.

the contrary; we then have to try to bring both optima into accordance by adding further components.

Figure 11 shows different diagrams obtained in the development of "visol" fuels. We are dealing here with a mixture of four components: two different visoles, the vinyl-butyl-ether (visole 1) and the butane-diol-divinyl-ether (visole 4), and two different organic amino compounds, aniline and methylaniline. The ignition delay is shown as a function of the composition of the amino mixture. The dotted lines correspond to the substances with 10 parts by volume; the broken lines, to the substances with 15 parts by volume; and the solid lines, to the substance with 20 parts by volume of amino mixture. Finally, the four diagrams differ in their visole composition. Without going into more detail, as for instance the conversion of a minimum into a maximum by changing the composition of the visole part, I want to draw attention to the extraordinary

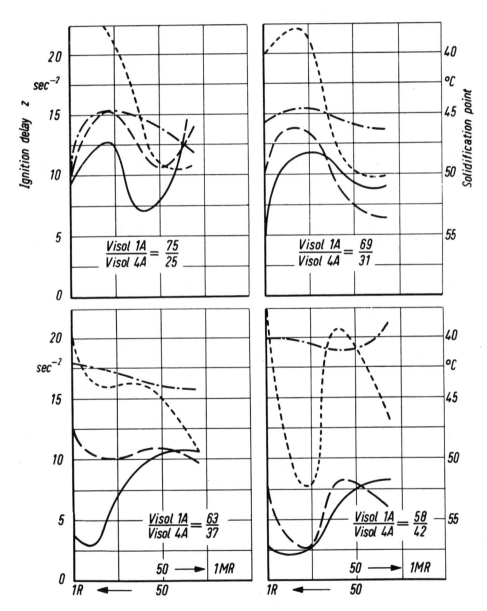

FIGURE 11.—Influence of the composition of the visol and amine composition in visol fuels (proportionality factor = parts by weight).

differences caused by small changes in the absolute contents of the amino components. This sensitivity made studies very difficult from the point of view of affinity; the systems shows all properties of multi-component systems and the technician is tempted to speak of a eutectic.

It should also be mentioned that the ignition delays given are not claimed to be absolute values. Ignition delay is more or less influenced by the way in which the components are brought together. We might even arrive at a point where an arrangement which is favorable for one combination of sub-stances results in long ignition delays for another fuel system. The ignition delay times were measured by a photoelectric cell by feeding the oxidizer uni-formly and reducibly into the fuel, which was kept in a crucible (Figure 12). Figure 13 shows a varia-tion of an apparatus we developed for the measure-ment of ignition delay at low temperatures.

Some remarks should be made on the ignition of hypergoles and the relation to the design of mixing

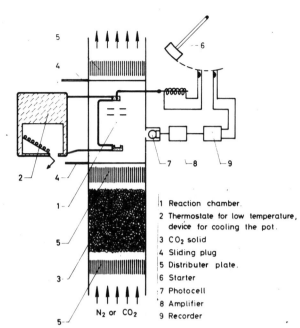

1	Reaction chamber.
2	Thermostate for low temperature, device for cooling the pot.
3	CO_2 solid
4	Sliding plug
5	Distributer plate.
6	Starter
7	Photocell
8	Amplifier
9	Recorder

FIGURE 13.—Ignition-delay apparatus for low temperature.

injectors. We found that generally the hypergoles cannot be ignited in every case by quick and inti-mate mixing in the stoichiometric ratio. We postu-lated a stoichiometric ignition ratio, that means the ratio of the primary reactions which are taking place at the boundary surface as the most important first step for immediate ignition of hypergolic sys-tems. But we could not complete our studies in this interesting field of theory and practice. From the development of suitable mixing injectors we learned that the energy used for atomizing has to be kept low. We used mixing arrangements which brought together both flows with a small amount of energy, but with split-up boundary surfaces, and they proved to be good.

This work, started in the thirties, was continued until the end of World War II, during which time about 1100 different combinations of hypergoles were investigated, leading us to a broad view of possible propellant systems.

To complete this review of research done in the beginnings of rocketry, I should like to report on our efforts to discover new materials and cooling systems for the rocket nozzle, which was exposed to a high thermal load uncommon at that time. These investigations were concentrated on "sweating" or "transpiration" cooling systems, today widely known and applied to turbine blades. It can be assumed that similar principles for the cooling of

FIGURE 12.—Device for measuring ignition delay.

rocket combustion chambers have been developed elsewhere, but I should like to mention at this point my former colleague Meyer-Hartwig who devoted intensive studies to these topics.

There are three significant effects which reduce the surface temperature: heat absorption by passing the cooling liquid through the porous wall, heat absorption by the evaporation of the cooling liquid, and the additional boundary layer consisting of the mass addition of cooling liquid at the surface of the wall. A temperature profile for the cooling of a solid and a porous wall is represented in Figure 14. At a gas temperature of 1100°C and a velocity of 600–700 m/s the surface temperature can be reduced to 100°C applying 0.04 g/(s·cm²) specific mass flow rate (Figure 15).

Figure 16 shows the application of porous material in a rocket nozzle. At a chamber pressure of 36 kp/cm² and a gas temperature of about 2500°K, 0.6 g/(s·cm²) of cooling liquid were fed through the nozzle wall, which amounts to less than 2 percent of the main mass flow rate of the combustion chamber. The porous materials used for the research in sweat-cooling were made from powdered steel and copper. The strength-to-weight ratio of this material was almost equal to that of the compact material.

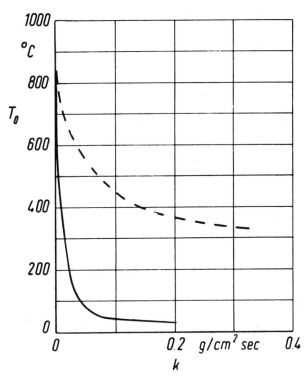

FIGURE 15.—Surface temperature as a function of specific coolant flow rate.

Figure 17 shows different test bars, orifices, and rocket nozzles developed in our laboratories. The development of porous materials for sweat-cooling was started with nonmetallic ceramics, but in connection with steel constructions a lot of difficulties arose due to differing rates of thermal expansion.

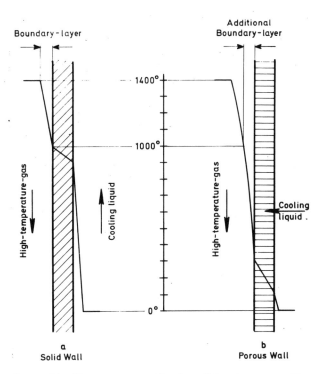

FIGURE 14.—Temperature profiles for solid and porous walls.

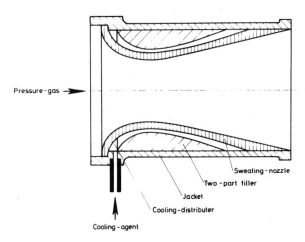

FIGURE 16.—Sweat-cooled material nozzle.

FIGURE 17.—Development of sweat-cooled materials.

Thus, we switched over to metallic materials. Taking advantage of the excellent properties of ceramics we tried to weld metal and ceramics. Zones of mixtures of ceramic and of increasing amount of metal were sintered to the ceramic (Figure 18). By this process advantage could be taken of the different properties of metal and ceramic. Today the mixtures of metal and ceramics are known as "cermets."

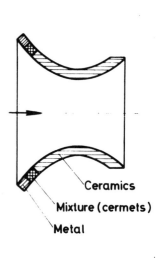

FIGURE 18.—Test rod and nozzle of compound material.

NOTES

1. "Some Special Problems of Power Plants," of which this paper is a revised and expanded version, was presented at the AGARD First Guided Missiles Seminar, Munich, Germany, April 1956, and appeared under the author's name in the *History of German Guided Missiles Development* (pp. 238–252), edited by Th. Benecke and A. W. Quick and published for and on behalf of The Advisory Group for Aeronautical Research and Development, North Atlantic Treaty Organization (AGARD) by the Wissenschaftliche Gesellschaft für Luftfahrt E. V. (Brunswick, Germany: Verlag E. Appelhans & Co., 1957). From this source are taken Figures 1–4, 6–11, 15, and 18 in this paper.—Ed.

12

On the GALCIT Rocket Research Project, 1936-38

Frank J. Malina, *United States*

Introduction

The following recollections are based on memory, on unpublished documents, and on published material available to me. I present them fully recognizing the fallibility of memory, and the unavoidable injection of personal evaluations and judgments. Although in our youthful enthusiasm we were already convinced, in 1936, that rocket research for space exploration was important, we made no systematic effort to preserve our papers and photographic records.

My interest in space exploration was first aroused when I read Jules Verne's *De la terre à la lune* in the Czech language as a boy of 12 in Czechoslovakia, where my family lived from 1920 to 1925. On our return to Texas, I followed reports on rocket work as they appeared from time to time in popular magazines. In 1933 I wrote the following paragraph for a technical English Course at Texas A.&M. College:

Can man do what he can imagine? – Now that man has conquered travel through the air his imagination has turned to interplanetary travel. Many prominent scientists of today say that travel through space to the Moon or to Mars is impossible. Others say, "What man can imagine, he can do." Many difficulties present themselves to interplanetary travel. The great distance separating the heavenly bodies would require machines of tremendous speeds, if the distances are to be traversed during the lifetime of one man. Upon arrival at one of these planets the traveler would require breathing apparatus, for the astronomers do not believe the atmosphere on these planets will support human life as our atmosphere does. If a machine left the earth, its return would be practically impossible, and those on the earth would never know if the machine reached its destination.

In 1934 I received a scholarship to study mechanical engineering at the California Institute of Technology. Before the end of my first year there I began part-time work as a member of the crew of the GALCIT (Guggenheim Aeronautical Laboratory, California Institute of Technology) ten-foot wind tunnel. This led to my appointment in 1935 as a graduate assistant in GALCIT.

The Guggenheim Laboratory, at this time, a few years after its founding, was recognized as one of the world's centers of aeronautical instruction and research. Under the leadership of Theodore von Kármán (1881–1963), GALCIT specialized in aerodynamics, fluid mechanics, and structures.[1-3] Von Kármán's senior staff included Clark B. Millikan (1903–1966), Ernest E. Sechler, and Arthur L. Klein.

The laboratory was already carrying out studies on the problems of high-speed flight, and the limits of the engine-propeller propulsion system for aircraft were beginning to be clearly recognized.

In 1935–36 William W. Jenney and I conducted experiments with model propellers in the wind tunnel for our master's theses. My mind turned more and more to the possibilities of rocket propulsion while we analyzed the characteristics of propellers.

In March 1935, at one of the weekly GALCIT seminars, William Bollay, then a graduate assistant to von Kármán, reviewed the possibilities of a rocket-powered aircraft based upon a paper published in December 1934 by Eugen Sänger (1905–1964), who was then working in Vienna.[4] Bollay carried out independent design and performance studies of rocket-powered aircraft and presented them on 27 March 1935 at a Caltech seminar on rockets.

Local newspapers reported on Bollay's lecture,[5] which resulted in attracting to GALCIT two rocket enthusiasts—John W. Parsons (1914–1952) and Edward S. Forman. Parsons was a self-trained chemist who, although he lacked the discipline of a formal higher education, had an uninhibited and fruitful imagination. He loved poetry and the exotic aspects of life. Forman, a skilled mechanic, had been working with Parsons for some time on powder rockets. They wished to build a liquid-propellant rocket motor, but found that they lacked adequate technical and financial resources for the task. They hoped to find help at Caltech. They were sent to me, and then began the series of events that lead to the establishment of the Jet Propulsion Laboratory.[6] On the following 4th of October, Bollay gave a lecture before the Institute of the Aeronautical Sciences in Los Angeles. He concluded by saying:

> The present calculations show that we can achieve (by means of rocket planes) higher velocities and reach greater heights than by any other method known so far. The high velocities should prove an attraction to the sportsman, to the military authorities, and perhaps to a few commercial enterprises. The high ceiling is of great interest to the meteorologist and the physicist. There are thus potent reasons for the further development of the rocket plane. I hope I have shown by these calculations that the idea of the rocket plane is not so fantastic as it at first appears and that at present it appears just at the border of the practically attainable and is certainly worthwhile working for. On the other hand, it seems improbable that the rocket plane will be a very hopeful contender with the airplane in ordinary air passenger transportation. For this purpose the stratosphere plane seems eminently more suitable.

Formation of the GALCIT Rocket Research Project

After discussion with Bollay, Parsons, and Forman, I prepared in February 1936, a program of work whose objective was the design of a high-altitude sounding rocket propelled by either a solid- or liquid-propellant rocket engine.

We reviewed the literature published by the first generation of space-flight pioneers—Tsiolkovskiy (1857–1935), Goddard (1882–1945), Esnault-Pelterie (1881–1957) and Oberth.[7] In scientific circles, this literature was generally regarded more in the nature of science fiction, primarily because the gap between the experimental demonstration of rocket-engine capabilities and the actual requirements of rocket propulsion for space flight was so fantastically great. This negative attitude extended to rocket propulsion itself, in spite of the fact that Goddard realistically faced the situation by decid-

ing to apply this type of propulsion to a vehicle for carrying instruments to altitudes in excess of those that can be reached by balloons, an application calling for an engine of much more modest performance.

We were especially impressed by Sänger's report of having achieved an exhaust velocity of 10,000 feet per second (specific impulse of 310) with light fuel oil and gaseous oxygen.[8] Unfortunately, we were never able to understand the method Sänger used for presenting his experimental results.

We concluded from our review of the existing information on rocket-engine design, including the results of the experiments of the American Rocket Society, that it was not possible to design an engine to meet specified performance requirements for a sounding rocket which would surpass the altitudes attainable with balloons. It appeared evident to us, after much argument, that until one could design a workable engine with a reasonable specific impulse there was no point in devoting effort to the design of the rocket shell, propellant supply, stabilizer, launching method, payload parachute, etc.

We, therefore, set as our initial program the following: (1) theoretical studies of the thermodynamical problems of the reaction principle and of the flight performance requirements of a sounding rocket, and (2) elementary experiments to determine the problems to be met in making accurate static tests of liquid- and solid-propellant rocket engines. This approach was in the spirit of von Kármán's teaching. He always stressed the importance of getting as clear as possible an understanding of the fundamental physical principles of a problem before initiating experiments in a purely empirical manner, for these can be very expensive in both time and money.

Parsons and Forman were not too pleased with an austere program that did not include the launching, at least, of model rockets. They could not resist the temptation of firing some models with black powder motors during the next three years. Their attitude is symptomatic of the anxiety of pioneers of new technological developments. In order to obtain support for their dreams, they are under pressure to demonstrate them before they can be technically accomplished. Thus one finds during this period attempts to make rocket flights, which, doomed to be disappointing, made support even more difficult to obtain.

The undertaking we had set for ourselves required, at a minimum, informal permission from Caltech and from the Guggenheim Laboratory before we could begin. In March, I proposed to Clark B. Millikan that I continue my studies leading to a doctorate and that my thesis be devoted to studies of the problems of rocket propulsion and of sounding-rocket flight performance. He was, however, dubious about the future of rocket propulsion, and suggested I should, instead, take one of many engineering positions available in the aircraft industry at that time. His advice was, no doubt, also influenced by the fact that GALCIT was then carrying out no research on aircraft power plants. I would like to add that later he actively supported our work.

I knew that my hopes rested finally with von Kármán, the director of GALCIT. Only much later did I learn that already in the 1920s, in Germany, he had given a sympathetic hearing to discussions of the possibilities of rocket propulsion,[9] and that in 1927 he had included in his lectures in Japan a reference to the problems needing solution before space flight became possible. He was at this time studying the aerodynamics of aircraft at high speeds, and was well aware of the need for a propulsion system which would surmount the limitations of the engine-propeller combination.

After considering my proposals for a few days, he agreed to them.[10] He also gave permission for Parsons and Forman to work with me, even though they were neither students nor on the staff at Caltech.[11] This decision was typical of his unorthodox attitude within the academic world. He pointed out, however, that he could not find funds in the budget of the Laboratory for the construction of experimental apparatus.

At Caltech, we were given further moral support by Robert A. Millikan (1868–1953), then head of the Institute, who was interested in the possibilities of using sounding rockets in his cosmic ray research, and by Irving P. Krick, then head of meterological research and instruction.

During the next three years we received no pay for our work, and during the first year we bought equipment, some secondhand, with whatever money we could pool together. Most of our work was done on weekends or at night.

We began our experiments with the construction of an uncooled rocket motor similar in design to one that had been previously tried by the American Rocket Society. For propellants we chose gaseous oxygen and methyl alcohol.

Our work in spring 1936 attracted to our group two GALCIT graduate students, Apollo M. O. Smith and Hsue-shen Tsien. Smith was working on his master's degree in aeronautics; Tsien, who became one of the outstanding pupils of von Kármán, was working on his doctorate. Smith and I began a theoretical analysis of flight performance of a sounding rocket, while Tsien and I began studies of the thermodynamic problems of the rocket motor.

Some of the members of our group in 1936 and Dr. von Kármán are shown in Figure 1. The work of our group, once it was approved by von Kármán, had the benefit of advice from von Kármán himself, C. B. Millikan, and other GALCIT staff members. We realized from the start that rocket research would require the ideas of many brains in many fields of applied science.

I was very fortunate at this time to enter von Kármán's inner circle of associates because he needed someone to prepare illustrations for the textbook *Mathematical Methods in Engineering* he was writing with Maurice A. Biot. Bollay had been assisting von Kármán with the manuscript of the book, and introduced me to him. When Bollay left for Harvard University in 1937, I also inherited his job as "caretaker" of the manuscript. Thereafter, I worked with von Kármán on many projects until his death in 1963. In a way be became my second father. We worked so closely together during the formative years of the Jet Propulsion Laboratory, until he went to Washington in 1944, that it is not always possible to separate the contribution either of us made to technical and organizational developments during the period 1939–44.

It is necessary to point out, however, that during the period of the GALCIT Rocket Research Project the initiative rested with our group, and it fell to me to hold the group together.

Relations between the Project and R. H. Goddard

The group heard with excitement in the summer of 1936 that Robert H. Goddard would come to Caltech in August to visit R. A. Millikan,[12] who was a member of a committee appointed by the Daniel and Florence Guggenheim Foundation to

FIGURE 1.—*a*, John W. Parsons; *b*, Theodore von Kármán; *c*, Frank J. Malina; *d*, Hsue-shen Tsien (Chien Hsueh-sen); *e*, Apollo M. O. Smith.

advise on the support given by the Foundation to Goddard for the development of a sounding rocket.[13] Millikan arranged for me to have a short discussion with Goddard on 28 August, during which I told him of our hopes and research plans. I also arranged to visit him at Roswell, New Mexico, the next month, when I was going for a holiday to my parents' home in Brenham, Texas.[14] I believe it was before Goddard's arrival in Pasadena that Millikan had already written for me a letter of introduction to him in connection with the possibility of my visiting his Roswell station.[15]

In Milton Lehman's biography of Goddard [16] appears a rather strange and inaccurate account of my visit to Roswell. No mention is made of the fact that R. A. Millikan had arranged for me to meet with Goddard during his visit to Caltech. Part of the account by Lehman reads:

The Goddards had no sooner returned to Mescalero Ranch at the end of August than they found one of Cal. Tech's graduate students waiting to see the professor. The same day Goddard received a note from Millikan asking him to extend "all possible courtesies" to the young student, Frank J. Malina.

My recollections of my visit to Roswell are that both Dr. and Mrs. Goddard received me cordially. My day with him consisted of a tour of his shop (where I was not shown any components of his sounding rocket), of a drive to his launching range to see his launching tower and 2000-pound-thrust static test stand, and of a general discussion during and after lunch. He did not wish to to give any technical details of his current work beyond that which he had published in his 1936 Smithsonian Institution report, with which I was already familiar. This report, of a very general nature, was of limited usefulness to serious students of the subject.[17] On 1 October 1936 I wrote to Goddard: [18]

I have just returned to the Institute after several weeks in Texas. I wish to thank you and your wife for the hospitality shown me and you for your kindness in allowing me to inspect that part of your work which you considered permissible under the circumstances.

I recall two special impressions he made on me. The first was a bitterness towards the press. He showed me a clipping of an editorial, which had appeared in the *New York Times* years earlier (13 January 1920), that ridiculed him, saying that a professor of physics should know better than to make space flight proposals, as they violated a

fundamental law of dynamics. He appeared to suffer keenly from such nonsense directed at him.

The second impression I obtained was that he felt that rockets were his private preserve, so that any others working on them took on the aspect of intruders. He did not appear to realize that in other countries were men who, independently of him, as so frequently happens in the history of technology, had arrived at the same basic ideas for rocket propulsion. His attitude caused him to turn his back on the scientific tradition of communication of results through established scientific journals, and instead he spent much time on patents, especially after he published his classic Smithsonian Institution report of 1919 on "A Method of Reaching Extreme Altitudes." [19]

As I departed, Goddard suggested that I come to work with him at Roswell when I completed my studies at Caltech. This was intriguing to me; but by the time I completed my doctorate in 1940 we had obtained governmental support for rocket research, and were building an effective research establishment.

A year later I wrote to Goddard in connection with an analysis of the flight performance of a sounding rocket with a constant thrust, which Smith and I were carrying out.[20] To the request for flight data on his rockets, he answered on 19 October 1937, as follows:

I have your letter of the fourteenth relative to data for your study of vertical rocket flight.

The gyroscopically stabilized flights described in the report to which you refer were, as therein stated, for stabilization during the period of propulsion, and not thereafter, and the trajectories were accordingly not vertical throughout the flights. The data regarding heights and speeds, while sufficiently accurate to describe the performance in general terms, would therefore hardly be satisfactory for exact calculations made under the assumption that the flights were vertical. Further, thrusts were not measured when the rockets were used for flights, and I have reason to believe that we did not always have the high efficiencies, in flight, that we obtained in certain of the static tests.

As stated in the paper, the main object was to obtain stabilization and satisfactory performance in flight, and I should prefer to have any analyses of performance made for flights in which height was the main consideration. We have had further stabilized flights since the paper was written, but the work is not yet sufficiently complete for publication.

The rockets used in the flights described were all 9 inches in diameter, and the initial altitude was about 4000 feet.[21]

In a letter home dated 23 October, I wrote:

Smith and I are working on the performance paper sporadically. I wrote to Goddard for some data not long ago; an answer arrived during the week. He wrote that he did not have the data desired. We have some data on his flights we want to use in our paper, now we are in a quandary over its use. We may write the paper as originally planned and let Goddard read it before publishing it.[22]

On 7 June 1938, I wrote home:

Had lunch at the Atheneaum with the head of the A.P. science news service last Wednesday. He is making a trip across the country looking for the spectacular. He saw Goddard and was impressed. Judging by his writeup of what he saw, Goddard is almost at the same place he was 2 years ago. We find it difficult to understand Goddard's method of attack of the whole research. Don't think it is the result of personal jealousy on our part. It would be to our benefit if he did get something significant.[23]

On 26 September 1938, I wrote:

The research is bogged down; however, some interesting news was brought by Kármán from New York. By the way, for some reason he thought I was going to be at the meeting in Boston. While in New York Kármán and Clark Millikan had a conference with Guggenheim and Goddard upon the latter's invitation.[24] It seems Goddard is beginning to believe that perhaps our group may be of some use to him. Kármán told him that we would be glad to co-operate with him if he kept no secrets from us. Don't know what will develop. Goddard may come to Pasadena in a couple of months.[25]

Von Kármán, in *The Wind and Beyond* writes:

The trouble with secrecy is that one can easily go in the wrong direction and never know it. I heard, for instance, that Goddard spent three or four years developing a gyroscope for his sounding rocket. This is a waste of time, because a high-altitude rocket does not need a complex tool like a gyroscope for stabilization in flight. At the start, the rocket can be stabilized by a launching tower somewhat taller than the one Goddard actually used. After emerging from the tower, if it has been boosted to enough speed, it can be stabilized accurately enough with fixed fins. Malina and his Jet Propulsion Laboratory team demonstrated this in 1945 when they launched the WAC Corporal, America's first successful high-altitude rocket, to a height of 250,000 feet.

I believe Goddard became bitter in his later years because he had had no real success with rockets, while Aerojet-General Corporation and other organizations were making an industry out of them. There is no direct line from Goddard to present-day rocketry. He is on a branch that died. He was an inventive man and had a good scientific foundation, but he was not a creator of science, and he took himself too seriously. If he had taken others into his confidence, I think he would have developed workable high-altitude rockets and his achievements would have been greater than they were. But not listening to, or communicating with, other qualified people hindered his accomplishments.[26]

With this background to the relations between Goddard and the Project, a summary of his effect on our work can be made. This appears needed, for erroneous impressions exist as to his influence on rocket research at Caltech.

As I pointed out earlier, the stimulus leading to the formation of the GALCIT Rocket Research Project was Sänger's work in Vienna.[27] Like Goddard, our group at first believed that the most promising practical application of rocket propulsion would be a sounding rocket for research of the upper atmosphere, which was of interest at Caltech in connection with cosmic ray studies and with meteorology requirements. Actually it did not turn out this way, for the first application of rocket power we successfully made was in assisting the takeoff of aircraft.

Our group studied and repeated some of Goddards' work with smokeless-powder impulse-type motors, upon which he had reported in his Smithsonian report of 1919.[28] Work on this type of solid-propellant rocket motor was, however, dropped by the group in 1939 in favor of developing one of the constant-pressure, constant-thrust type. Goddard's smokeless powder rocket engine did, however, find application in armament rockets during World War II.

To the best of my recollection, we studied only a few of the patents Goddard had taken out up to that time. As is well known, patents are not equivalent to know-how and rarely provide the analytical basis for engineering design. His publications, together with those of Tsiolkovskiy, Esnault-Pelterie, Oberth, and Sänger, provided important leads, but much work remained to be done before rocket engines became a useful reality.

There is no doubt that had Goddard been willing to co-operate with our Caltech group, his many years of experience would have had a strong influence on our work. As it happened, our group independently initiated the development of liquid and solid propellants different from those that Goddard studied. When finally in 1944 I initiated the construction of the WAC Corporal sounding rocket at the Jet Propulsion Laboratory, it bore little technical relation to Goddard's sounding rocket of 1936, about which we still did not have any detailed information.

Research Undertaken by the Group

On 31 October 1936, the first try of the portable test equipment was made for the gaseous-oxygen-methyl-alcohol rocket motor in the area of the Arroyo Seco back of Devil's Gate Dam, on the western edge of Pasadena, California, a stone's throw from the present-day Jet Propulsion Laboratory. I learned several years later from Clarence N. Hickman that he and Goddard had conducted smokeless-powder armament rocket experiments at this same location during World War I.

On 1 November, I wrote home as follows:

This has been a very busy week. We made our first test on the rocket motor yesterday. It is almost inconceivable how much there is to be done and thought of to make as simple a test as we made. We have been thinking about it for about 6 months now, although we had to get all the equipment together in two days, not by choice, but because there are classes, and hours in the wind tunnel to be spent. Friday we drove back and forth to Los Angeles picking up pressure tanks, fittings and instruments. Saturday morning at 3:30 a.m. we felt the setup was along far enough to go home and snatch 3 hours of sleep. At 9:00 a.m. an Institute truck took our heaviest parts to the Arroyo, about 3 miles above the

Rose Bowl, where we found an ideal location. Besides Parsons and me, there were two students working in the N.Y.A. working for us. It was 1:00 p.m. before all our holes were dug, sand bags filled, and equipment minutely checked. By then Carlos Wood and Rockefeller had arrived with two of the box type movie cameras for recording the action of the motor. Bill Bollay and his wife also came to watch from behind the dump.

Very many things happened that will teach us what to do next time. The most excitement took place on the last "shot" when the oxygen hose, for some reason, ignited and swung around on the ground, 40 feet from us. We all tore out across the country wondering if our check valves would work. Unfortunately Carlos and Rocky had to leave just before this "shot" so that we have no record on film of what happened. As a whole the test was successful.[29]

A number of tests were made with this transportable experimental setup (see Figures 2 and 3); the last one on 16 January 1937 when the motor ran for 44 seconds at a chamber pressure of 75 pounds per square inch.[30]

FIGURE 2.—Members of GALCIT rocket research group during early test (1936): from left, Rudolf Schott, Apollo M. O. Smith, Frank J. Malina, the late Edward S. Forman (died 1973), and the late John W. Parsons.

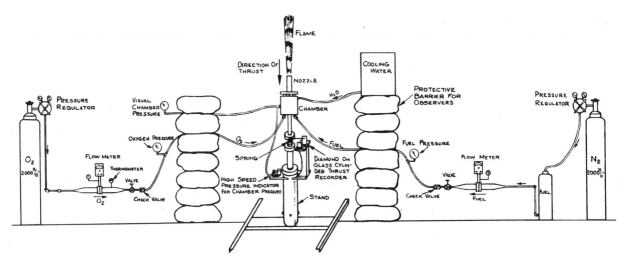

FIGURE 3.—Schematic diagram of test setup similar to one used by GALCIT rocket research group on 11 November 1936. Propellant was gaseous oxygen/methyl alcohol.

In March 1937, Smith and I completed our analysis of the flight performance of a constant-thrust sounding rocket. The results were so encouraging that our Project obtained from von Kármán the continued moral support of GALCIT. We were authorized to conduct small-scale rocket motor tests in the laboratory. This permitted us to reduce the time we wasted putting up and taking down the transportable equipment we had used in the Arroyo Seco. Von Kármán also asked me to give a report on the results of our first year's work at the GALCIT seminar at the end of April.

The unexpected result of the seminar was the offer of the first financial support for our Project. Weld Arnold (1895–1962), then an assistant in the Astrophysical Laboratory at Caltech, came to me and said that in return for his being permitted to work with our group as a photographer he would make a contribution of $1,000 for our work. His offer was accepted with alacrity, for our Project was destitute.

This enabled Parsons and me to give up our effort to write an anti-war novel with a plot, of course, revolving around the work of a group of rocket engineers. We had hoped to sell it for a large sum to a Hollywood studio as a basis for a movie script to support the work of the project! This was of some relief to me, for I could then spend less time in Parson's house, where he was accumulating tetranitromethane in his kitchen.

Arnold, who commuted the five miles between

Glendale and Caltech by bicycle, brought the first 500 dollars for our project in one- and five-dollar bills in a bundle wrapped in newspaper! We never learned how he had accumulated them. When I placed the bundle on the desk of C. B. Millikan with the question "How do we open a fund at Caltech for our project?," he was flabbergasted.

What has been called the original GALCIT rocket research group was now complete. It consisted of Parsons, Forman, Smith, Tsien, Arnold, and myself. In June 1937, studies made by the group up to that time, including Bollay's paper of 1935, were collected together into what our group called its "bible." [31]

The "bible" contained the following papers:

1. "Proposed Investigations of the GALCIT Rocket Research Project; Discussions of Laboratory for Conducting Tests, and Reports of Experiments Conducted during the Fall of 1936," by F. J. Malina, 10 April 1937.

2. "Analysis of the Rocket Motor," by F. J. Malina, 10 April 1937.

3. "The Effect of Angle of Divergence of Nozzle on the Thrust of a Rocket Motor; Ideal Cycle of a Rocket Motor; Ideal Rocket Efficiency and Ideal Thrust; Calculation of Chamber Temperature with Dissociation," by H. S. Tsien, 29 May 1937.

4. "A Consideration of the Applicability of Various Substances as Fuels for Jet Propulsion," by J. W. Parsons, 10 June 1937.

5. "Rocket Performance" (Rocket Shell as a Body of Revolution), by F. J. Malina and A. M. O. Smith, 15 April 1937.
6. "Performance of the Rocket Plane," by W. Bollay (1935).

The paper on the performance of a sounding rocket by Smith and myself became in 1938 the first paper published by the Institute of Aeronautical Sciences (now American Institute of Aeronautics and Astronautics) in the field of rocket flight.[32] Smith and I had worked on this paper for many days and nights. On 13 December 1937, I wrote home:

> Smith and I were much disappointed last week when we found a French paper with a study similar to ours. Have decided not to send our paper to France. (REP-Hirsch Prize competition). The finding does not affect the N.Y. presentation.
>
> Caltech has been rather unlucky in having other men beat them to publication. My room-mate [Martin Summerfield] also has the same misfortune.[33]

The French paper referred to above was "Les Fusées volantes météorologiques" published in October 1936 by Willy Ley and Herbert Schaefer in *L'Aerophile*.[34] Smith's and my paper was, however, more general in discussing the influence of design parameters, and more suitable for application to particular cases of a sounding rocket propelled by a constant-thrust rocket engine. My paper on the analysis of the rocket motor, including Tsien's calculation of the effect of the angle of divergence of the exhaust nozzle on the thrust of a rocket motor, was published by the *Journal of the Franklin Institute* in 1940.[35] The paper by Parsons led eventually to the development of red fuming nitric acid as a storable oxidizer, and he also anticipated the use of boron hydride as a fuel.[36] Many of his suggestions were incorporated in patents which he and I prepared in 1943 and assigned to the Aerojet-General Corporation of which we were co-founders in 1942.[37]

When von Kármán gave the group permission to make small-scale experiments of rocket motors at GALCIT, we decided to mount a motor and propellant supply on a bob of a 50-foot ballistic pendulum, using the deflection of the pendulum to measure thrust. The pendulum was suspended from the third floor of the Laboratory with the bob in the basement. It was planned to make tests with various oxidizer-fuel combinations.

We selected the combination of methyl alcohol and nitrogen tetroxide for our initial try. Our first mishap occurred when Smith and I were trying to get a quantity of the nitrogen tetroxide from a cylinder that we had placed on the lawn in front of Caltech's Gates Chemistry Building. The valve on the cylinder jammed, causing a fountain of the corrosive liquid to erupt from the cylinder all over the lawn. This left a brown patch there for several weeks, to the irritation of the gardener.

When we finally tried an experiment with the motor on the pendulum, there was a misfire, with the result that a cloud of nitrogen tetroxide and alcohol permeated most of GALCIT, leaving behind a thin layer of rust on much of the permanent equipment of the Laboratory. We were told to move our apparatus outside the building at once. Thereafter we also were known at Caltech as the "Suicide Squad."

We remounted the pendulum in the open from the roof of the building and obtained a limited amount of useful information. We made the first, or one of the first, experiments in America with a rocket motor using a storable liquid oxidizer. On the basis of this experience with nitrogen tetroxide, Parsons later developed red-fuming nitric acid as a storable oxidizer which is still being used today.

Although rocket research unavoidably involves experimentation of a dangerous nature, to my knowledge no one has suffered a fatal injury up to the present day at JPL. Unfortunately, Parsons's familiarity with explosives led to contempt, and in 1952, when moving his Pasadena home laboratory to Mexico, he dropped a fulminate of mercury cap which exploded and killed him. I wish to take this occasion to express my appreciation for his work, which was of great significance in the history of the development of American rocket technology, both as regards storable liquid propellants and composite solid propellants.[38]

During this period Tsien and I continued our theoretical studies of the thermodynamic characteristics of a rocket motor. To check our results, steps were taken to design and construct a test stand for a small rocket motor burning gaseous oxygen and ethylene gas. Von Kármán reviewed our plans and agreed that we could build the apparatus, shown in Figures 4 and 5, on a platform on the eastern side of GALCIT. In 1939 this apparatus exploded. I escaped serious injury only because

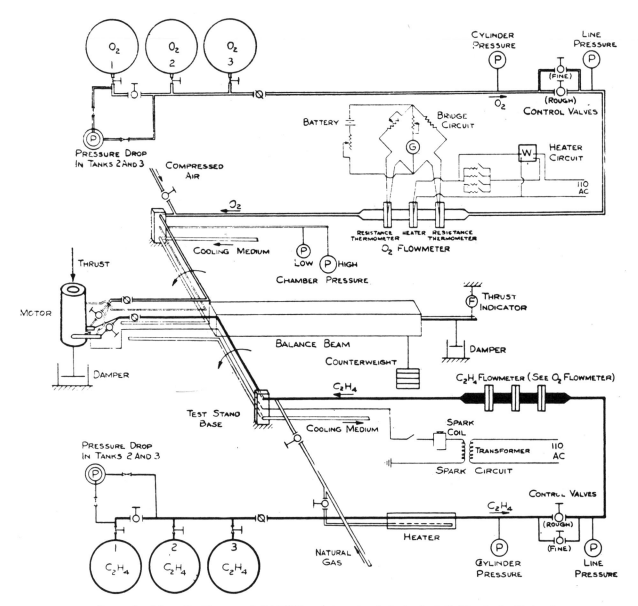

FIGURE 4.—Schematic diagram of GALCIT rocket motor test stand at California Institute of
Technology.

von Kármán had called me to bring a typewriter
to his home. Parsons and Forman were shaken up
but unhurt.

Smith made simple experiments to determine the
material from which we should make the exhaust
nozzle of the motor. He describes these experiments
as follows in a recent letter to me:

Sometime, perhaps in the 1937–1938 school year, perhaps
before [it was in the spring of 1938], we began investigation
of materials—ceramics, metals, carborundum, etc. I developed
a standard simple test. I would use the largest tip (No. 10, I

believe) on an oxy-acetylene torch and play it over a specimen
for one minute. Some super refractories spalled and popped
like a pan of popcorn and some just melted. You obtained
a ½" cube of molybdenum and I tested that. It did not melt,
but when I removed the neutral protecting atmosphere of
the torch, before my very eyes I watched it literally go up in
smoke. While cooling, it dwindled from about a ½" cube to
a ¼" cube giving off a dense white smoke. As part of this
phase you and I visited the Vitrefax Corporation in Hunting-
ton Park to get help from them about super refractories. One
important refractory was forcefully brought to our attention.
We watched them make mullite and saw large graphite
electrodes working unscathed in large pots of boiling super

FIGURE 5.—Overall view of GALCIT test stand at Caltech (top), details of control panel (center), and ethylene tanks mounted in balance structure (bottom). From *Popular Mechanics* (August 1940).

refractory. This opened our eyes to the possibilities of graphite. It tested well under the torch. Later, shortly before I left Caltech in June 1938, I happened to try the torch on a ½" x 2" x 12" long piece of copper bar stock. The torch could not hurt this piece at all and this test opened our eyes to the possibilities of massive copper for resisting heat.[39]

The first combustion chamber liner and exhaust nozzle of the motor were made of electrode graphite. Later the exhaust nozzle was made of copper. An experiment made in May 1938, at a chamber pressure of 300 pounds per square inch for a period of one minute, showed that the graphite had withstood the temperature and that the exhaust nozzle throat, which was 0.138 inch in diameter, suffered only an enlargement of 0.015 inch.[40] The motor delivered a thrust of the order of 5 pounds.

In March 1938, A. Bartocci in Italy published the results of his extensive experiments with a rocket motor of dimensions similar to ours with cold oxygen gas.[41] His results were in close agreement with the theoretical analysis which Tsien and I had made. A report of the first series of experiments with our apparatus is contained in my doctorate thesis of 1940.[42]

In the winter of 1938, Tsien and I also extended the study, by Smith and me, of the performance of a sounding rocket to the case of propulsion by successive impulses from a constant-volume solid propellant rocket engine.[43] We had reviewed Goddard's 1919 paper on "A Method of Reaching Extreme Altitudes"[44] and decided to find a mathematical solution for the flight calculation problem, which Goddard had not carried out. We did this in spite of the difficult practical problem of devising a reloading mechanism for such a rocket engine, for at that time no propulsion method could be discounted.

Parsons and Forman built a smokeless powder constant-volume combustion rocket motor similar to the one tested by Goddard. With it they extended Goddard's results.[45] To my knowledge, no practical solution has ever been found for a long-duration solid-propellant rocket engine using the impulse technique. The use of impulses from small atomic explosions has been considered; however, no actual tests of such a system have been as yet reported.

The negative conclusions we reached as regards the practicability of devising an impulse-system rocket engine for long duration propulsion made us turn to the study of the possibility of developing a composite solid propellant which would burn

in a combustion chamber in cigarette fashion. Parsons decided first to try extending the burning time of the black-powder pyrotechnic skyrocket. He finally constructed a modified black-powder 12-second, 28-pound-thrust rocket unit in 1941.[46] The results of L. Damblanc of France with black-powder rockets published in 1935 were known to us.[47]

During the summer of 1938, Smith began working in the engineering department of the Douglas Aircraft Company, where he is still employed. Arnold left Caltech for New York, and completely vanished as far as we were concerned. It was not until 1959 that I learned that he was a member of the Board of Trustees of the University of Nevada. We then corresponded until his death in 1962. Tsien was able to devote less time to the work of the project, as he was completing his doctorate under von Kármán. I struggled on with Parsons and Forman, little suspecting that in the next few months the project would become a fullfledged GALCIT activity supported financially by the Federal government.

We also had less time to devote to rocket research, for we had to support ourselves. Parsons and Forman took part-time jobs with the Halifax Powder Company in the California Mojave Desert, and I began to do some work on problems of wind erosion of soil with von Kármán for the Soil Conservation Service of the U.S. Department of Agriculture.[48]

The work of the group on rocket research at GALCIT, from the beginning, attracted the attention of newspapers and popular scientific journals. Since our work was not then classified as "secret," we were not averse to discussing with journalists our plans and results. There were times that we were abashed by the sensational interpretations given of our work, for we tended to be, if anything, too conservative in our estimates of its implications.[49]

The fact that our work was having a real impact in America came from two sources. In May 1938, von Kármán had received an inkling that the U.S. Army Air Corps (now the U.S. Air Force) was becoming interested in rocket propulsion; as I will indicate later, however, it was only at the end of the year that we learned why.

Then in August 1938, Ruben Fleet, president of the Consolidated Aircraft Company of San Diego, California, approached GALCIT for information on the possibility of using rockets for assisting the take-off of large aircraft, especially flying boats. I went to San Diego to discuss the matter, and prepared a report, "The Rocket Motor and its Application as an Auxiliary to the Power Plants of Conventional Aircraft," [50] in which I concluded that the rocket engine was particularly adaptable for assisting the take-off of aircraft, ascending to operating altitude and reaching high speeds. The Consolidated Aircraft Company appears to have been the first American commercial organization to recognize the potential importance of rocket assisted aircraft take-off. It was not, however, until 1943 that liquid-propellant rocket engines, constructed by the Aerojet-General Corporation, were tested in a Consolidated Aircraft Company flying boat on San Diego Bay.[51]

In October 1938, a senior officer of the U.S. Army Ordnance Division paid a visit to Caltech, and informed our group that on the basis of the Army's experience with rockets he thought there was little possibility of using them for military purposes!

I had learned during the year of the REP-Hirsch International Astronautical Prize, which was administered by the Astronautics Committee of the Société Astronomique de France. The prize, named for the French astronautical pioneer Robert Esnault-Pelterie (REP) and the banker rocket-enthusiast of Paris, André-Louis Hirsch (1900–1962), consisted of a medal and a cash sum of 1000 francs. As the money contributed by Arnold was rapidly being used up, I decided to enter the competition by sending a paper on some of my work in the hope of augmenting the funds of the Project. Not until 1946, when in Prague, did I learn that the prize had been awarded to me in 1939.[52] The outbreak of the Second World War in Europe had prevented the Astronautics Committee from notifying me. In 1958, Andrew G. Haley (1904–1966), then president of the International Astronautical Federation, arranged for the medal to be presented to me by André-Louis Hirsch at the IXth International Astronautical Congress at Amsterdam, but by then the prize was worth a fraction of its former value. As it turned out, however, government support for our rocket research was forthcoming before the contribution of Arnold was spent, and when I left JPL to work at UNESCO in Paris in 1946, 300 dollars still remained in the Arnold fund.

In December 1938, after giving a talk entitled "Facts and Fancies of Rockets" at a Caltech luncheon of the Society of the Sigma Xi, I was informed by von Kármán, R. A. Millikan, and Max Mason that I was to go to Washington, D. C., to give expert information to the National Academy of Sciences Committee on Army Air Corps Research. R. A. Millikan and von Kármán were members of this Committee.

One of the subjects on which Gen. H. A. Arnold, then Commanding General of the Army Air Corps, asked the Academy to give advice was the possible use of rockets for the assisted take-off of heavily loaded aircraft. In response, I prepared a "Report on Jet Propulsion for the National Academy of Sciences Committee on Air Corps Research," which contained the following parts: (1) Fundamental concepts, (2) Classification of types of jet propulsors, (3) Possible applications of jet propulsion in connection with heavier-than-air craft, (4) Present state of development of jet propulsion, and (5) Research program for developing jet propulsion.[53] The word "rocket" was still in such bad repute in "serious" scientific circles at this time that it was felt advisable by von Kármán and myself to follow the precedent of the Air Corps of dropping the use of the word. It did not return to our vocabulary until several years later, by which time the word "jet" had become part of the name of our laboratory (JPL) and of the Aerojet-General Corporation.

I presented my report to the Committee on 28 December 1938, and shortly thereafter the Academy accepted von Kármán's offer to study, with our GALCIT Rocket Research Group, the problem of the assisted take-off of aircraft on the basis of available information, and to prepare a proposal for a research program. A sum of 1,000 dollars was provided for this work. It is interesting to note that when Caltech obtained the first governmental support for rocket research, Jerome C. Hunsaker of the Massachusetts Institute of Technology, who offered to study the de-icing problem of windshields, which was then a serious aircraft problem, told von Kármán, "You can have the Buck Rogers' job." [54]

Parsons and Forman were delighted when I returned from Washington with the news that the work we had done during the past three years was to be rewarded by being given government financial support, and that von Kármán would join us as director of the program. We could even expect to be paid for doing our rocket research!

Thus in 1939 the GALCIT Rocket Research Project became the Air Corps Jet Propulsion Research Project. In 1944 I prepared a proposal for the creation of a section of jet propulsion within the Division of Engineering at Caltech. It was decided that it would be premature to do so. Instead, von Kármán and I founded JPL. Of the original GALCIT Rocket Research Group only I remained at Caltech during the whole period, although Tsien had returned from M.I.T. in 1943 to work with us again. Parsons and Forman were employed, beginning in 1942, by the Aerojet-General Corporation; Smith was at the Douglas Aircraft Company; and Arnold's whereabouts were then unknown to us.

In conclusion, I wish to express my appreciation to William Bollay and A. M. O. Smith for their help to me during the preparation of this memoir, to Mrs. Robert H. Goddard for granting me permission to quote from my correspondence with her husband, to Lee Edson for providing me with text from Th. von Kármán's autobiography before its publication, and to George S. James for retrieving several references and illustrations used in the text.

NOTES

Under the title *O nauchno issledovatel'skoy rabote gruppi GALCIT v 1936–1938*, this paper appeared on pages 69–84 of *Iz istorii astronavtiki i raketnoi tekhniki: Materialy XVIII mezhdunarodnogo astronavticheskogo kongressa, Belgrad, 25–29 Sentyavrya 1967* [From the History of Rockets and Astronautics: Materials of the 18th International Astronautical Congress, Belgrade, 25–29 September 1967], Moscow: Nauka, 1970.

1. *Guggenheim Aeronautical Laboratory—The First Twenty-Five Years* (Pasadena: California Institute of Technology, 1954).

2. Theodore von Kármán (with Lee Edson), *The Wind and Beyond* (Boston: Little, Brown and Co., 1967).

3. Frank L. Wattendorf and Frank J. Malina, "Theodore von Kármán, 1881–1963," *Astronautica Acta*, vol. 10, p. 81, 1964.

4. Eugen Sänger, "Neuere Ergebnisse der Rakenflugtechnik," *Flug*, Sonderheft 1 (December 1934), Vienna, H. Pittner.

5. William Bollay, "Performance of the Rocket Plane," GALCIT Rocket Research Project, Report 5, 27 March 1935; "Rocket Plane Visualized Flying 1200 Miles an Hour," *Los Angeles Times*, 27 March 1935.

6. F. J. Malina, "The Jet Propulsion Laboratory: Its Origins and First Decade of Work," *Spaceflight*, September 1964, pp. 160–65; "Origins and First Decade of the Jet Propulsion

Laboratory," in *The History of Rocket Technology*, edited by Eugene M. Emme (Detroit: Wayne State University Press, 1964), pp. 46–66; and "The Rocket Pioneers," *Engineering and Science*, vol. 31, no. 5 (February 1968), pp. 9–13 and 30–32.

7. Th. von Kármán and F. J. Malina, "Los Comienzos de la Astronautica," ch. 1 in *Ciencia y tecnologia del espacio* (Madrid: *I.N.T.A.E.T.*, 1967). F. J. Malina, "A Short History of Rocket Propulsion up to 1954," in O. E. Lancaster, *Jet Propulsion Engines*, vol. 12, High Speed Aerodynamics and Jet Propulsion (Princeton: Princeton University Press, 1959).

8. See note 4.

9. Th. von Kármán, "Jet Assisted Take-off," *Interavia*, vol. 7, 1952, pp. 376–79; and *The Wind and Beyond* (see note 2), pp. 236–38.

10. *The Wind and Beyond*, pp. 234–35 and 238–40.

11. "Undergraduates Plan Rocket Study with New Society," *Science Newsletter*, vol. 31, 8 May 1937, p. 296; and "Notes and News," *Astronautics*, no. 39, January 1938, pp. 2 and 16.

12. Milton Lehman, *This High Man* (New York: Farrar, Straus and Co., 1963), pp. 234–35.

13. Esther C. Goddard and G. Edward Pendray, Editors, *The Papers of Robert H. Goddard* (New York: McGraw-Hill Book Company, 1970) (hereafter cited as *Papers*), vol. 2, pp. 665, 746, 804–06, 834, 919; and vol. 3, pp. 1199, 1353.

14. "Excerpts from Letters Written Home by Frank J. Malina Between 1936 and 1946," (unpublished; hereafter cited as Letters).

15. Goddard, *Papers*, 2:1012–13, 1023.

16. See note 12.

17. Robert H. Goddard, "Liquid-Propellant Rocket Development," *Smithsonian Miscellaneous Collections*, vol. 95, no. 3, 10 pp., 11 pls., 16 March 1936.

18. Goddard, *Papers*, vol. 2, p. 1027.

19. In *Smithsonian Miscellaneous Collections*, vol. 71, no. 2, December 1919.

20. Goddard, *Papers*, vol. 2, pp. 1089–91.

21. See note 20.

22. Letters (note 14).

23. Letters (note 14).

24. Goddard, *Papers*, vol. 3, p. 1199.

25. Letters (note 14).

26. *The Wind and Beyond* (see note 2), pp. 240–242.

27. See note 4.

28. See note 19; also John W. Parsons and Edward S. Forman, "Experiments with Powder Motors for Rocket Propulsion by Successive Impulses," *Astronautics*, no. 43 (August 1939), pp. 4–11.

29. Letters (note 14).

30. "Schematic Diagram of GALCIT Proving Stand," *Astronautics*, no. 41 (July 1938), p. 1; and, same issue, F. J. Malina, "Rocketry in California, Plans and Progress of the GALCIT Rocket Research Group," pp. 3–6.

31. F. J. Malina, Hsue Shen Tsien, Apollo M. O. Smith, and William Bollay, "Report of the GALCIT Rocket Research Project," Report RRP-1, Guggenheim Aeronautical Laboratory, California Institute of Technology, 1937, unpublished.

32. F. J. Malina and A. M. O. Smith, "Flight Analysis of a Sounding Rocket," *Journal of the Aeronautical Sciences*, vol. 5, 1938, pp. 199–202.

33. Letters (note 14).

34. Willy Ley and Herbert Schaefer, "Les Fusées volantes météorologiques," *L'Aerophile*, vol. 44, 1936, pp. 228–32.

35. F. J. Malina, "Characteristics of the Rocket Motor Unit Based on the Theory of Perfect Gases," *Journal of the Franklin Institute*, vol. 230, no. 4, 1940, pp. 433–54.

36. J. W. Parsons, "A Consideration of the Practicability of Various Substances as Fuels for Jet Propulsion," GALCIT Rocket Research Project, Report 7, 10 June 1937, unpublished.

37. F. J. Malina and J. W. Parsons, U. S. Patents 2,573,471, 2,693,077, and 2,774,214. Originally filed 8 May 1943.

38. See note 6.

39. A. M. O. Smith in letter to the author, 29 December 1966.

40. See note 2 and also 42, below.

41. A. Bartocci, "La forza di reazioni nell'efflusso di gas," *L'Aerotecnica*, March 1938.

42. F. J. Malina, Doctor's Thesis, California Institute of Technology, 1940.

43. H. S. Tsien and F. J. Malina, "Flight Analysis of a Sounding Rocket with Special Reference to Propulsion by Successive Impulses," *Journal of the Aeronautical Sciences*, vol. 6, 1938, pp. 50–58.

44. See note 19.

45. See Goddard, *Papers*, vol. 3, p. 1199; and *The Wind and Beyond* (note 2), pp. 240–42.

46. See note 6.

47. Louis Damblanc, "Les fusées autopropulsives à explosifs," *L'Aerophile*, vol. 43, 1935, pp. 205–09, 241–47.

48. *The Wind and Beyond* (note 2), pp. 206–07.

49. See note 5 and "Designs Rocket Ship to Fly at 4,400 Miles an Hour," *Chicago Daily News*, 12 April 1935; "Pasadena Men Aim at Rocket Altitude Mark," *Pasadena Star News*, 15 July 1938; Scholer Bangs, "Rocket Altitude Record Sought," *Los Angeles Examiner*, 15 July 1938; William S. Barton, "Our Expanding Universe," *Los Angeles Times*, 26 November 1939; and "Seeking Power for Space Rockets," *Popular Mechanics*, August 1940, pp. 210–13.

50. F. J. Malina. "The Rocket Motor and Its Application as an Auxiliary to the Power Plants of Conventional Aircraft," GALCIT Rocket Research Project, Report 2, 24 August 1938, unpublished.

51. C. W. Schnare, "Development of ATO and Engines for Manned Rocket Aircraft," American Rocket Society, Preprint 2088-61, p. 7; and R. C. Stiff, Jr., "Storable Liquid Rockets," American Institute of Aeronautics and Astronautics, Preprint 67-977, p. 2 and fig. 11.

52. Prix et médailles déscernés par la Société, *Bulletin de la Société Astronomique de France*, vol. 53, 1939, p. 296.

53. F. J. Malina, "Report on Jet Propulsion for the National Academy of Sciences Committee on Air Corps Research," (Jet Propulsion Laboratory Report, Misc. No. 1), 21 December 1938 (unpublished).

54. Review by Th. von Kármán of C. M. Bolster, "Assisted Take-off of Aircraft" (James Jackson Cabot Fund Lecture, Norwich University, Northfield, Vermont, Publication no. 9, 1950.—Ed.), *Journal of the American Rocket Society*, no. 85, June 1951, p. 92; *The Wind and Beyond* (note 2), p. 243.

13

My Contributions to Astronautics

HERMANN OBERTH, *German Federal Republic*

As a boy of eleven during the winter of 1905–06, I read Jules Verne's *From the Earth to the Moon* and *A Trip around the Moon.* If we disregard the novelistic side of these books, the following essential parts remain: Three travelers were shot in a projectile to the moon with a giant gun, called the "Columbiade." It was planned to fall onto the moon, easing the fall with powder rockets. Since the book was written in 1860, other types of rockets were unknown. The projectile, however, missed the moon and returned in an astronomically impossible, but literally very interesting, trajectory to the earth, falling onto the Pacific from which it was recovered.

I was fascinated by the idea of space flight, and even more so, because I succeeded in verifying the magnitude of the escape velocity. Although I had not yet learned anything about infinitesimal calculus, by that time I did have the following information: In high school we had learned the laws of free fall. Moreover, we had learned that at an altitude of 6370 km (two radii away from the center of the earth) gravity is only a quarter, and at an altitude of n radii from the center it is only $1/n^2$ as great as it is on the surface of the earth (one radius distance from the center). I then divided the distance into intervals so small that gravity could virtually be considered as a constant, and I calculated the velocity increase for the greatest accelerations in these intervals. Then I did the same for the smallest accelerations of gravity in these intervals. In this manner, I found that the escape velocity of 12,000 yards per second, which Jules Verne had used, was indeed within these two limits. Likewise I found that the time of flight was correct, if it is assumed that the projectile was traveling at minimum velocity.

Nevertheless, I soon saw that space flight in this way was impossible. Apart from all questions of technical rationality there was one physiological impossibility. Sitting in a car which is accelerating, we are pressed back in our seats. The greater the acceleration, the more intense the pressure. If the acceleration were as great as that of free fall, that is, 9.8 m/sec², the pressure experienced by a body would equal its own weight. With increasing acceleration, the ratio would increase. Assuming it were possible to reach a velocity of 11,000 m/sec at a distance of 300 m, this pressure would be more than 20,000 times as much as the passenger's own weight.

Against this handicap Jules Verne proposed a water buffer; and he succeeded with it, too—on paper, at least! Actually, this solution would be worthless, since man's internal organs could not tolerate this acceleration. Therefore, shooting someone into space with a gun would not work, and I had to look for different kinds of space ships.

Aside from some impracticable ideas, I was pushed more and more towards rocket propulsion. I cannot say that I favored it very much, because of the danger of explosion. I was also worried about the disproportion between the propellant to be taken along and the rest of the mass of the spacecraft; but I saw no other way out.

Jules Verne's idea of retarding the fall onto the moon by rockets had surprised me very much in the beginning, because there was nothing the escaping gas could push against. But, I said to myself: When someone jumps from a boat to the shore, the boat will receive an impulse in the opposite direction. If we place a pole in outer space, away from the earth's atmosphere and field of gravitation, and move it in a certain direction with a certain speed, it will maintain its direction and speed as long as nothing else happens. But, when a space pilot, sitting on the pole, cuts little pieces off the end of the pole, and throws them backwards, then not only will these small pieces change their speed, but also the remaining part of the pole will get an impulse in the opposite direction. The forward speed of the pole will be increased less if the cut-off pieces are small and move slowly, and more if the pieces are large and move at high speed.

In the same way, the increase in speed would be equally high if, instead of one big piece, many small pieces were to be exhausted or thrown off. It does not matter whether these pieces push against something, or whether they sail through the vacuum of space. There would also be an increase in speed if the thrown-off parts were gas molecules. The increase can be considerable when large quantities of gas are exhausted at high speed.

In general, it is not as important how much knowledge a person has, but, rather, what he does with his knowledge. In this sense, there were many stumbling blocks in the field of rocketry. Knowledgeable engineers and even university professors had postulated that repulsion would not work in a vacuum. I nevertheless continued in my belief that it would prove out in actual fact. There was even a colonel, head of the German Missile Post in East Prussia, who in 1927 tried to prove the impossibility of space travel. Among other things, he said that although the law of the conservation of the center of gravity was valid, the gas would expand so much in outer space that it would lose its entire mass and therefore would not have any moment of inertia. To the contrary, I maintained that a pound of propellant would always remain a pound of propellant, no matter how much space into which it might expand.

From 1910 to 1912, I learned infinitesimal calculus in the Bischof-Teutsch-Gymnasium in Schässburg. This school, more humanistic than scientific in nature, resembled a car which has only small headlights in front, but which illuminates very brightly the way it has already traveled, thus helping light the way for others. I also had bought the book, *Mathematik für Jedermann* [Mathematics for Everybody], by August Shuster, which covered differential calculus and helped me overcome a certain lack of training.

As a student I had little occasion to do experiments. In order to accomplish something with my time, I pondered the theoretical problems of rocket technology and space travel, and attempted to solve some of them. No one of whom I had knowledge had done so thoroughly. Dr. Goddard in 1919, for instance, wrote that it would be impossible to express for a rocket trajectory the interactions of propellant consumption, exhaust velocity, air drag, influence of gravity, etc., in closed numerical equations.[1] In 1910 I had begun to investigate these mathematical relationships and to derive the equations; these investigations were completed by 1929.

One of my first discoveries was the optimum speed at which losses in performance, caused by air drag and gravity, were reduced to a minimum. I found this by a sort of differentiation process and called the term $\bar{v}$. When a rocket rises perpendicularly to the earth's surface with the velocity $\bar{v}$, the air drag is equal to the weight of the rocket. If the rocket rises faster, it has to fight against its weight for a shorter time; but since the air drag increases with the square of the velocity, the total losses are greater; and if it rises too slowly, it has to fight against its own weight for a longer time.

All rockets built before 1920 had flown too fast. Early rockets also were not large enough, for there is a kind of competition between the weight of the rocket and the air density. If, or example, $\bar{v}c = 2gH$, then the optimum speed does not change at all when the rocket rises. Consequently the rocket can only escape from the atmosphere if the ratio between takeoff mass and burnout mass is infinite; that is, if the propellant weighed infinitely as much as the rest of the rocket. In this equation c denotes the exhaust velocity, H the height at which the air pressure will have decreased to $1/e$, which is 1 divided by the base of natural logarithms ($1/2.71828 = 0.36788$ of the initial value), and g denotes the acceleration of gravity.

If the rocket were small, then even $\bar{v}$ would decrease with time: the air does not become thinner at the same rate at which the rocket loses weight. The rocket will, so to speak, remain stuck in the air. If the rocket, however, is big and heavy, the forces caused by the drag will be less in comparison to the other forces. In this case, $\bar{v}$ is higher, and the rocket reaches thinner layers of air sooner. For example, a cannon ball will not be retarded as much by a headwind as a gun bullet traveling at the same speed.

If the rocket carries enough propellant, the rocket can leave the earth and even escape the earth's field of gravitation. At inclined trajectories the optimum speed is the one at which the air drag is equal to the weight times the sine of the angle at which the rocket rises.

Concerning the propellant taken along, the following rule applies: the propellant will be the more effective, the higher the exhaust velocity it can produce and the more of it that can be carried compared to the rest of the rocket mass. In space with no atmosphere, and no gravitation, the increase in speed $V_2 - V_1$ of a rocket would equal its exhaust velocity if it were e times (i.e., 2.718) heavier with filled tanks than with empty ones. If the ratio of the masses were e times $e = e^2$ (7.389), the increase in speed would be $v_2 - v_1 = 2c$. At a ratio of e^2 times e, which means a take-off mass 20 times the burn-out mass, $v_2 - v_1 = 3c$, etc. From this it can be seen that $v_2 - v_1$ can well be greater than c; thus, the statement made by Professor Dr. Kirchberger and Dr. von Dallwitz-Wegner is not correct: "The propellant does not even contain enough energy to lift its own weight beyond the earth's field of gravitation. How should it be able to take along the weight of the rocket, too?" [2]

The fact which proves these two professors wrong is that the propellant, to a large extent, remains in the earth's field of gravitation and gives only part of its energy to the rocket in the form of thrust.

Later on, the requirement for stages developed out of these formulas. If there is a small rocket on top of a big one, and if the big one is jettisoned, and the small one is ignited, then their speeds are added. Councillor Lorenz, for example, had said that he never understood this principle.[3] In this case, the mass ratios have to be multiplied with each other, and when calculating the lower rocket, one has to take into account the entire mass of the upper one as payload.

These are only a few examples. I had entered an entirely new field of science with these calculations and could, by using my formulas, determine the important parameters for building a rocket. This is the advantage of such algebraic formulas. An electronic brain of today will calculate infinitely faster and more accurately; but it gives only certain numerical answers and not the general rela-

tionship. By the way, I refer intentionally to "an electronic brain of today," because computer technology is growing at such a fast rate. These machines can compute, in a very short time, certain common traits that statisticians would require years to find out—if they could do it at all. No one can predict the performance of future computers.

The rocket at that time resembled a talented but poor boy with a small job in a big firm. Since he is not trained, he cannot work effectively, and since he cannot produce in an outstanding manner, no one's attention is drawn to him. If some of his friends were to say, "He is capable of doing better work," the people in authority would not believe it. I am thinking of the great but entirely misunderstood German inventor, Hermann Ganswindt, of whose inventions and tragic fate I did not learn until 1926. He invented the helicopter; the free-wheeling mechanism; and in 1895(!) he proposed a space ship powered by rocket propulsion.[4] I am also thinking of that Russian high-school teacher, Konstantin Eduardovitch Tsiolkovskiy, who in 1896 also proposed a space ship powered by rocket propulsion.[5] He wasn't recognized until after 1924 when, working independently, western physicists had similar ideas. Tsiolkovskiy's editor wrote in 1924: "Do we have to import everything that has already been born in our unmeasurable country and which had to perish because of neglect?" [6]

But I can tell a story myself.

In fall 1917 I made a presentation to the German Ministry of Armament and proposed a long-range rocket powered by ethyl alcohol, water, and liquid air, somewhat similar to the V-2, only bigger and not so complicated. In the appendix, I expanded the principles mentioned in the text and proved them mathematically.

In spring 1918 I received my manuscript back. The reviewer apparently had not read the appendix at all, for he only answered: "According to experience these rockets do not fly farther than 7 km, and taking into account the Prussian thoroughness which is applied at our missile post, it cannot be expected that this distance can be surpassed considerably."

I also experimented at the swimming school at Schässburg. I filled a bottle a third to a half full with different liquids, corked it, and jumped with it from a springboard into the water, holding the bottle with its neck down. When I moved the tip of the bottle slightly downward near the end of my free fall, in order to compensate for the retarding effect of the air drag, I saw that the liquids floated freely inside the bottle. While doing these experiments, I recognized that a human being could most assuredly endure this condition for one to two seconds. It was clear to me that he could endure weightlessness for days, physically. Whether he also could endure it psychologically was questionable. However, an experiment which, by the way, almost cost my life, brought me this confirming reassurance.

One cold morning in fall 1911 I was all alone in our swimming pool at the school. While attempting to cross the pool under water, diagonally, I hit a wall which seemed almost perpendicular to me. Feeling that I had missed my way, I swam along that wall to the left side until I tried to rise to the surface again—but I could not find the surface anywhere. From several encounters I finally recognized that this "wall" was the bottom. I pressed against it and got to the surface in time to give you this account today.

On my way home I thought about the incident and concluded that we are informed about our orientation in space by (1) the Venier particles in the vestibule of the inner ear, (2) tensions in the muscles and tissue of our body, and (3) the parts of skin against which the ground exerts a pressure.[7]

Because of the cold water in the pool, and the excess of carbon dioxide in my blood, my equilibrium sensors had become insensitive. For the same reason, the sensing of the muscles was not entirely effective any longer; and there was no surface at all touching the body since it was floating free in the water. Though the Kantian category of "above" and "below" was not ineffective, the feeling for the direction of a perpendicular line was lost.

This meant that I had undergone the psychological experience of weightlessness! It was not a dramatic experience such as jumping off a trampoline and experiencing a sudden fall. Rather, it was experienced gradually by a numbing of the senses.

In order to examine psychological effects, it is not necessary to create situations by real causes. It suffices to feign it to our senses. When the mother receives the news of her son's death, and believes it, she will react in exactly the same manner as if he had died; even if, in fact, he is still alive. Thus, if a psychologist wants to study the effects of such news,

he does not have to kill the mother's son. In the same way, we can study the psychological effects of weightlessness if we know how to simulate it.

For three years during World War I, I had access to all drugs at a hospital and a military pharmacological supply station. With the help of these drugs I numbed the sense of equilibrium in my muscles and skin; so that by floating under water with my eyes closed; and by using an airhose wound around my body, I could extend the psychological experience of weightlessness for hours. I noticed that I did not become nauseated when using these drugs. During an actual space flight, a rendezvous maneuver does not take more than a couple of hours; and during the rest of the flight, gravitation can be produced by rotation and by centrifugal force. I do not believe in the need of exposing man to unnatural conditions. In my opinion, it is the aim of technology to provide man with conditions in space which correspond to his nature. I have been of this opinion since I was young, so no one can talk of calcification on my part.

I do not mean to say, however, that the effects on man of weightlessness over long durations should not be studied. Everything suitable for research should be investigated scientifically. But a perfect technology should not make man live in adverse conditions.

Today we know that there are people who think weightlessness is a pleasant feeling and who have endured it without permanent harm. I am not surprised, but only puzzled about the little faith that was given to my observations and conclusions of so long ago.

After World War I, I changed from medicine to physics and turned to some German physicists and engineers with my ideas, but without success. Today, I know why. People are too busy and overly strained. If an ordinary professor wants to do his job correctly, he first must be very fast at writing and reading, because a publication is expected of him every year, no matter whether or not he has anything to say. Second, he has to keep up to date on his discipline. In the third place, he has to be a manager and a real diplomat to maintain the status of his institute. Fourth, he must be talented in writing and presenting understandable lectures because he has to teach his students. And fifth, he has to be gifted as a research scientist; an effort that exceeds even the gift of inventing something.

But, which human being is excellently gifted in all these fields and is able to enjoy some of those activities which often provide no monetary return?

More could be achieved in science, by far, if these matters were separated from each other. People with a gift or teaching should have no other obligations than to teach. Research scientists endowed by God with their gift, should not be bothered by anything else. And managing should be left to those born for it. But especially the following should be considered: People with a gift for fast and voluminous writing and reading should be employed to record everything currently known in manuals. These would be divided like the Bible into books, chapters and verses so that they could be referred to quickly. Yearly supplements should be published and from time to time the manual should be revised. I do not have to mention that such manuals should have an alphabetical index so that the author could quickly find the passage he wants to refer to. People who perform serious scientific work should be reminded not to write about anything already contained in the manual but to refer to all the passages in the manual related to their particular subject.

As things stand today, the average scientist looks at the entire body of scientific knowledge like a stuffed goose looks at its food—for God's sake, no more! He studies only his special subject and is often a layman on others. He often opposes new ideas outside his specialty. If asked why he does not take interest in subjects other than his own—subjects in which all the world is interested—the easiest answer is, "I do not think anything of it." If he did approve of another specialty, he would have to occupy himself with the subject, and would lose valuable time in the area in which he is most proficient.

In his defense, it must be said that out of a thousand proposed inventions, only one, at the most, is worthy to be examined more closely! Good ideas often take decades to establish themselves. This being so, which person has not committed an error in his life? If I did not know something 20 years ago and know it today, I do not have to be treated as though I still did not know it. For instance, my very highly esteemed colleague, Professor Klaus Oswatitsch, is now a member of the International Academy of Astronautics, although 15 years ago he maintained that it would be unworthy of a serious scientist to occupy himself with astronautics, especially manned space travel. And he even carried on a controversy with me in a Salzburg periodical.

In any event, it turned out to be impossible to get authoritative scientists to listen to me or to think about my early proposals. In order to force them to examine my ideas, I had to turn to interesting the public in space travel.

The results of my investigations had been compiled in a manuscript originally intended only to prove the possibility of space travel. But then I began to fear that I would be reproached with: "Dear friend, what you have calculated is all right, but today's technology cannot build such a thing." In order to avoid this reproach, I began investigating solutions for problems not readily understood by an engineer of that day. I continue to be surprised at how much of my studies has entered modern space technology. Among them, unfortunately, were theoretical things I would have carried out better had I been doing the development work on the rocket. And on the other hand, sometimes I did not want to state everything I knew because I did not want to be superfluous in the future development of rockets. I wanted to work as a technician and consulting engineer. Of course, some things I did not mention were subsequently invented by other people, independently of me. I want to mention the swiveling motor as an example. My intention to build it can be deduced from the fact that I left out the part between the pump and the combustion chamber and rudders in the explanatory drawings for the construction of a rocket (Figures 1 and 2) in my first two books.[8]

Other things were not mentioned in order to keep these drawings from becoming too complex. For example, I knew at that time the optimum ratio of rocket stages, but mentioned it for the first time in 1941 in a secret note. At that time I knew most of the things I published in 1958 in my book *Das Mondauto*.[9] Other things I showed in the design drawings but did not mention in the text included the bell shape of the nozzles for high expansion or the film-cooling of the thrust chambers.

But it was no work of witchcraft to invent those things I had prophesied. My formulas showed me what to pursue and what to ignore. For instance, the requirement of a high exhaust velocity led logically to the use of liquid propellants because

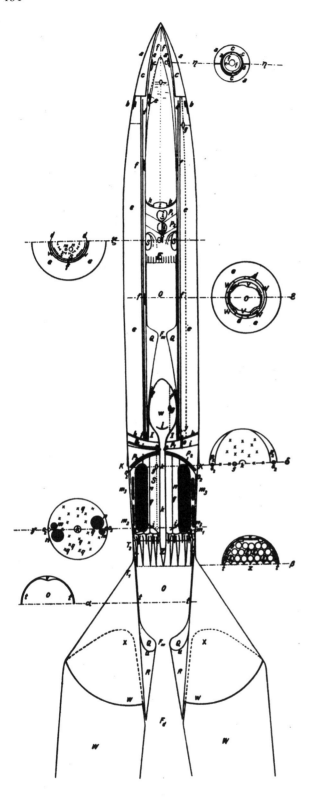

FIGURE 1.—Model B rocket. From Oberth, *Wege zur Raumschiffahrt*, 1929.

they provide a greater specific impulse. From the requirement for a lightweight rocket structure came the realization that ceramic materials could not be used for rockets with liquid propellants. In these rockets the combustion chamber has to be light in weight and must have a thin wall, and the walls have to be kept cool by flowing the fuel around them. With this method, regenerative cooling is accomplished. The pressure in the combustion chamber must not be too low, otherwise the gas exhausts at too low a velocity. The tanks, however, should be under low pressure so that the walls do not have to be too thick. From this consideration the need for fuel pumps resulted. By the way, the paper also contained a relatively simple mathematical criterion for determining the advantage or disadvantage of using a device which increased the exhaust velocity but diminished the mass ratio of empty rocket to filled rocket.

In spite of regenerative cooling I did not want the temperature of the combustion chamber to be too high, especially because the titanium and vanadium-steel alloys of today were not known at that time. A means of decreasing the temperature of the combustion chamber without reducing the exhaust velocity is available by adding another element to the propellant which does not burn but only evaporates, thus creating a specifically light vapor. When combining hydrogen and oxygen, for example, the excess of hydrogen creates that effect (Esnault-Pelterie called it the "Oberth-effect").

In this way I had, in the 1920s, experimentally achieved a propulsion system which reached exhaust speeds of 3,900 m/sec to 4,0000 m/sec. I used the propellants, however, in their gaseous state because in Transylvania I could neither obtain them in liquid form nor find means to liquefy them.

I wrote about this to some friends in Vienna; whereupon a professor of the Vienna Technical University answered that I must be a fraud. He had calculated that hydrogen and oxygen, even when used in their stoichiometrically correct proportion, could not provide more than 3,200 m/sec because of dissociation. However, he did not think of the fact that dissociation is practically zero because of the excess of hydrogen and the low temperature. Pure hydrogen can be lighter and achieve a greater exhaust velocity at low temperature than dissociated or even undissociated H_2O vapor at high temperature. Today the Americans use H_2 and O_2 in their

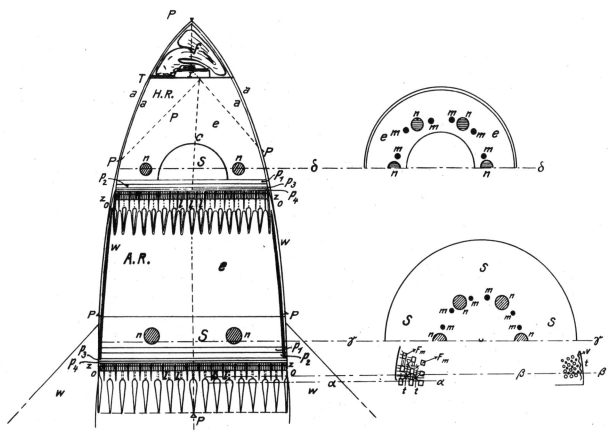

FIGURE 2.—Model E rocket. From Oberth, *Wege zur Raumschiffahrt,* 1929.

hydrogen-oxygen engines in propellant ratios of 1:4 to 1:5 (instead of the stoichiometric ratio of 1:8) and produce exhaust velocities up to 5,000 m/sec. For the same reason, I proposed to add water to the alcohol in the first stages, even though these engines do not develop the high exhaust velocities of hydrogen-oxygen engines. Water has since been used in almost all engines burning alcohol. The demand for specifically heavier fuels in the first stages, even though they do not develop such high exhaust velocities, and for lighter fuels with higher exhaust velocities in upper stages, also resulted from the mathematical formulas in my writings. I tried to avoid static reinforcements by keeping the tanks under a light overpressure internally. This principle has been applied practically to the Atlas booster by Karel J. Bossart, who developed it to technical maturity.[10]

Another proposal of mine which has found application is the use of parachutes for landing rocket vehicles.

Later on, I had proposed electricity for the steering mechanism. For example, for the speed-control system, I proposed that a mass should act against an elastic resistance; its deflection would then be a function of the acceleration. The mass was to act in such a way on a potentiometer (a variable electric resistor) that a current proportional to the acceleration would be produced. When this current is integrated, speed will be indicated. This instrument can also be used to close the fuel valves automatically, when the desired speed is reached.

The attitude of the rocket was to be controlled by a gyroscope which caused the rudders to deflect by electric control as soon as the gyroscope and rocket axes were not parallel.

In my book I also proposed a centrifuge, with an arm 35 meters long, to examine systematically the resistance of man to high accelerations, to train man at high accelerations, and to select among the applicants for space travel those with the best abilities.

Regarding space capsules, I proposed to paint them black on one side and leave them shiny on the other, and to turn the desired side to the sun. I also proposed a spiral tube which had the function of cleaning the air by distillation. When shadowed by the spacecraft, the tube would cool down, and condense out the wastes of the spacecraft, because they all have a higher freezing point than oxygen, nitrogen, and argon, which would remain as gases. These would first pass through a filter, and then be warmed to a convenient temperature on the sunny side of the spacecraft. The tube could be cleaned by turning the cold side to the sun and evaporating the condensates. During this process the condensates could also be retained, cooled again, and stored for certain purposes. I also proposed a giant space mirror in that book in order to offer something sensational to the reader.

I had submitted this manuscript of the University of Heidelberg as a thesis for a Ph.D., but it was refused. Councillor Max Wolf, who was an astronomer, could not accept it because it dealt mainly with physical-medical subjects; he gave me a certificate, however, stating that he thought the work was scientifically correct and ingenious.

With that certificate I offered my book to the publishing firm of R. Oldenbourg in Munich. This little book, which appeared in 1923 under the title *Die Rakete zu den Planetenräumen,*[11] fulfilled its purpose. It stimulated public interest, and numerous authors explained the difficult content to the layman, among them Max Valier, Otto Willi Gail, Willy Ley, Karl August von Laffert, and Felix Linke.[12]

In 1928 Fritz von Opel revealed his famous rocket-powered car. Maybe it will be of interest to you to know that when I visited him, his first words were, "Professor, do not judge me solely by the rocket-powered car. I do serious work, too." A rocket engine works most efficiently when the gas velocity ejected rearward is matched by the forward velocity of the vehicle. In the case of the rocket-powered car, the efficiency was very poor. Opel knew that, but he showed his rocket car for publicity. This, however, did not prevent Professor Kirchberger, who was not aware of that fact, from calculating the efficiency of Opel's rocket car from the consumed fuel and the power output. Then he put the result into calculations for space rockets so as to prove that space travel is impossible (or at

least that he himself could not have invented it). As I said, Opel used his car only for advertising purposes, and he succeeded—public interest was very much stimulated.

During the years from 1922 to 1928 I finally learned that I was not alone in my ideas regarding rocketry. As early as 1922 I had heard of Dr. Robert H. Goddard and had written to him, whereupon he sent me his publication "A Method of Reaching Extreme Altitudes." [13] In 1924 I heard of Konstantin Tsiolkovskiy for the first time. In 1925 he sent me his book *Rakyeta v kosmeetcheskoye prostranstvo,*[14] and I was helpèd with the translation by one of my students, Arzamanoff, a Russian emigrant. Then in 1924, the city engineer of Essen, Walter Hohmann, published his book about rocket trajectories in interplanetary space.[15] He had made these calculations for his own enjoyment but had not published them because he feared ridicule. When he saw that such far-out ideas could indeed be published, he ventured into the public limelight. One of his calculated trajectories was later used for the calculation of the trajectory for a spacecraft to Mars, and another for a spacecraft to Venus. In 1926 I heard for the first time of Hermann Ganswindt.[16] In 1929 I wrote about him: "Germany possesses the peculiar gift of producing great men and then letting them perish through neglect!"

In 1929 I published *Wege zur Raumschiffahrt,*[17] in which I reported most of my theories on space travel and my inventions. I described manned space travel in detail, proposed the inclined trajectory towards the east for ascending space ships, investigated the relationships between consumption of propellant and gain of energy, commented on most of the errors in the literature of the day concerning rockets, and finally, described an electrostatic space ship.

It is well known that manned space travel has required fewer sacrifices than the development of aviation. The main reason for this is that aviation meant a leap into an unknown element, whereas in space travel, most of the problems were solved theoretically before being taken up practically. And, in all humility, I think I contributed to that with my theoretical preparatory work!

The time finally came when the German scientific world had to take a stand on the question of space travel. But, believe me, I was amazed upon seeing the lack of general education, the disinterest in new

FIGURE 3.—Set of "Frau in Mond" with (from left) Otto Kanturck (who built sets), Hermann Oberth, Fritz Lang (boy in front of him is one of the actors), the cameraman, Hermann Ganswindt, and Willy Ley. Photo from Willy Ley collection.

ideas, and the vanity and self-complacency of certain people! Up to that time, subconsciously, I had envisioned a kind of worship of scientific research; and I had considered German scientists as absolutely the best.

Why, for example did Councillor Lorenz invent one objection after the other to space travel, one more senseless than the other, and why did he, as second chairman of the VDI (Association of German Engineers), make it impossible for me to comment on his objections in the VDI periodical.[18] I think he did this because he had said once that space flight was impossible, and he did not want to retract his statement. He had overlooked the fact that the problem of repulsion is mainly a problem of impulse, that propellants not only possess chemical

but also a high kinetic energy which is destroyed partly by the gas exhausting backward, but which has to re-appear somewhere; that the amount of this energy can only be calculated according to the laws of thrust; and that the rocket is always at rest with respect to itself. Another time he integrated in wrong intervals. If a student of his had done so in an examination, he probably would have failed him. About the inclined trajectory towards the east, which I had proposed, he said that every sensible human being would have to understand that a rocket will be most efficient if the thrust is always in one direction, upwards and perpendicular to the earth.

In addition to Lorenz, I would like to mention a certain major from the Reich Ministry of Arma-

FIGURE 4.—Professor Hermann Oberth on the studio grounds of the UFA, during the filming of "Frau in Mond." Photo from Frederick I. Ordway III collection.

ment who in 1928 still insisted to me that rockets flying farther than artillery shells would be of no military interest.

Professor Dr. von Dallwitz-Wegner maintained that a change of speed of 30 m/sec² would be experienced by a man jumping off a train going at 100 km/hr.[19] Apparently he confused speed with acceleration.

Why do I say all this? Everything mentioned has been disproved and the people of that time are dead and forgotten. Is it necessary to exhume dead bodies?

Ladies and gentlemen, I am not exhuming dead bodies. I am talking about something living! When

listening to the objections of today's scientists against new inventions and discoveries, the same thing is found again. For example, let us look at the rediscovery of Atlantis by Pastor Spanuth, or at the objection against parapsychology, or at research on Unidentified Flying Objects. Even in the field of astronautics it appears quite often in Germany that people such as A. F. Staats, Hermann Langkraer, or Schönenberger go unnoticed, whereas others who cannot measure up to them get the lion's share of research funds.

However, I do not want to close on a bitter note. Instead let me tell you of a personal experience that has a brighter side. First, in 1927, the Verein

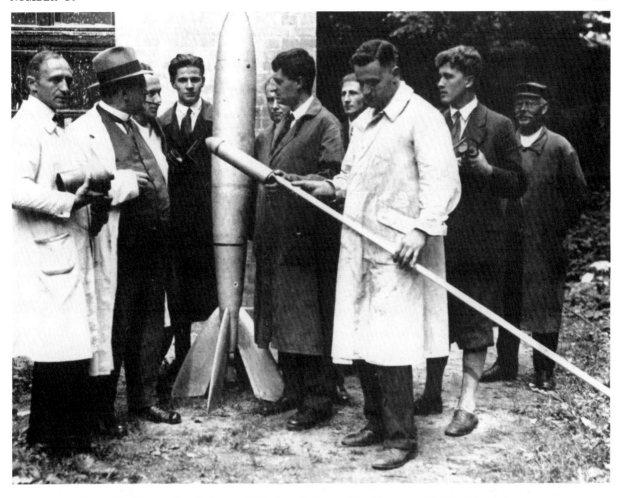

FIGURE 5.—Photo taken 5 August 1930 after Professor Oberth's successful "Kegelduse" test on grounds of Chemisch-Technische Reichsanstadt, Berlin-Plotzensee. From left: Dr. Rudolf Nebel, Dr. Ritter (of Chemisch-Technische Reichsanstadt), Mr. Bermueller, Kurt Heinisch, next man unidentifiable (almost covered by Oberth), Professor Hermann Oberth, next man unknown, Klaus Riedel ("Riedel II") in white coat, Wernher von Braun, next man unknown. Photo from Fredrick I. Ordway III collection.

für Raumschiffahrt [Association for Space Travel] was founded in Breslau,[20] and in 1928 Fritz Lang (see Figure 3), made his well-known film "Frau in Mond" (The Girl in the Moon).[21] During that time I began my first firing tests at the UFA site in Berlin (Figure 4). Subsequently I received certification for the first European rocket engine firing with gasoline and liquid oxygen,[22] (Figure 5). The affair, by the way, was nevertheless disgraceful. First, I was not a trained mechanic; and Henry Ford was right when he said that one should not invent an engine if one could not assemble it with one's own hands. Let me tell you, that man was right. Realizing this, I set to work and in 1932 I passed my examination as lock-

smith and then taught the courses of practical engineering at the Mediasch High School. Later, I also learned design engineering.

Second, my nerves were almost shattered by an explosion in the fall of 1929.[23] Had I been as serene as I am today, I would have left everything as it was and cured my neurosis. But I did not want to give up the exceptional opportunity to conduct experiments, so I continued working. The explosion had made it clear to me that considerably faster combustion of gasoline and liquid oxygen was possible in a limited, narrow space; and I discovered the atomization phenomenon of burning liquid propellant droplets. This had been the only physical-technical question that had troubled me secretly.

Fourteen days later I had my slit injector and nozzle. Another seven days later my cone combustion chamber was ready to fire. With that the door to space travel was pushed open. However, as a consequence of my tension and taut nerves I had committed several grave blunders, especially in treating people.

But as I said, the combustion chamber for liquid propellants was invented, and it has been hailed as a major contribution to astronautics. I was helped with my experiments by students of the Technical University of Berlin. Among them was Wernher von Braun, who has since made space travel a reality.

NOTES

Under the title *Mop raboty po astronavtike*, this paper appeared on pages 85–96 of *Iz istorii astronavtiki i raketnoi tekhniki: Materialy XVIII mezhdunarodnogo astronavticheskogo kongressa, Belgrad, 25–29 Sentyavrya 1967* [From the History of Rockets and Astronautics: Materials of the 18th International Astronautical Congress, Belgrade, 25–29 September 1967], Moscow: Nauka, 1970.

1. Robert H. Goddard, "A Method of Reaching Extreme Altitudes," *Smithsonian Miscellaneous Collections*, vol. 71, no. 2, December 1919, p. 1:

The problem was to determine the minimum initial mass of an ideal rocket necessary, in order that on a continuous loss of mass, a final mass of one pound would remain, at any desired altitude.

An approximate method was found necessary, in solving this problem . . . , in order to avoid an unsolved problem in the Calculus of Variations. The solution that was obtained revealed the fact that surprising small initial masses would be necessary . . . .—Ed.

2. Dallwitz-Wegner, "Über Raketenpropeller und die Unmöglichkeit der Weltraumschiffahrt mittels Raketenschiffen" [The Rocket Propeller and the Impossibility of Space Travel by Means of Rocket Ships], *Autotechnik*, 1929; K. Holzhausen, "Schuss und Rakete in den Weltenraum" [Projectiles and Rockets in Interstellar Space], *Maschinen-Konstrukteur*, vol. 61, no. 18 (15 September 1928), pp. 436–437, and, same issue, H. Oberth, "Das Wesen der Rakete" [Principle of the Rocket], pp. 438–441.—Ed.

3. H. Lorenz, "Die Moglichkeit der Weltraumfahrt" [The Possibility of Space Travel], *Zeitschrift des Vereins Deutscher Ingenieure*, vol. 71, no. 19, 7 May 1927, pp. 651–657, and Supplements 1 (vol. 71, no. 32, 6 August 1927, p. 1128) and 2 (vol. 71, no. 35, 27 August 1927, p. 1236); and "Der Rakentenflug in der Stratosphäre" [Rocket Flight in the Stratosphere] and "Die Ausfuhrbarkeit der Weltraumfahrt" [The Feasibility of Space Travel], *Jahrbuch der Wissenschaftlichen Gesellschaft fur Luftfahrt*, 1928. Hermann Oberth, "Ist die Weltraumfahrt Möglich? [Is Space Travel Possible], *Die Rakete*, no. 11 (15 November 1927), pp. 144–52, and no. 12 (15 Decem-

ber 1927), pp. 163–66. Accounts of the Lorenz-Oberth debate at the WGL meeting appear in Willy Ley, *Rockets, Missiles, and Men in Space* (New York: The Viking Press, 1968), pp. 109–110; and Theodore von Karman, with Lee Edson, *The Wind and Beyond* (Boston: Little, Brown and Co., 1967), pp. 236–37.—Ed.

4. Ley, op. cit. (note 3), pp. 85–93.

5. Konstantin E. Tsiolkovskiy, "Issledovaniye mirovykh prostranstv reaktivnymi priborami [Investigation of Outer Space by Means of Reactive Devices], *Nauchnoye Obozreniye* [Science Review], no. 5 (May 1903), pp. 44–75, and *Rakyeta v kosmeetcheskoye prostranstv* [The Rocket into Cosmic Space] (Kaluga, 1924), 32 pp.—Ed.

6. Tsiolkovskiy, *Rakyeta v kosmeetcheskoye prostranstv*, p. iii; and W. Ley, op. cit. (note 3), p. 96.—Ed.

7. I was exposed to medical information early in life because my father was a physician and a good friend of the town's physician, Dr. Fritz Kraus. We visited him very often. He was a man with an incredible amount of knowledge; and the conversations between my father and him were always highly interesting and instructive. It was stated incorrectly, therefore, in 1958 that I had acquired only a little general education at the age of 30. I was also a very eager reader of the Monthly Popular Science Journal *Kosmos*.

8. Oberth, *Die Rakete zu den Planetenräumen* [The Rocket into Interplanetary Space] (Munich-Berlin: R. Oldenbourg, 1923), 92 pp.; and *Wege zur Raumschiffahrt* [Means for Space Travel] (Munich-Berlin: R. Oldenbourg, 1929), 431 pp.

9. Oberth, *The Moon Car*, translated by Willy Ley (New York: Harper & Brothers, 1959), 98 pp.

10. John L. Chapman, *Atlas: The Story of a Missile* (New York: Harper & Brothers, 1960), pp. 86–92.—Ed.

11. See note 8.

12. Valier, *Der Vorstoss in den Weltenraum* [The Advance into Space] (Munich-Berlin: R. Oldenbourg, 1924), 134 pp.; Gail, *Mit Raketenkraft ins Weltenall: Vom Feuerwagen zum Raumschiff*, [With Rocket Propulsion into Space: From Rocket Cars to Space Ship] (Stuttgart: K. Thienemann, 1928), 106 pp.; Ley, *Die Fahrt ins Weltall* [The Journey into Space] (Leipzig: Hachmeister & Thal, 1926); and Linke, *Das Raketen-Weltraumschiff* [The Rocket Spaceship] (Hamburg, 1928), 100 pp.

13. See note 1 and Esther C. Goddard and G. Edward Pendray, Editors, *The Papers of Robert H. Goddard* (New York: McGraw-Hill Book Company, 1970), vol. 1, pp. 485–86 and 545.—Ed.

14. See note 5.

15. Hohmann, *Die Erreichbarkeit der Himmelskörper* [The Attainability of Celestial Bodies] (Munich-Berlin: R. Oldenbourg, 1925), 88 pp.

16. See note 4.

17. See note 8.

18. See note 3.

19. See note 2.

20. 5 June 1927, see Heinz Gartman, *The Men behind the Space Rockets* (New York: David McKay, 1956), pp. 48–73.

21. Ley, *Rockets, Missiles, and Men in Space* (see note 3), pp. 114–24.

22. Ibid., pp. 121–24.

23. Ibid., p. 118.

14

Early Rocket Developments of the American Rocket Society

G. EDWARD PENDRAY, *United States*

The first issue of the *Bulletin of the American Interplanetary Society*, better known later as the American Rocket Society,[1] appeared in June 1930. It consisted of four single-spaced mimeograph pages, carrying news of the Society's founding on 4 April of the same year;[2] a summary of a paper on "The Historical Background of Interplanetary Travel" by Fletcher Pratt, the writer and historian; an item about the tragic death of the German rocket pioneer, Max Valier, which had occurred in the previous month; a prediction by Robert Esnault-Pelterie, the French aircraft builder and inventor, "A trip to the Moon may be possible within fifteen years"; and an announcement that the Society was undertaking "a survey of the entire field of information relating to interplanetary travel."

This latter survey was the beginning of the Society's program to promote the development of rockets. As planned, it was to consist of a series of studies by various members of the Society, summarizing the literature then available on the physics, chemistry, technology, and history of rockets, as well as current thinking on what later came to be known as astronautics. Several of these summary papers were completed and presented at subsequent Society meetings. Others were begun but later abandoned, for it early became evident that a wide gap existed between current ideas and technical literature about rockets and the practical task of developing them as potential vehicles for space exploration.

Dr. Robert H. Goddard, the American rocket and space flight pioneer, was then at work on his highly significant rocket development in Massachusetts, and was soon to continue it on a greatly increased scale in New Mexico, financed by a grant from Daniel Guggenheim. Dr. Goddard had published very little, his principal paper having been "A Method of Reaching Extreme Altitudes," brought out by the Smithsonian Institution in December 1919, dealing entirely with solid propellant rockets.[3] From time to time newspaper stories indicated that he was making considerable progress, but members of the Society could learn almost nothing about the technical details of this work.

There had appeared in American newspapers and popular magazines, however, numerous articles about rocket experiments in other countries, especially in Europe. These included the work of Oberth, Heylandt, Valier, Esnault-Pelterie, the Verein für Raumschiffahrt, and others.

At the time of the Society's founding I had been elected vice-president, with the assignment of helping to get a research program going. Early in 1931 it became possible for Mrs. Pendray and me to go abroad, and we planned our trip in such a way as to enable us to see, we hoped, what some of the European experimenters were doing. The Society named us its official representatives, but in view of the state of the treasury, we paid for the trip ourselves. Mrs. Pendray was one of the twelve founders of the Society, which number also included myself.

After some unsuccessful attempts to get in contact with Darwin O. Lyon[4] in Italy and Robert Esnault-Pelterie in France, both of whom were away at the time of our arrival, our journey at length brought us to Berlin, where we found Willy Ley very much at home and eager to show us the work of the Verein für Raumschiffahrt, which was engaged in a modest experimental program at the "Raketenflugplatz," its "rocket flying field" at Reinickendorf on the outskirts of Berlin.

We had not previously met Ley, one of the founders, and at that time secretary of the VfR, but had corresponded with him. There was, however, something of a communications problem; Ley's English wasn't very good at that time, and our German was nonexistent. It was not easy to carry on technical conversations, but with the aid of drawings, sketches, and patient explanation on Ley's part, we managed it after a fashion.[5]

Ley and his VfR associates, who included Rudolph Nebel, Klaus Riedel, and several others, then gave us the most memorable experience of the entire trip—a proving-stand test (Figure 1) of a small liquid-propellant rocket motor employing liquid oxygen and gasoline. Mrs. Pendray and I were not aware at the time that Goddard's successful shots since 1926 had been accomplished with liquid propellants, and this experiment at the Raketenflugplatz was the first of its kind we had witnessed. Upon our return I reported fully to the Society, on the evening of 1 May 1931, both the method and the promise of the German experiments.[6]

A few days later Hugh F. Pierce, who was subsequently to become president of the Society and one

of the four original founders of Reaction Motors, Inc., proposed that the Society delay no longer the beginning of its own experimental program. An Experimental Committee was formed, with myself as chairman, and the Society's Rocket No. 1 was designed by Pierce and me. It was patterned in general after the "Two-Stick Repulsor" rocket of the VfR, designs for which I had discussed with Ley in Berlin.[7]

The rocket (Figure 2) was constructed in a small machine shop Pierce had established in the basement of the apartment house where he lived. The propellant tanks consisted of two parallel cylindrical tubes of aluminum, each 5½ feet long and

FIGURE 2.—ARS No. 1, during a demonstration and lecture at New York University (Washington Square Campus), in spring 1932. Hugh F. Pierce, who constructed the rocket, is packing the parachute in its container (made from a ten-cent-store saucepan) as G. Edward Pendray, co-designer of the rocket, holds the parachute. The cone-shaped nose was designed to open up at the height of the flight and eject the parachute. The parachute itself, made by Mrs. Leatrice M. Pendray from a scaled-down design for a professional aviation parachute, was of silk pongee. Photo from Pendray Collection, Princeton University Library.

FIGURE 1.—Author in 1931 visiting the proving ground of the Verein für Raumschiffahrt near Berlin. An early type of liquid-fuel rocket motor is in the thrust frame. From left, Willy Ley, Klaus Riedel, Rudolf Nebel, G. Edward Pendray.

FIGURE 3.—a, Testing ground, on a farm loaned to the Society near Stockton, New Jersey, used for test of ARS No. 1 on 12 November 1932. Near the trench is Mrs. Pendray, charter member of the society and an active participant in the experimental program. Working at the wooden launching rack are Pendray (left), Pierce (rear, facing camera); David Lasser (overcoat and hat) one of the founders of the society and its first president, and Dr. William Lemkin, member of the Experimental Committee.

b, Pouring liquid oxygen into the tank of ARS No. 1 preparatory to testing, Pendray, chairman of the ARS Experimental Committee. On brace of the launching rack is electrical apparatus designed by Pierce for remote ignition and release of rocket.

Photos from Pendray Collection, Princeton University Library.

2 inches in diameter. They were clamped at the top by a yoke, or framepiece, which supported the motor and its cooling jacket, the turn-on valves that could be operated electrically, and a cone-shaped nosepiece containing a parachute. At the rear of the rocket were four fixed vanes of sheet aluminum for guidance in vertical flight.

The propellants were gasoline and liquid oxygen, forced into the motor by gas pressure at approximately 300 psi. The oxygen pressure was produced by partial evaporation. The gasoline was pressurized by nitrogen supplied from an auxiliary tank. The parachute mechanism was kept closed by the pressure of nitrogen in the gasoline tank, and was set to spring open when the pressure dropped at the termination of firing. The motor was an aluminum casting, 3 inches in outside diameter and 6 inches long, with walls 1/2 inch thick. Loaded with fuel, this first ARS rocket weighed 15 pounds. The motor was designed to provide a thrust of 60 pounds, giving an expected acceleration of 3G at launching.

The first static test of the rocket occurred on 12 November 1932, on a farm near Stockton, New Jersey.[8] Members of the Society had hauled lumber and built a small wooden launching rack (Figure 3), equipped with a spring-operated measuring device. In the test the motor burned satisfactorily for a period of from 20 to 30 seconds, and provided the expected 60 pounds maximum thrust.

During these ground tests, however, the rocket was accidentally damaged, and as a consequence, was never flight tested. Its fragility, and the difficulty of getting all the parts to operate satisfactorily at the right time—still a problem with rockets—caused the members of the experimental group to decide on a thorough reconstruction, of such a radical nature as to constitute a new rocket.

This task was put in the capable hands of Bernard Smith, a young member with considerable mechanical aptitude, later Technical Director of the Naval Weapons Laboratory at Dahlgren, Virginia. Smith removed the superstructure containing the parachute, the water jacket, and other items that had proved to have little or no value. He clamped the motor securely between the upper portion of the two propellant tanks, substituted light balsa-wood fins for the aluminum vanes, and rounded the forward end of the rocket with a streamlined aluminum bonnet containing a large inlet port for air

cooling. Smith's drawing of this rocket is shown in Figure 4.

This rocket, known as ARS No. 2 (see Figure 5), was shot from a temporary proving field at Marine Park, Great Kills, Staten Island, New York, on 14 May 1933.[9] It reached an altitude of about 250 feet, after firing about two seconds, and was still going well when the oxygen tank exploded, apparently as the result of a stuck safety valve. It had been calculated that the rocket would reach an altitude of about a mile, but of course the bursting oxygen tank released the pressure, the motor ceased functioning, and the rocket dropped into the water of lower New York Bay, from which it was rescued by rowboat.

In spite of the accident, the members of the Society's Experimental Committee considered the shot successful. It was the first liquid propellant rocket

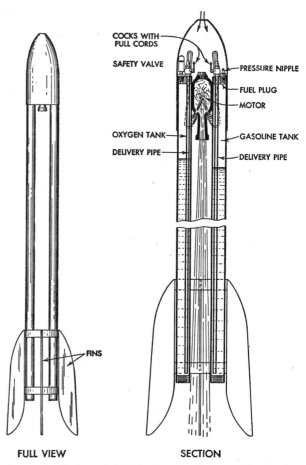

FIGURE 4.—Design of ARS Rocket No. 2. From *The Coming of Age of Rocket Power* (New York: Harper & Brothers, 1945) p. 124.

FIGURE 5.—*a*, Setting the propellant valves of ARS No. 2 rocket just prior to test at Marine Park on 14 May 1933. From left, Laurence Manning, Carl Ahrens, Bernard Smith (who designed and built the rocket), G. Edward Pendray, Alfred Best, and Alfred Africano—all members of the Experimental Committee. The rocket stands in its launching tower, complete except for a nose cone which was slipped over the valve assembly just before the shot. It had no parachute or other landing equipment. The launcher was aimed with a five-degree tilt to seaward, where rocket was expected to land.

b, The take-off of rocket shown in 5*a*. It was about 6 feet tall and weighed about 15 pounds loaded and ready for the shot. Propellants used were gasoline and liquid oxygen pressured by nitrogen drawn from the pressure cylinder standing to the right of the launcher. At the end of the countdown, when the ignition apparatus failed to work, Smith ran out and ignited it with a gasoline torch. Here, he is returning to the barricade. The rocket is already in the air. Note crude barricades for protection of participants and spectators.

c, Post-mortem on flight shown in 5*b*. From left, Max Kraus, secretary of the Society; Pendray (behind rocket) and Smith.

Photos from Pendray Collection, Princeton University Library.

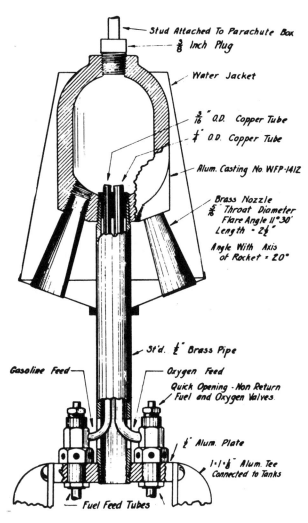

Stud Attached To Parachute Box

⅜ Inch Plug

Water Jacket

³⁄₁₆" O.D. Copper Tube

¼" O.D. Copper Tube

Alum. Casting No. WFP-1412

Brass Nozzle
⅝ Throat Diameter
Flare Angle 11°30'
Length - 2¼"
Angle With Axis
of Rocket - 20°

St'd. ¼" Brass Pipe

Oxygen Feed

Quick Opening - Non Return
Fuel and Oxygen Valves

Gasoline Feed

¼" Alum. Plate

1·1·⅜" Alum. Tee
Connected to Tanks

Fuel Feed Tubes

FIGURE 6.—Detail of ARS Rocket No. 4. From *Astronautics*,
no. 30 (October-November, 1934), p. 3.

The design designated as ARS No. 4, constructed by John Shesta and a small group he had selected to aid him, was completed first. As can be seen in Figures 6 and 7a, its motor was placed ahead of the center of gravity as in the case of all these early rockets, on the theory—mistaken, as it later proved —that greater flight stability could be achieved in that configuration. ARS Rocket No. 4 had a single motor with four nozzles. The nozzles were so placed as to direct the jet gases rearward but slightly away from the sides of the cylindrical gasoline tank, on the upper end of which the motor was mounted. The oxygen tank was mounted directly behind the gasoline tank, in tandem fashion. A small cylindrical case for a parachute projected ahead of the motor, and the motor itself was encased in a water-jacket.

The first attempt to fire this rocket failed.[12] Examination revealed that the fuel inlet ports were not large enough and the rocket, though it fired, failed to develop enough power to rise. For the second attempt, it was slightly modified by enlarging the fuel ports and omitting the water jacket. The shot (Figures 7b, c) occurred on 9 September 1934, also at Marine Park, Staten Island.[13] The slender rocket rose from the launching rack most satisfactorily, and in flight performed excellently for a few seconds, until one of the four nozzles burned out. The rocket, which had by this time reached an altitude of several hundred feet, yawed over, went into a long, fast trajectory over New York Bay, and struck the water still vigorously firing. Calculations based on the data of three observers at triangulation stations, and confirmed by motion picture and still photographs, indicated that at its maximum the velocity of this rocket exceeded 1,000 feet per second.

ARS No. 3, designed by Bernard Smith and myself, was completed next. In this one (Figures 8 and 9), the propellant tanks were nested one inside the other, with the gasoline tank inside, surrounding a long motor nozzle, which ran the length of the rocket, and the oxygen tank on the outside, surrounding the gasoline tank. This design produced a compact, professional looking rocket, but it was very troublesome to construct because of the many welded seams. What was worse, it proved impossible to fuel or shoot, because the liquid oxygen, exposed to so much warm metal in the large outer tank,

any of us had seen get off the ground, and considering the state of the art at that time, it was something of an achievement. It was not history's first operating liquid-propellant rocket, of course, the Verein für Raumschiffahrt had anticipated us by a few months, and Goddard by seven years and two months, his first successful liquid-propellant shot having been made near Auburn, Massachusetts, on 16 March 1926.[10]

Following the shot of ARS No. 2, plans for new rockets began to burgeon in the Society. Designs for several were submitted, and the three most promising ones were quickly approved by the Experimental Committee.[11]

FIGURE 7.—*a,* Preparing for a ground firing test of ARS No. 4 at Marine Park in summer 1934. From left, John Shesta, designer and builder of the rocket; Carl Ahrens, member of the group which aided in its construction; and Pendray. In this preliminary version, no means were provided for cooling the four nozzles of the rocket motor. The test indicated need for several modifications, including addition of a water jacket to cool the nozzles.

b, ARS No. 4 in flight at Marine Park on 9 September 1934. It emerged from the launcher satisfactorily, and performed very well for the first few seconds, reaching an altitude of several hundred feet, at which point one nozzle burned out, causing the rocket, still firing rapidly, to tilt over toward New York Bay, where it struck the water at a velocity that observers at three triangulation stations estimated to be in excess of 1,000 feet per second.

c, Post-mortem on flight shown in Figure 11. Shesta, left, holds the propellant-tank portion of the rocket; Pendray points to the damaged but unopened parachute case.

Photos from Pendray Collection, Princeton University Library.

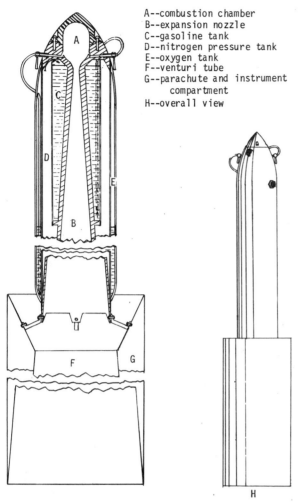

A--combustion chamber
B--expansion nozzle
C--gasoline tank
D--nitrogen pressure tank
E--oxygen tank
F--venturi tube
G--parachute and instrument
        compartment
H--overall view

FIGURE 8.—Detail of ARS Rocket No. 3. From *Astronautics*,
no. 27 (October 1933), p. 3.

FIGURE 9.—ARS Rocket No. 3, at Marine Park for launch
attempt in September 1934. From left, Shesta, Pendray, and
Smith. The gasoline tank is being pressurized with nitrogen
through a valve in the cone. The oxygen fill-hole is visible
just below the pressure inlet. Photo from Pendray Collection,
Princeton University Library.

simply evaporated and blew out of the fill-hole as
fast as it could be poured in.[14]

The other rockets which had been designed by
Committee members were in various stages of construction, but one by one they were abandoned, for
it had become clear that building and shooting
whole rockets, when so many components—particularly the motor—were in such an unsatisfactory
state of development, was really not productive.
The Experimental Committee had already devised
a small proving stand for individual motor tests,
with a view to developing a motor that would work
reliably and not burn out. John Shesta designed
this first ARS proving stand, and in constructing it
used the tanks, valves, and other parts of his rocket,
ARS No. 4.

With this equipment the Society then began a
long, often discouraging, but finally successful series
of motor development tests. These were conducted
at various places and sometimes under great difficulties because, in the vicinity of New York, rocket
shots or motor tests were not welcomed by neighbors, or approved by the police, and there was no
way of obtaining permission to carry on such experiments in peace. As a consequence the Society
performed many of these tests under some harass-
ment, and found frequent and unannounced moving of the testing ground to be a wise and sometimes
necessary precaution. Despite these problems, the
tests provided much data, increasing sophistication,
useful experience and know-how, and finally culminated in the development of a practical liquid-
cooled regenerative motor designed by James H.
Wyld, a long-time member of the Experimental

FIGURE 10.—Liquid-propellant motor under test at the ARS testing ground at Crestwood, New York, in 1935. Dials on the panel mounted on a sawhorse registered pressure in each propellant tank and in the motor, thrust, and the time in seconds. Motion pictures of dials preserved data for later study. Photo from Pendray Collection, Princeton University Library.

Crestwood.[17] A Nichrome nozzle stood up well in this series, but not perfectly. All the others burned out.

A third series was shot at Crestwood on 25 August 1935. There were five runs, and this time various fuels as well as nozzles and cooling systems were tried.[18] A fourth series of tests was made at the same place soon afterward, on 20 October 1935.[19]

By this time a great deal of information had been obtained. It had been definitely shown that water would not work effectively as a coolant in these small motors, and also that alcohol was a better fuel for small motors than gasoline. It began to be clear that no uncooled motor, of whatever available material, would stand up under more than a few seconds of firing, and that some dynamic means of cooling must be devised. The tests also indicated

Committee. Development of this motor led directly to the founding on 18 December 1941 of Reaction Motors, Inc., later a division of Thiokol Chemical Corporation, by Lovell Lawrence, John Shesta, James H. Wyld, and Hugh F. Pierce, all of whom had been active in the Society's experimental program.[15]

Until the beginning of these tests the Society had been using cast aluminum motors, some cooled with water, others depending on the metal mass to soak up heat during the relatively short period of firing. In the proving stand tests, motors and nozzles of carbon steel, stainless steel, Nichrome, carbon, "hard-surfacing" metals, and other allegedly heat-resistant materials were tried. Various members suggested tests to be run, or constructed motors to be tested.

In the first series of runs undertaken at Crestwood, New York, a suburb of New York City, on 21 April 1935, five types of motors were tested (Figure 10), but none stood up.[16] Three months later, a new series of motors was ready. To simplify changing styles, shapes, and nozzle material on the proving stand, a "sectional motor" had been constructed (Figure 11), the nozzle and body sections of which could readily be replaced by others of different shape or material after each run. Six runs were made in the second series of tests, also at

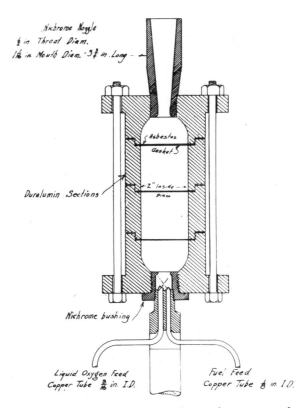

FIGURE 11.—Segmented liquid-propellant rocket motor made to facilitate tests of various motor shapes and materials. By increasing or reducing the number and shape of segments, the size and shape of the combustion chamber could be quickly altered. Nozzles of various shapes and materials could also be readily tested. The design and the actual motor and alternative parts were by Shesta, in late 1935. From Pendray Collection, Princeton University Library.

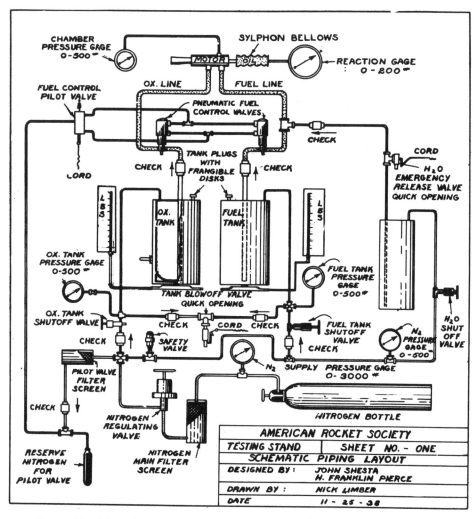

FIGURE 12.—Schematic Diagram of Proving Stand No. 2. From *Astronautics*, no. 42 (February 1939), p. 1.

that the Society's first proving stand, while practical for short runs of motors of less than one hundred pounds thrust, was too small for the sort of tests now indicated. Shesta was asked to build a new, bigger and better stand, aided by Wyld, Alfred Africano, Peter van Dresser, and others. The group immediately started work on the project.[20]

During the period required for completion of the new stand (Figures 12 and 16), the Experimental Committee turned to the problem of aerodynamic design, and began a series of tests, with solid-propellant rockets of many sizes and shapes, undertaken to determine empirically some of the principles of rocket stability and guidance in flight, as well as the mechanics of catapults and other

launching schemes, flight stabilization devices, and parachutes and parachute releases.

These tests were carried on at several sites, principally one near Pawling, New York. The solid-propellant rocket vehicles tested, shown in Figures 13 and 14, were made by members of the Society, and consisted of head-drive and tail-drive types, long bodies, short bodies, finned and unfinned rockets, and many other varieties all propelled by commercial skyrocket motors. The tests continued at intervals over about four years, beginning in the summer of 1935 and continuing until November 1939. The results of all these tests were reported in detail in *Astronautics*.[21]

During the latter part of this period the liquid-

FIGURE 13.—H. F. Pierce, with solid-fuel rockets of various designs tested by the Committee to determine the best aerodynamic shape and other characteristics of high-altitude rockets. These tests took place principally at a site near Pawling, New York, where this picture was taken in 1935, during one of the earliest series. These rockets and those in Figure 14, were constructed by various members of the Experimental Committee and were powered by commercial 4-pound and 6-pound skyrocket motors.

FIGURE 14.—Members of the ARS Experimental Committee at Midvale, New Jersey, in summer 1937. From left, Shesta, Healy, Pendray, and Africano.

Photos from Pendray Collection, Princeton University Library.

propellant motor tests were resumed, and now began to repay the effort. Motors of increasing effectiveness and sophistication began to appear for testing. The Wyld regenerative motor (Figure 15) most successful of all, was first presented in idea form in an article by Wyld in the April 1938 *Astronautics.* The same issue carried an article describing a new experimental motor by Midshipman Robert C. Truax of the United States Naval Experiment Station, and an account of its performance at tests carried out at Annapolis.[22]

Shortly after disclosing his idea, Wyld constructed a working model of his motor. It received its first test on the Society's new proving stand (Figure 16) at New Rochelle, New York, on 10 December 1938,

delivering a thrust of somewhat over 90 pounds and producing a jet velocity of well over 6,000 feet per second. Because of an oxygen shortage at the test site that day, the first run was brief—only about 13½ seconds.[23] Also tested, earlier on this day, were a tubular monel motor built by Pierce and a tubular regenerative motor submitted by Truax.

The Wyld motor (Figure 17) was subsequently tested more fully in runs on the ARS No. 2 proving stand at Midvale, New Jersey, on 8 June 1941,[24] and again on 22 June and 1 August.[25] Other interesting motors also tested on these occasions included those submitted by Africano (Figure 18),[26] with the Society, co-winner of the REP-Hirsch Prize in 1936;[27] by Robertson Youngquist (Figure 19), then a stu-

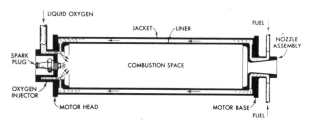

FIGURE 15.—Design for the Wyld liquid-propellant rocket
motor, the first successful regenerative motor of its type, and
culmination of the American Rocket Society's long series of
experiments aimed at developing an efficient, burnout-
resistant rocket motor. From *Astronautics*, no. 40 (April 1938),
p. 11.

dent at the Massachusetts Institute of Technology; [28] and by Nathan Carver, a long time member
of the Society.[29] Active experimentation by the Society and its Experimental Committee as a group
ceased after the 1 August 1941 tests. A photograph
of the Wyld motor in operation during this last
test series is shown in Figure 20.

During the experimental period, several other
rockets and motors were built and tested as well by
members individually, including Pierce, Constantine P. Lent, and others.[30] On 2 February 1936 a
well-publicized "mail rocket" shot occurred at
Greenwood Lake, a small body of water which lies
on the border of the states of New York and New
Jersey. The project, sponsored by F. W. Kessler, a
Brooklyn philatelist, was designed by Dr. Alexander
Klemin, of the Guggenheim School for Aeronautics
at New York University, and a group of associates
including Pierce, Carver, and Ley.[31] Two rockets—
actually small gliders equipped with liquid-propellant rocket motors—were prepared for the shot.
The excessive power of the motors, and other
mechanical problems, caused the gliders to perform
erratically, but one craft nevertheless succeeded in
crossing the ice of the lake from one state to the
other, thus validating the regular postage and
special rockets stamps on the mail they carried.

Reaction Motors, Inc., continued its successful
development of the Wyld motor, at first with the aid
of the Society's second proving stand, borrowed
from the ARS for that purpose. The Society later
formally presented the stand to RMI's historical
museum, and in 1965 RMI in turn presented it to
the National Air and Space Museum of the Smithsonian Institution, in Washington, D.C.

FIGURE 16.—The American Rocket Society's second proving
stand for tests of liquid-propellant motors. Larger, sturdier,
and with a larger propellant capacity than the first, it was
constructed by John Shesta, aided by several other members
of the ARS Experimental Committee. The series, date and
run were chalked on the blackened board at the right (date
of this test was 10 December 1938). The dials registered
pressure in the propellant tanks and motor, thrust, time in
seconds, and other data, all preserved on motion picture for
later study. From left, Shesta (behind the stand), Louis
Goodman, and Alfred Africano. Photo from Pendray Collection, Princeton University Library.

The end of active rocket experimentation on the
part of the Society was brought about principally
by the imminence of World War II; the development of renewed interest by the United States military authorities in rockets, particularly solid propellant rockets; and the realization by most of us
that small-scale development and testing such as
could be done by the Society, with the resources
available to it, had been carried about as far as was

FIGURE 19.—MIT motor of Robertson Youngquist during test.

FIGURE 17.—James H. Wyld and a model of his liquid-propellant regenerative rocket motor at Midvale, New Jersey, on 8 June 1941, just prior to a successful test of the motor. In subsequent tests on the ARS No. 3 proving stand, which provided larger fuel capacity and hence longer runs, the Wyld motor did not burn out, and it delivered a thrust of somewhat more than 90 pounds and a jet velocity of well over 6,000 feet per second.

FIGURE 18.—H. F. Pierce making final adjustments preparatory to testing a large liquid-propellant motor, designed and constructed by Alfred Africano, on the ARS No. 3 proving stand on 22 June 1941.

Photos from Pendray Collection, Princeton University Library.

FIGURE 20.—Wyld motor in action. From *Astronautics*, no. 50 (October 1941), p. 8.

possible: subsequent development would necessarily depend on massive support, large-scale engineering teamwork, and government interest. In the end, so it proved.

Meanwhile the American Rocket Society continued to develop rapidly as a technical society, especially after about 1944. By 1 February 1963, when it merged with the Institute of the Aerospace Sciences to form the American Institute of Aeronautics and Astronautics, the American Rocket Society had more than 20,000 members.[32] The combined organization, of course, is now almost twice that size, and is, I believe, the largest technical society in the world devoted to the more rapid development of the related sciences of aeronautics and astronautics.

NOTES

Under the title *Ranniy period deyatel'nosti Amerikanskogo raketnogo ovshchestva*, this paper appeared on pages 97–108 of *Iz istorii astronavtiki i raketnoi tekhniki: Materialy XVIII mezhdunarodnogo astronavticheskogo kongressa, Belgrad, 25–29 Sentyavrya 1967* [From the History of Rockets and Astronautics: Materials of the 18th International Astronautical Congress, Belgrade, 25–29 September 1967], Moscow: Nauka, 1970.

G. Edward Pendray has been closely associated with the development of rockets since 1929, being one of the founders and a director and advisor of the American Rocket Society (which merged in January 1963 with the Institute of the Aerospace Sciences to form the American Institute of Aeronautics and Astronautics). He wrote the influential book, *The Coming Age of Rocket Power* (New York: Harper & Brothers, 1945), in which many of the details here presented are to be found on pages 118–130. With Mrs. Esther C. Goddard, he edited a collection of Dr. Goddard's research

notes published as *Rocket Development: Liquid-Fuel Rocket Research, 1929–1941* (New York: Prentice-Hall, Inc., 1948; rev. ed., paperback, 1961) and also with Mrs. Goddard, he recently completed editing *The Papers of Robert H. Goddard* (New York: McGraw-Hill Book Company, 1970).

1. "The Forthcoming Annual Meeting," *Astronautics* (official publication of the American Interplanetary Society), no. 28 (March 1934); reprinted edition (New York: Kraus Reprint Corporation, 1958), p. 7. The name of the American Interplanetary Society was changed to the American Rocket Society at the annual meeting on the evening of 6 April 1934.

2. G. Edward Pendray, "The First Quarter Century of the American Rocket Society," *Jet Propulsion* (Journal of the American Rocket Society), vol. 25, no. 11 (November 1955), p. 586.

3. Robert H. Goddard, "A Method of Reaching Extreme Altitudes" (*Smithsonian Miscellaneous Collections*, vol. 71, no. 2, 69 figs., 11 pls., December 1919) and "Liquid Propellant Rocket Development" (ibid., vol. 95, no. 3, 10 pp., 11 pls., 16 March 1936) were republished by the American Rocket Society in one volume entitled *Rockets* in 1945, with a new foreword by Dr. Goddard and Pendray. Goddard began correspondence with Pendray early in the history of the American Interplanetary Society. Both men wrote each other and occasionally met throughout Goddard's life. One result of this association was the American Rocket Society combined edition of Goddard's classic reports. (See Esther C. Goddard and G. Edward Pendray, editors, *T⸱: Papers of Robert H. Goddard* (New York: McGraw Hill Book Company, 1970), vol. 2, pp. 795–96, 1073, 1074 and 1084; and vol. 3, pp. 1346, 1540–45, 1548–56, 1581, and 1598—Ed.)

4. "Has Two-Step Rocket Ready," *Bulletin, American Interplanetary Society*, no. 6 (January 1931); reprinted edition (New York: Kraus Reprint Corporation, 1958), p. 1; "American Rocket Pioneers, No. 3, Dr. Darwin O. Lyon," *Journal of the American Rocket Society*, no. 61 (March 1945), p. 11.

5. Willy Ley, in a footnote on page 129 of his *Rockets, Missiles, and Men in Space* (New York: Viking Press, 1968), comments on a misunderstanding regarding the evolution of the German VfR Miraks which apparently resulted from these conversations.

6. Pendray, "The German Rockets," *Bulletin, American Interplanetary Society*, no. 9 (May 1931), pp. 5–12.

7. Pendray, "The Conquest of Space by Rocket," *Bulletin, American Interplanetary Society*, no. 17 (March 1932), pp. 3–7. Discusses the evolution of ARS Rocket No. 1.

8. Pendray, "History of the First A.I.S. Rocket," *Astronautics*, no. 24 (November-December 1932), pp. 1–5; and Pendray, "Why Not Shoot Rockets?" *Journal of the British Interplanetary Society*, vol. 2, no. 2, 1935, pp. 9–12. This account discusses the cost of ARS Rocket No. 1.

9. Pendray, "The Flight of Experimental Rocket No. 2," *Astronautics*, no. 26 (May 1933), pp. 1–13.

10. Goddard, "Liquid-Propellant Rocket Development" (see Note 3), pp. 2–3.

11. "Three New Rockets Being Built," *Astronautics*, no. 27 (October 1933), pp. 1–8; and "Society's Rockets Near Completion," *Astronautics*, no. 28 (March 1934), pp. 2–6.

12. "Rocket Experiments of 1934," *Astronautics*, no. 29 (September 1934), pp. 1–3.

13. "The Flight of Rocket No. 4," *Astronautics*, no. 30 (October-November 1934), pp. 1–4.

14. "Test Report on Rocket No. 3," *Astronautics*, no. 30 (October-November 1934), pp. 5–6.

15. "December 18, 1941—Reaction Motors, Inc., was organized to continue development of Wyld thrust chamber." This statement was attributed to Lovell Lawrence in letter from H. A. Koch, Reaction Motors Division, Thiokol Chemical Corporation to A. J. Kelley, Aerojet-General Corporation, 7 July 1961, regarding preparation of chronology by George S. James for American Rocket Society Space Flight Report to the Nation.

16. John Shesta, "Report on Rocket Tests," *Astronautics*, no. 31 (June 1935), pp. 1–6; and, same issue, p. 12, Nathan Carver, "Flame Data for Test Runs."

17. "Report on Motor Tests of June 2nd," *Astronautics*, no. 32 (October 1935), pp. 3–4.

18. Alfred Africano, "Report on the Rocket Motor Tests of August 25th," *Astronautics*, no. 33 (March 1936), pp. 3–5.

19. "Rocket Motor Tests of October 20, 1935," *Astronautics*, no. 34 (June 1936), p. 5.

20. "ARS No. 2 Proving Stand," *Astronautics*, no. 40 (April 1938), pp. 15–17.

21. Pendray, "Rocket Tests at Pawling," *Astronautics*, no. 38 (October 1937), pp. 9–10; and, same issue, pp. 10–12, Africano, "Report on Model Flight Tests." Peter van Dresser, "Dry Fuel Experiences," *Astronautics*, no. 41 (July 1938), pp. 9–12. Africano, "New Model Stability Tests," *Astronautics*, no. 44 (November 1939), pp. 1–6; and, same issue, pp. 11–13, Roy Healy, "Model Rockets." Shesta, "Powder Flight Tests," *Astronautics*, no. 45 (April 1940), p. 3.

22. Robert C. Truax, "Gas, Air, Water," *Astronautics*, no. 40 (April 1938), pp. 9–11; and, same issue, pp. 11–12, James H. Wyld, "Fuel as Coolant."

23. John Shesta, H. Franklin Pierce, and James H. Wyld, "Report on the 1938 Rocket Motor Tests," *Astronautics*, no. 42 (February 1939), pp. 2–6.

24. Reports on these tests were published in *Astronautics*, no. 49 (August 1941), as follows: Shesta and Healy, "Report on Motor Tests, pp. 3–5; J. J. Pesqueira and Cedric Giles, "Report on Flame and Sound," pp. 6–7; Cedric Giles, "The Nozzle-less Motor," pp. 8–10, and "Mr. Carver Explains," p. 10.

25. Reports on these tests were published in *Astronautics*, no. 50 (October 1941), as follows: Healy and Shesta, "Report on Motor Tests of June 22," pp. 3–6; Lovell Lawrence, Jr., "Timing and Ignition Control," p. 6; Africano, "The Africano Motor," p. 7; and Healy, "Wyld Motor Retested," p. 8.

26. See *Astronautics*, no. 49, p. 7.

27. [Award of REP-Hirsch Prize for 1936], *Astronautics*, no. 35 (October 1936), p. 17. Africano, "The Design of a Stratosphere Rocket," *Journal of the Aeronautical Sciences*, vol. 3, June 1936, pp. 287–290.

28. See *Astronautics*, no. 50, pp. 4–5.

29. See *Astronautics*, no. 49, p. 10.

30. "Tubular Motors," *Astronautics*, no. 37 (July 1937), pp. 9–10; and, same issue, p. 11, "Spear Rocket."

31. "The First Rocket Air Mail Flight," *Popular Mechanics*, vol. 65, no. 5 (May 1936), pp. 641–642. Alexander Klemin, "On the Aerodynamic Principles of the Greenwood Lake Rocket Aeroplane," *Astronautics*, no. 36 (March 1937), pp. 7–9. [Results of Greenwood Lake Motor Tests; comments by Nathan Carver], *Astronautics*, no. 38 (October 1937), p. 16. Jesse T. Ellington and Perry F. Zwisler, *Rocket Mail Catalog: 1904–1967* (New York, 1967), p. 215.

32. "ARS Membership Votes Merger With IAS," *Astronautics*, vol. 8, no. 1 (January 1963), p. 9.

15

Ludvík Očenášek: Czech Rocket Experimenter

Rudolph Pešek and Ivo Budil, *Czechoslovakia*

The first Czechoslovak rockets were launched at the end of the 1920s. The largest public demonstration, of a whole range of rockets, including two-stage ones, was held on 2 March 1930 near Czechoslovakia's capital city Prague. The rockets, some of which are shown in Figure 1, were about 20 inches in length and one at least reached the remarkable altitude, for that time, of 4,700 feet.

They were designed, constructed and tested by the Czech inventor and entrepreneur Ludvík Očenášek (1872–1949). This typically self-made man had an unusually wide span of interests, both technical and political, which warrants our interest in his life work. He is shown in Figure 2 with his son, Miroslav, a graduate electrical engineer who worked with his father on one of the latter's projects, a hydrodynamic boat.

Born into a poor mining family, Ludvík Očenášek taught himself to be a mechanic, and while working at that trade succeeded in completing his education in a middle vocational school. At the age of 22, after working in a patent office, he opened in Prague his own machine shop which in time grew into a medium-sized industrial plant. At first his plant limited itself to electrical appliances, but later proved equally successful in producing a variety of technical developments such as an improved bicycle; crystals for radio receivers; a system of underground loudspeakers that he perfected and produced for stadiums; and eventually new machines for the pharmaceutical industry, and military weapons. His enterprise did not restrict itself to the mass production of existing products, however; the plant also produced the new inventions Očenášek had patented. His original workshop, where he developed his first "noiseless" machine-gun, is shown in Figure 3.

Creativity marked his entire life, from the merry-go-round he designed and constructed at the age of eight to the new type of recoil device for firearms—for which a patent was awarded to him two days after his death on 10 August 1949. In the first decade of the 20th century, his interest centered on aviation. In 1905 Očenášek designed and built an aeronautical rotary engine (Figure 4), which was similar to the subsequently famous French Gnome engine. This eight-cylinder radial rotary engine was introduced in 1908 at the industrial exposition in Prague. A letter describing it was published in the French review *Le Monde Industriel*.[1] The motor is preserved in Prague's Technical Museum. Another French journal, *Encyclopédie Contemporaine*[2], praised Očenášek's engine for its light weight and high output. It developed 12 horsepower and weighed only 165 pounds (13.8 lb/hp).

Očenášek of course built his radial rotary airplane engine because he wanted to fly. In 1910 and 1911 he built a monoplane which ranged among the largest aircraft of its time (see Figure 4). It had a wing span of 39 feet (12 m), an over-all length of 36 feet (11 m), and its propeller diameter was 8½ feet (2.6 m). Its "Gnome type" rotary engine developed 50 horsepower. The plane's total loaded weight, with pilot, 75 kilograms of fuel and 8 kilograms of lubricant, amounted to approximately 1325 pounds (600 kg). The entire flying machine could be transported in three crates and assembled in two hours.

In this plane, through constant improvements, Očenášek on 30 November 1910 attained a maximum flight distance of not quite 100 feet (30 m). However, when his chief mechanic Serntner, during a test flight in 1911, lost control and the plane burned, Očenášek was obliged to abandon his ex-

FIGURE 1.—Some of the solid propellant rockets developed by Ludvík Očenášek.

pensive experiment in aviation. Meanwhile his firm, transformed into a limited liability stock company, declared bankruptcy.

A similar interest by Očenášek in rocketry and jet-propelled boats marked the decade from 1928 to 1938. These years, just before World War II are also characterized by Očenášek's efforts to improve the weaponry of the Czechoslovak armed forces. Toward the end of his life he supported himself as

a self-employed designer and builder of machinery for the pharmaceutical industry. As late as 1949, when he was 77, he won three prizes for his apparatus in this field.

Such is the irony of fate, however, that Ludvík Očenášek gained high recognition in his own country not as an inventor but as a fighter for Czechoslovak independence. Toward the end of World War I he became a member of the Mafia, which was

FIGURE 2.—Ludvík Očenášek (1872–1949) and his son Ing. Miroslav Očenášek (1898–1955).

then a secret underground organization of patriots striving for national liberation from the Austro-Hungarian Empire. He detected the existence of a secret telephone line between the Austro-Hungarian and German general staffs, tapped the conversations, and passed the resulting intelligence to the resistance movement. In 1918 he took an active part in organizing the Czechoslovak army. This gained him immense popularity during the 1920s. A small footnote to Očenášek's life story is that in his old age, during World War II, he again participated actively in the resistance, this time against the Nazis, and under the German occupation was followed and interrogated by the Gestapo. During the Prague uprising of May 1945, at the age of 73, he fought on the barricades, rifle in hand, and sustained serious multiple wounds.

The name of Očenášek did win world fame once in connection with rocketry, early in 1930. This was due to a journalist's hoax. A newspaperman ran a fanciful article in his Christmas (1929) issue to the effect that Ludvík Očenášek was planning to send his rocket to the moon in 1930 with a crew of nine aboard. The lunar space ship was described as having six rockets for thrust and two for braking. The news item was picked up and copied by papers in Austria, Denmark, Germany, Italy, the Netherlands, Poland and Switzerland, Očenášek took it as the joke for which it was meant. This did not, however, prevent him from receiving several hundred letters from all over Europe, and even from the United States, written by volunteers eager to accompany him on his trip to the moon. Perhaps one of these would-be moon-trotters, Miss Sally Gallant of New Castle, Pennsylvania, is still alive. Her letter was typical of many American offers:

I am five feet four inches tall, weight 138 pounds, am blonde, speak Polish and English. I work as a nurse, I am 20 years old, and would like to fly with you to the moon.[3]

Of course that newspaper prank did have its kernel of truth—Očenášek's serious experiments in rocketry. He began them in 1928, inspired by reports of successful experiments performed by Dr. Robert H. Goddard, engineer Max Valier, Professor Hermann Oberth and others. He corresponded with Professor Oberth, who at Očenášek's invitation, came to see him in Prague. The two are shown together in the Czechoslovak capital in Figure 5. Incidentally, in the same city Očenášek met with another pioneer of high altitude flights, Professor August Piccard.

Očenášek thoroughly studied Goddard's initial results and similarly concluded that gunpowder was not the ideal propellant for rocket acceleration.[4] He planned to use liquid propellants as advocated by both Goddard and Oberth, such as alcohol or hydrogen and oxygen. His objective however was far less fantastic than a flight to the moon. His aim was to utilize rockets for delivering mail between continents via high altitude trajectories.

Fortunately a series of photographs of Očenášek's 1930 rocket tests have survived, and these are shown in Figure 6. The motion pictures of these public demonstrations on 2 March 1930 constitute a unique document.

However, more concrete data is lacking thus far. Očenášek feared that once again, as in the case of

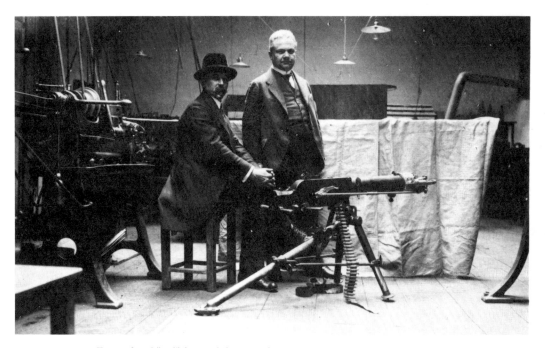

FIGURE 3.—Očenášek's workshop and his first noiseless machine gun.

FIGURE 4.—*a,* Očenášek's aircraft rotary engine of 1908, which produced 12 hp at 600 rpm and weighed 165 lb (75 kg); *b,* his monoplane of 1910–1911, showing placement of rotary engine; *c,* control surfaces of the monoplane.

FIGURE 5.—Ludvík Očenášek and Professor Hermann Oberth in Prague.

his radial aircraft engine, he might be deprived of priority in his invention, and, therefore, concealed technical details. Only a single model has survived to the present day. It apparently is a second stage which still contains its unburned propellant charge. Ludvík Očenášek's daughter has kept it, propellant charge and all, in her household for nearly 40 years. Chemical analysis reveals that the propellant consists of ordinary gunpowder loaded in a specially shaped paper container which by its form constitutes a nozzle.

After further experimentation, Očenášek is said to have devised a ground-launching apparatus to aid in overcoming the obstacles to rapid rocket acceleration. This equipment reportedly proved successful, and was tested by having it catapult a heavy sack of sand straight up into the air. Information on this device, however, has not yet been verified.

Ludvík Očenášek was obliged to foresake further investigation in the rocket field, owing to the depression of the 1930s, which caused him to lose his business enterprise and left him with no funds for such research. However he continued to believe in the feasibility of his idea—the transporting mail from Europe to America by rocket. He was certain it would be developed in the immediate future. In April 1930, *The New York Sun* carried an article on his activities in which he stated:

Indeed, rockets with human crews (to quote the terminology of that time) are not improbable, although in this case many difficult problems concerning the physiological reactions of the human body will arise.[5]

However, Očenášek did not abandon his attempts to find some practical application of the jet propul-

sion principle. Since rocket flights were too fantastic for his time, he tried to adapt the reaction principle to powering a boat for shallow waters. He found support and encouragement in the Bata Shoe Company. The company welcomed a source of cheap motive power for its flat-bottomed river craft which delivered its footwear via the shallow unregulated rivers of central Europe.

In 1933 he tested his first hydrodynamic boat (No. 1), a small craft on which the entire four-horsepower power plant was mounted as an auxiliary power package. These trials proved promising. Streams of water were forced through jet nozzles placed just above the surface of the water in the river (see Figure 7). He subsequently constructed a larger boat (No. 2) weighing 1.4 metric tons to carry six passengers (Figure 7c). With the equipment still relatively unperfected, this craft achieved good results. With a draft of 7 inches (18 cm) it attained speeds of 9 miles per hour (14 kph) and above all displayed considerable towing potential for pulling barges, with unusual maneuverability.

In 1935 the Czechoslovak armed forces ordered such a jet-powered boat (No. 3) from Očenášek, and added it as an operational unit to its Danube River fleet. Under full load, the boat could cruise at 15 miles per hour (24 kph), developed a pull of 1650 pounds (750 kg) and could haul 300 metric tons of freight at 5 miles per hour (8 kph). A publicity film about Očenášek's hydrodynamic boat was prepared at the time, but we have thus far been unable to find a copy. Latest reports suggest it may have been sent to Amsterdam.

Further orders for boats came in. Očenášek's son assembled four such boats in Poland; interest was expressed by Japan, Rumania, and the Netherlands. There exists a project design for a very large passenger-carrying river craft. But World War II and the occupation of Czechoslovakia in 1939 put an end to all of Očenášek's activities in this direction. Thus, his most outstanding technical achievement never was able to realize its potential.

In the years just before World War II, however, Očenášek had turned again to the technology of military weapons, out of a desire to improve the arsenal of Czechoslovakia's Army. And once again he worked with rockets. If we know little of his first generation of rockets, of the latter military ones we knew even less. Ludvík Očenášek performed these experiments secretly in an unknown rock

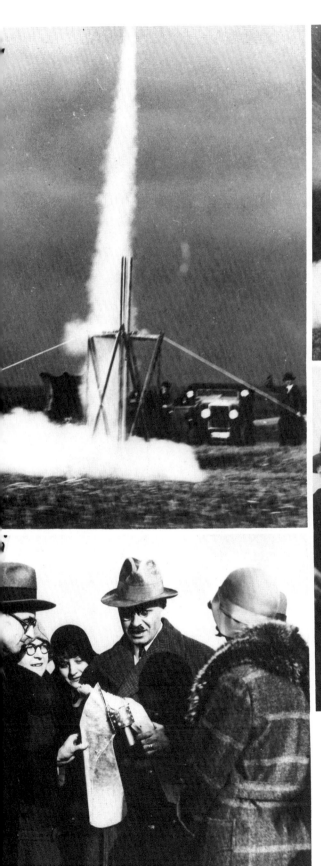

FIGURE 6.—*a*, Launching site and rack used during a demonstration of Očenášek's solid propellant rockets on White Mountain, near Prague, 2 March 1930; *b*, Očenášek preparing rocket for launch; *c*, demonstration rocket being placed in rack; *d*, larger rack used for some rockets; *e*, Očenášek inspecting rocket prior to launch; *f*, two-stage rocket, being placed in launcher; *g*, successful launch from larger rack; *h*, explosion of rocket during take-off; *i*, Očenášek and his son inspecting rockets following tests; *j*, Miroslav Očenášek and co-worker inspecting damage to fins and nozzle of demonstration rocket following test.

FIGURE 7.—*a*, Oćenášek's water-jet propelled boat No. 1, showing exhaust nozzles; *b*, rear of boat No. 1; *c*, water-jet propelled boat No. 2; *d*, boat No. 3 during demonstration test; *e*, water exhaust ducts of boat No. 3.

quarry near Prague. Even his family learned of this activity only by chance, when he come home one day injured. Naturally, since that work involved military secrecy no photographs of the actual devices have been found. All we have located is a photograph (Figure 8) of two models of these rockets. The projectiles were streamlined and provided with fins. At their rear was located a metal cartridge for the solid propellant. These rockets, moreover, were launched by being fired from a gun. Thus they were really a combination of projectile and rocket, a grenade-rocket similar to the British infantry anti-tank grenade rocket (PIAT) of World War II. The projectile, according to confirmed reports, had a range of 1.6 miles (2.5 km) with little dispersion.

Očenášek wanted to share the designs for this new weapon with Czechoslovakia's foreign allies. In this he was unsuccessful, and the plans remained all through the war sealed up in the house where he lived. He died on 10 August 1949 and his son died six years later, on 3 August 1955. His tombstone at the Olsary Cemetery is shown in Figure 9.

(Professor Pešek's presentation concluded with a motion picture film showing the 2 March 1930 public demonstration of Ludvík Očenášek's first-generation rockets at the White Mountain near Prague.)

FIGURE 9.—Očenášek's grave in the Olsary cemetery in Prague.

FIGURE 8.—Two models of Očenášek's grenade rocket.

NOTES

1. M. Guérin, "Nouveau moteur à explosion et lampe à arc-systeme L. Očenášek," *Le Monde Industriel*, 13th year, 31 December 1908, pp. 438–39.

2. Louis Davia, "Exposition jubilaire de Prague," *Encyclopédie Contemporaine*, 1908, p. 204.

3. Theodor Prochazka, "Seek to Go on Flight to Moon; Five Men and a Girl in U.S. Write to Inventor; Take Joke Story Seriously," *The New York Sun*, 20 March 1930, p. 24.

4. Goddard, "A Method of Reaching Extreme Altitudes," *Smithsonian Miscellaneous Collections*, vol. 71, no. 2, December 1919, pp. 67–68.

5. Theodor Prochazka, "Mail by Rocket Is Latest Plan; Czech Inventor Working on Device to Cross Ocean; Confident He Will Succeed," *The New York Sun*, April 1930. See also "News From Abroad," *Bulletin of the American Interplanetary Society*, no. 1 (June 1930), p. 4.

16

Early Experiments with Ramjet Engines in Flight

YU. A. POBEDONOSTSEV, *Soviet Union*

. . . currently the application of ramjets for space vehicles can be seen in their use for accelerating a rocket within the limits of a continuous atmosphere up to a velocity of mach 7–10.
Academician B. S. Stechkin

Development of space rockets represents an extremely complex scientific problem. But among the many problems, solution of which determines progress in rocketry, that of the energy content of the propellant heads the list. It can be said with good reason that the launching of sputniks, rocket flight to the Moon, Venus and Mars, manned orbital flights, and soft landing on the Moon—all these remarkable achievements are the gigantic strides in the development of Soviet science and rocket-power engineering. It is quite evident that the development and modification of jet engines and the selection of the most efficient propellants for them is still going to be one of the fundamental determinative tasks of cosmonautics for many decades to come, as it was at the very outset of the cosmic era.

Conducting research of energy content of propellants on a wide scale, Soviet scientists from the very beginning advanced and developed the concept of using air-breathing engines in space engineering in addition to other types of rocket engines.

At the beginning of this century K.E. Tsiolkovskiy put forward the concept of using engines propelled by air oxygen for the boost of spacecrafts during their flight in the atmosphere.[1]

F.A. Tsander, as well as other scientists, has devoted much of his effort to the investigation of this problem.[2]

The concept of using air-breathing engines to boost space rockets is universally recognized at the present time. Numerous theoretical and experimental studies published in the world press indicate that the use of air-breathing engines in the first stages of carrier rockets permits a severalfold increase of the mass of sputniks to be orbited, while maintaining unchanged the launching weight, or even decreasing it appreciably, yet maintaining the payload weight.

In 1907–13 René Lorin, a French engineer, suggested the concept of a ramjet engine.[3] Its first theoretical foundation, the design and experiments with ramjet engines, however, were carried out much later by Soviet scientists.

One of the closest disciples and followers of N.Ye. Zhukovskiy, Boris Sergeyevitch Stechkin, now Academician, delivering a course of lectures on hydrodynamics at the Mechanics Department of the Moscow N. E. Bauman Higher Technical School in 1928 expounded his new theory of ramjet engines. Strictly following the classical principles of gas dynamics, he derived for the most general case the equation for thrust and efficiency of ramjet engines in a resilient medium.

The problem of the reactive force of fluid flow, passing through a jet engine (for an incompressible fluid, when there is no thermal aspect) was developed in detail earlier by N.Ye. Zhukovskiy and expounded in his classic works *On Reaction of Fluid Inflow and Outflow* and *Contribution to the Theory of Ships Propelled by the Reactive Force of Water*.

B.S. Stechkin investigated in a similar way the

resilient medium flow for the first time. Moreover he showed how the efficiency of a ramjet engine could be determined if the external energy was partially or fully supplied to the air, and he investigated the case of air flow compression due to the loss of free stream momentum, as was suggested by René Lorin in his time. In this case the air characteristics are changed according to the "Brayton cycle" and its thermal efficiency will equal the difference between unity and the ratio of air temperature at the completion of compression to its initial value at the inlet to the engine.

Rumors about this lecture quickly spread among the advanced scientific and technical circles at that time interested in rocketry, and B.S. Stechkin was asked to deliver the lecture once more for a wider audience.

Soon such a lecture was held at one of the public lecture halls of the Soviet Army House. The hall was overcrowded and many of those who wished to be present failed to get in. Then Boris Sergeyevitch was asked to publish the lecture. With the aid of his students and disciples Stechkin prepared the lecture for publication as the article "Theory of a Ramjet Engine," first published in February 1929, thus becoming known not only to specialists in the USSR but in other countries as well.[4] In this article the equations of ramjet engine thrust and efficiency were given for the first time.

Soon after the publication of Stechkin's work, reviews, comments, and references to it, as well as unanimous recognition of USSR priority in this field, began to appear in the technical literature abroad. For instance, the famous Italian scientist Arturo Giovanni Crocco in his monograph "Superaviation and Hyperaviation," published in 1931, wrote that "the classic theory of ramjet engines had been formulated for the first time in the USSR by the Moscow professor Stechkin." [5]

The theory worked out by B.S. Stechkin opened the way for practical works in developing ramjet engines.

In autumn 1931 in the USSR a group of ardent enthusiasts and advocates of rocket engineering was set up as a voluntary society which afterwards was named the Group for Study of Jet Propulsion (GIRD). Mainly they were young students and aviation specialists who set for their task the practical development of jet vehicles. GIRD conducted its work in teams while general guidance was ef-

fected by the Technical Council composed of the most qualified specialists. Sergei Pavlovitch Korolyev, who afterwards became an Academican and a spacecraft designer, was Chairman of the Technical Council.

One of GIRD's team, headed by myself, was entrusted with investigations and experimental testing of ramjet engine performance. At the beginning we devoted several months to theoretical calculations and research into possible fields of such engines application. Then the time was ripe to commence the practical work, i.e., investigations of models and separate units of ramjet engines.

Test stand IU-1 was constructed in GIRD by March 1933. It comprised a high-pressure compression station, a battery of tanks accumulating the air compressed up to 200 kg/cm² and a stop valve measuring the air supply from the gas pressure tanks to the receiver. The latter damped the pressure fluctuations of the air supplied to the experimental engine. The design of the test stand, preserved among other papers of that time, is shown in Figure 1, and the ramjet engine model being tested is shown in Figure 2. Air entered the model at various preset values of excess pressure which simulated the dynamic pressure in the inlet diffuser of the engine.

Experimental laboratories as well as workshops and design rooms of GIRD were housed at that time in the basement of an apartment building.

The first test of IU-1 was carried out on 26 March

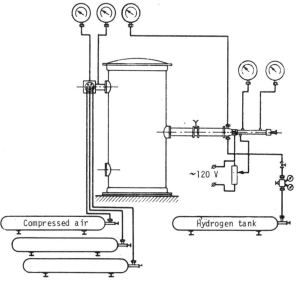

FIGURE 1.—Diagram of IU-1 facility for ramjet engine testing (from GIRD archives).

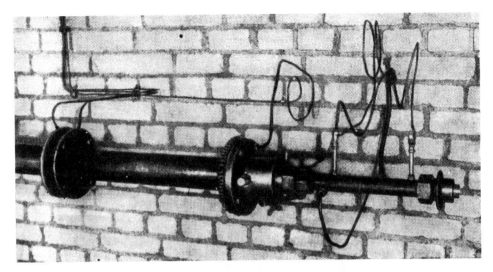

FIGURE 2.—Experimental ramjet engine.

1933. The test records of this new field of engineering, i.e., engineering of ramjet engines, have been preserved to this day.[6] Record No. 1 briefly stated:

At 2:30 a.m. the knife switch of the facility electric motor was activated. . . . The compressor was stopped at 2:45 a.m. . . . After 15 minutes had elapsed pressure in the final compression stage had reached 190 atm.

Owing to the participation and support of the whole personnel of GIRD the testing and the final adjustment of the facility successfully advanced and after six tests it was fully prepared for the investigation of the ramjet engine model.

Figure 3 shows the ignition of various combustible air-fuel mixtures and their rates of combustion.

It was decided to carry on the experiments on ramjet engine models in the IU-1 test stand with gaseous hydrogen, the most available and convenient from the point of operation, which when mixed with air is ignited in a very wide range and ensures the highest rate of combustion.

In the early morning of 15 April 1933 the first test of the ramjet engine model was conducted. It lasted 5 minutes. The conclusion of the test results stated: "The first starting of the engine has proved the theoretical suppositions about jet engines propelled by a gaseous propellant." The test marked the beginning of experimental research on ramjet engines.

Four days after the first test the second one was carried out on the IU-1 stand. This time the engine was tested at pressures in the combustion chamber varying from 1 to 3.2 atm. During the test period the engine was started 3 times and it was established that "under normal engine performance the ignition of hydrogen-air mixture should be done only once, on starting the engine. The combustion chamber having been heated, the ignition may be cut off and the power is adjusted only by means of air and propellant supply."

As the work of testing the ramjet engine models proceeded, the methods of investigation were gradually modified. From 9 June 1933, the thrust developed by the engine under the test was measured during experiments on the IU-1 test stand.

To make the ramjet engine effective not only at supersonic velocities but at subsonic ones as well, designs of ramjet engines were researched in which the air, in addition to being compressed in the diffuser due to the air flow kinetic energy, was also compressed by means of certain devices. One of such design was the pulse-jet engine (PuVRD), with the valve at the entry (the prototype jet engine of a pilotless "flying bomb" known later in Germany as the V-1).

To investigate the possibility of developing the pulse-jet engine in GIRD, in June 1933 an experimental combustion chamber with a valve labelled EK-3, was constructed.

The test of pulse-jet engines in 1933 in GIRD permitted a determination of the main problem occurring when developing the design of engines of such type, and an estimate of the volume and difficulties of their solution. It was decided for the

Ignition limits of combustible mixtures			Spec. wt.
I Gases		% gas (by vol) in mixture	
Acetylene	C_2H_2		1.173
Hydrogen	H_2		0.09
Carbon dioxide	CO		1.25
Water (blue) gas	$CO+H_2$		
Hydrogen sulfide	H_2S		
Ethylene	C_2H_4		1.26
Dithiane	C_2N_2		
Ethane	C_2H_6		1.357
Methane	CH_4		0.717
Ammonia	NH_3		0.711
Butylene	C_4H_2		
Propylene	C_3H_6		
Pentane	C_5H_{12}		
Propane	C_3H_8		2.02
Butane	C_4H_{10}		
II Vapors			
Carbon bisulfide	CS_2		
Ethyl ether	$C_4H_{10}O$		
Methyl alcohol	CH_4O		
Ethyl alcohol	C_2H_6O		
Acetone	C_3H_6O		
Oil			
Benzene	C_6H_6		
Toluole	C_7H_8		

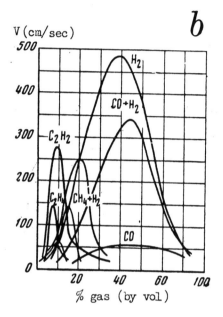

FIGURE 3.—Parameters of fuel-air mixtures used in tests: *a*, Ignition limits of combustible mixtures; *b*, burning rate of mixture versus combustible gas content.

immediate years to direct all efforts toward research on ramjet engines.

Experimental works on investigating the ramjet engines, from April 1933 in GIRD, were conducted for the whole year without interruption. Success of the first investigations made it possible to commence the construction and testing of a ramjet engine in free flight. A bold idea discussed and approved by the GIRD Technical Council was to arrange for the engine to be tested in the body of an artillery projectile and to test ramjet engines at supersonic velocities, i.e., in the region where the ramjet engines are the most efficient. It was necessary to prove experimentally the feasibility of developing a ramjet engine—an engine which at that time had been built nowhere in the world—and also to prove in practice the correctness of theoretical statements, i.e., to prove in principle that an engine of such a type is capable of developing thrust. At that time, when the question was still being raised as to whether it was advisable to work on developing ramjet engines at all, an answer could only be given by an actually operating ramjet engine having shown its working ability in flight.

Selection of the propellant for such a ramjet engine model was of great significance. As a result of a thorough investigation of all conditions of a ramjet engine performance during the forthcoming tests, the following requirements were suggested for the propellant: (1) it should be solid; (2) it should be inflammable and should have a high combustion rate in a wide range of air mixtures; and (3) it should have calorific capacity per liter as high as possible. Having investigated a number of propellants we decided to choose white phosphorus as the one most convenient for the purpose (see figure 4).

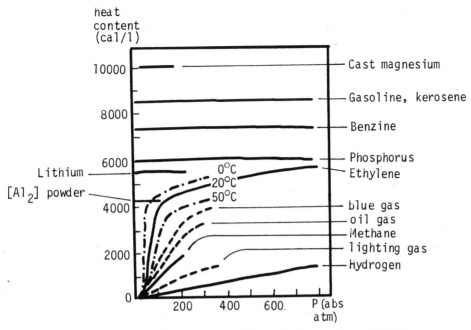

FIGURE 4.—Calorific content per liter of fuel at various pressures.

As the work procedure has shown, our choice of propellant was a good one. At the same time, we also decided to use "solid benzene" as a propellant. Therefore the ramjet engine intended for the operation on an artillery projectiles was designed with due regard to the possibility of using both phosphorus and benzene.

To prepare a ramjet engine model for free flight testing, a special mobile test stand was constructed in which the rotating combustion chamber of a jet engine was installed and on 12 July 1933, at one of the proving grounds near Moscow, the first test of the phosphorus-operated combustion chamber in the rotating ramjet engine was carried out. The aim of the first test was to investigate the properties of phosphorus as a propellant for a jet engine, and in particular for an engine installed on an artillery projectile.

The whole second half of 1933 was devoted to the preparation of the ramjet engine to the flight tests.

Owing to the harmonious and cohesive work of a small group of the third team of GIRD, all the bench tests and preparatory work that had been set by the program to pave the way for the beginning of flight tests were effected in a short period of time, and in autumn 1933 the ramjet engines were given their first flight tests.

The ramjet engine models had the contour of a long-range shell of a 76-mm (3-in.) cannon (Figure 5). The internal part of a ramjet engine comprised an entry channel, a combustion chamber and a nozzle. The propellant grain was placed directly in the combustion chamber. In order to prevent the penetration of combustion gases into the internal cavity of the engine, the exit nozzle was plugged with a metal stopper (part 4 in Figure 6) prior to firing the cannon. After the ramjet engine had cleared the cannon channel, the plug would detach from the projectile and fall near the cannon.

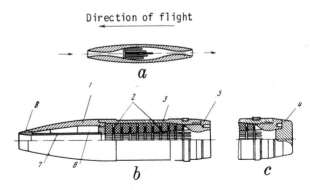

FIGURE 5.—Ramjet engine under study: a, Plan view; b, design; c, rear part of missile, with plug.

1, ogival part (nose)   5, nozzle
2, fuel cap   6, cavity for payload
3, shell body   7, intake channel
4, plug   8, air inlet

The first version of the projectile with a ramjet engine was provided with an empty cavity for housing the payload (see 6 in Figure 5).

The propellant grain was a metal frame filled with white phosphorus (2 in Figure 6). Inside the grain, along its axis, was a conical cavity positioned with its wide end towards the exit nozzle. In order to prevent the propellant grain from premature self-ignition during the transportation and preparation for model testing, the phosphorus grains were coated on all sides with a thin layer of varnish. The longitudinal ribs of the metal frame of the grain were manufactured of 2-mm-thick sheet steel and the transverse plates were of electron, a magnesium alloy. It was understood that the electron plates would burn together with phosphorus and thus considerably increase the total calorific capacity of the grain.

For the first tests, 10 projectiles with ramjet engines were prepared. They were fired from the 76-mm cannon of 1902 pattern at 20° angle of elevation. The speed of the projectile as it left the barrel of the cannon was 588 m/sec.

Prior to firing the projectiles with ramjet engines two shots were fired with a modernized shrapnel-filled shell, which fell at a distance of 7200 m. Then projectile No. 1 was fired without propellant. Instead of a phosphorus grain the frame of the grain filled with sand of the same weight was fitted in its chamber. The flight of this projectile was accompanied by strong whistling. Its flight range was roughly estimated at 2000–3000 m, since the point

of impact could not be determined because all the observers had been positioned further down range. Then 9 shots were fired with ramjet engines, with results as shown in Table 1.

TABLE 1.—*Results of first test*

Test no.	d_f (mm)	d_o (mm)	d_{cr} (mm)	d_{cr}/d_f	q (kg)	q_t (kg)	Range (m)
0 [a]	—	—	—	—	6.30	—	7200
1 [b]	28	28	32.0	1.140	6.17	—	2000
2	30	28	32.0	1.070	6.13	0.380	5300
3	30	28	34.5	1.150	6.18	0.340	8000
4	25	25	29.0	1.160	6.20	0.400	5350
5	30	25	31.0	1.030	6.22	0.390	4900
6	28	25	32.0	1.140	6.35	0.390	5300
7	30	25	34.0	1.135	6.25	0.415	6000
8	30	28	32.0	1.070	6.23	0.390	4500
9	25	25	28.0	1.120	6.30	0.415	3200
10	30	28	32.0	1.070	6.06	0.430	6000

[a] Modernized shrapnel-filled shell.   [b] Without fuel.

Data from these first tests confirmed the possibility of using the artillery cannon for catapulting ramjet engines, and the experiment proved the absolute safety of firing projectiles of the adopted design. In all cases the ignition of propellant in the chamber of the ramjet engine did not fail, the propellant having ignited 10–15 m away from the cannon.

The first tests of ramjet engines in flight, carried out in September 1933, proved that an engine of such a type was capable of operation. The increase in flight range of the projectile with a ramjet engine (projectile no. 3) of almost 1 km compared to that of a standard projectile is the most convincing evidence of this fact. The increase was obtained in spite of the fact that, from an aerodynamic point of view, a projectile with a through bore is much less efficient than a conventional one and, therefore, at that part of flight trajectory where the engine was out of operation the projectile with a ramjet engine experienced higher drag than a standard projectile. In all cases the projectiles with operating ramjet engines flew further than a projectile of the same weight and shape but without propellant. Thus, the only explanation of the flight range increase can be the fact that the ramjet engine developed some positive thrust during the flight. This fact was of a great fundamental significance.

The results of these flight tests of artillery projectiles with ramjet engines made it possible not only

FIGURE 6.—Combustion elements of ramjet engines developed by GIRD.

1, ogival part (nose)   3, shell body
2, fuel charge   4, plug

to establish the fact of positive performance of a ramjet engine, but also to determine the amount of thrust developed. Based on the preliminary calculations, the values were defined for drag experienced by the projectile body and for thrust developed by a ramjet engine. When the flight velocity with which the shell escaped the cannon barrel was 588 m/sec, the calculated drag was 20 kg and the ramjet engine thrust equalled 18 kg; i.e., it was somewhat less than the drag (Figure 7). Therefore, the engine was able to compensate 90% of the drag, but was not able to overcome it completely or to impart positive boost to the projectile. As the projectile drag exceeded the engine thrust, its velocity should decrease as the flight proceeded. The decrease of velocity caused even greater difference between the drag and the thrust. Thus, as at the moment of escaping the cannon, at the initial velocity stated, so in further flight the designed thrust of ramjet engines was less than the drag. This did not in any way confuse us, as the results of flight tests, even with such a thrust-drag ratio, enabled us to establish the fact of the ramjet engine operation and to determine the degrees to which the thrust obtained in practice approximated that designed.

Processing the flight-test data showed that the actual drag in fact exceeded that calculated and the actual thrust was somewhat below that designed. It could be explained by a number of causes, such as deformation of the metal frame of the phosphorus grain, inadequate flight stability of projectiles with ramjet engines, and so on.

Disclosure of the causes for the decrease in thrust,

compared with the designed value, and the increase in drag was a valuable result of the first set of experiments. As soon as the causes of the deficiency in ramjet engine performance were known, it became possible to look for methods to eliminate them and to modify the engine.

After the first set of experiments the second set of flight tests on ramjet engines were carried out in February 1934 and the third, in 1935. Six additional models of ramjet engines were designed for these tests, which were positioned in the body of a 76-mm projectile. Some versions of ramjet engines comprise several groups differing in the size of diffuser entry section or nozzle throat, and some test models of projectiles with ramjet engines differed in the amount of propellant used.

The second version of projectiles with ramjet engine differed from the first one only in the design of the phosphorus-grain frame. To decrease the distortion of the longitudinal ribs of the frame it was decided to make it possible for the grain to rotate freely in the chamber. With such a design, the rise of the grain angular velocity occurred not instantly, but gradually, thus preventing distortion of the grain ribs. Owing to the modifications of the jet engine design, the results of the test were appreciably better.

To prevent fuel loss, the grain framework of the third version of the engine was made so as to decrease the ejection of bits of phosphorus, and phosphorus with lower melting temperature was used. Due to this modification of the propellant grain, the value of specific impulse in the engines of the third version increased to 423 kg sec/kg of propellant.

In these engines the propellant grain framework was intended to retain phosphorus during the period of the projectile boost inside the cannon, and then it was used as a propellant. That is why the test of this group of projectiles was quite significant. Up to that time, the interesting concepts of F.A. Tsander and Yu.V. Kondratyuk, of using metal propellant in jet engines, were developed only theoretically or by means of experimental testing under bench conditions. Ramjet engines designed by the GIRD third team were the first jet engines in the world operated in flight using metal propellant not in the form of powder but as an element of structure.

During these tests the projectiles with ramjet engine covered a distance of 12 km (Table 2).

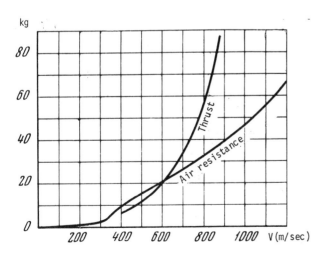

FIGURE 7.—Air drag versus thrust developed by ramjet engine.

TABLE 2.—*Results of flight tests on air-breathing jet engines of versions 2, 3, 4, 5, and 6*

Version	d_f (mm)	d_{cr} (mm)	d_{cr}/d_f	q (kg)	q_t (kg)	w_o (m/sec)	Range (m)	P	No. Shots	Diagram of jet engine
2	28	34	1.22	5.600	0.300	600	8500	185	5	
	28	35	1.25	5.600	0.300	600	10000	320	5	
	28	36	1.29	5.600	0.300	600	9500	300	5	
	28	37	1.32	5.600	0.300	600	9500	300	5	
3	28	35	1.25	6.200	0.277	680	10700	423	10	Second version, stabilized phosphorus cap Electron metal shell
	30	35	1.17	6.200	0.270	680	10500	400	10	
4	30	35	1.17	6.095	0.645	680	12500	346	3	
5	30	35	1.17	5.850	0.400	680	11807	364	4	
	30	35	1.17	5.925	0.580	680	12021	334	6	
6	30	35	1.17	5.662	0.620	680	12100	396	5	
	30	35	1.17	5.867	0.620	680	10600	330	5	

During the test quite high efficiency was obtained. Its value in the best experiments was as high as 16 percent, and taking into account that a large part of propellant was exhausted from the engine at the initial moment of the projectile flight in the air, the actual efficiency was considerably higher.

Figure 8 displays the dependence of the flight range of the projectile with a ramjet engine (which was obtained from the results of the trial firing) on the ratio of diameter of the engine nozzle throat (d_{cr}) to the diameter of the air inlet (d_f). As seen from the curve in figure 8, the optimum value of the relation $d_{cr}:d_f$ is quite close to the value 1.25–1.27; the curve has a gently sloping maximum, and its

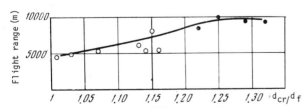

FIGURE 8.—Flight range versus ratio of nozzle diameter to air intake diameter.

further increase in this case evidently leads to some decrease in flight range, though a slight one.

A brief enumeration of the results of the first experiments with ramjet engines shows that even then, at the very outset of the rocketry development and with very limited experimental possibilities, the research workers tried to investigate the performance of the new-type engines as thoroughly as possible and to comprehend the regularities governing the processes which occurred in them.

The principal result of these experiments demonstrating the success of the work commenced at GIRD on ramjet engines was the experimental proof of the capabilities of these engines. The main question, Will a ramjet engine perform? was clearly answered: "Yes, a ramjet engine designed on the basis of Stechkin's theory is able to run in flight and to develop thrust." It was an important conclusion.

One more fact of historical significance should be noted. Ramjet engines of GIRD design were the first jet engines to attain supersonic velocity. Not a single rocket in the world had achieved such a velocity by that time.

The study of projectiles with ramjet engines was carried out by the personnel of the GIRD third

team, which included M.S. Kisenko, A.B. Ryazan-
kin, G.V. Shibalov, I.A. Merkulov, L.E. Bryuker and
O.S. Oganesov.

The experiment confirmed the workability of
engines of such a type; therefore, the theoretical
conclusions of B.S. Stechkin as well as of other
Soviet and foreign scientists, and primarily those of
F.A. Tsander and Italian Academician A. Crocco,
were proved valid.

Having completed these first experiments the scientists were faced with the second task: to solve the
problem of possible practical use of ramjet engines
on vehicles having scientific or defense significance.

NOTES

Under the title *O pervykh ispytaniyakh v polete pryamoto-
'nykh vozdushno-reakyivnykh dvigateley,* this paper appeared
on pages 109–121 of *Iz istorii astronavtiki i raketnoi tekhniki:
Materialy XVIII mezhdunarodnogo astronavticheskogo kon-
gressa, Belgrad, 25–29 Sentyavrya 1967* [From the History of
Rockets and Astronautics: Materials of the 18th International
Astronautical Congress, Belgrade, 25–29 September 1967],
Moscow: Nauka, 1970.

1. Konstantin Eduardovich Tsiolkovskiy, "Issledovaniye
mirovykh prostranstv reaktivnymi priborami," [Investigation
of Outer Space by Means of Reactive Devices], *Nauchnoye
obozreniye* [Science Review], no. 5, May 1903. An English
translation of this paper appears on pp. 24–59 of *Works on
Rocket Technology, by K. E. Tsiolkovskiy,* NASA TT F-243,
November 1965, which is a translation of *Trudy po raketnoy
tekhnike,* M. K. Tikhonravov, ed., (Moscow: Oborongiz,
1947).—Ed.

2. F. A. Tsander, *Problema poleta pri pomoshchi reaktivnykh apparatov: Mezhplanetnyye polety* [Problems of Flight
by Jet Propulsion: Interplanetary Flights] (Moscow, 1932).
Available in English as NASA TT F-147.—Ed.

3. René Lorin, "Note sur la propulsion des vehicules
aériens," *l'Aerophile,* vol. 15, November 1907, pp. 321–22;
and "Une expérience simple relative au propulseur á réaction directe," *L'Aerophile,* vol. 21, 15 November 1913, p. 514.
—Ed.

4. B. S. Stechkin, "Teoriya vozdushnogo reaktivnogo dvigatelya" [Theory of the Ramjet Engine], *Tekhnika Vozdushnogo
Flota* [Air Force Technology], no. 2, February 1929.—Ed.

5. G. A. Crocco, "Iperaviazione e superaviazione," [Hyper-
aviation and Superaviation] *L'Aerotecnica,* vol. 11, October
1931, pp. 1173–1220.—Ed.

6. Here and elsewhere, cited from papers in the GIRD
archives.

17

First Rocket and Aircraft Flight Tests of Ramjets

YU. A. POBEDONOSTSEV, *Soviet Union*

Introduction

The development of space rockets presents a rather complex scientific problem. Among all the problems which affect the successful development of space technology that of rocket power engineering is the most important one. We may confidently say that the launching of Earth satellites, rocket flights to the Moon, Venus, and Mars, manned orbital flights, and soft landing on the Moon are the significant steps in the development of the Soviet space technology. Therefore it is quite clear that the creation and improvement of rocket engines and the choice of the most efficient propellants for them will remain one of the key and governing problems in modern space technology for many decades to come, just as at the dawn of the space age.

The first to advance and substantiate the idea of applying engines using atmospheric oxygen for boosting space vehicles during their motion in the atmosphere was Konstantin Eduardovich Tsiolkovskiy.[1]

Fridrikh Arturovich Tsander and other investigators made a great contribution to the study of this problem.[2]

At present the idea of using ramjet engines for boosting space rockets is generally recognized. Numerous theoretical and experimental investigations published in the world press show that the use of ramjet engines in the first stages of carrier-rockets will allow a severalfold increase in the mass of a satellite put into orbit, with the rocket launching weight being unchanged.

Academician Boris Sergeyevich Stechkin, one of the closest pupils and followers of N.E. Zhukovski, delivering lectures on hydrodynamics at the Me-

chanics Department of the Moscow N.E. Bauman Higher Technical School in 1923, set forth a new theory of a ramjet engine. Strictly following the classic gas-dynamics laws, he derived for the most general case equations for the thrust and efficiency of a ramjet engine operating in an elastic medium.

For an incompressible fluid, without thermal effects being considered, the problem of a reaction force of a fluid jet through a jet engine was developed in detail earlier by N.Ye. Zhukovskiy and presented in his classical works: "On Reaction of Fluid Inflow and Outflow" and "Contribution To the Theory of Ships Propelled by the Reactive Flow of Water."

The analogous investigation of the compressible flow was carried out for the first time by B.S. Stechkin. He detailed the problem of energy input to the air jet inside the ramjet; and he concluded that the law of heat transfer to the air can be arbitrary, but the integral defining the operation must be taken in a closed loop (in the coordinates pv) presenting the process of changing the state of the air passing through the ramjet. Thus, the thermal efficiency of the heating cycle of the air in a ramjet was immediately determined. The total efficiency of a ramjet was defined as the product of the thermodynamic efficiency and the propulsion-unit efficiency, or, as it is now called, "the efficiency of motion" or "propulsive efficiency."

In addition, he showed how to define the efficiency of a ramjet engine when the air gets energy partly or wholly from the outside, and considered the case of air-jet compression at the expense of a free stream impulse loss, as it was proposed by René Lorin.[3] In this case the air passes on the Brayton cycle and its thermal efficiency will equal the difference between unity and the ratio of the air temperature at the completion of compression to its initial temperature at the inlet to the engine.

Soon after the publication of B.S. Stechkin's work, comments on and references to it began to appear in the technical literature abroad. Soviet Union priority in this field was unanimously acknowledged. For example, G. A. Crocco, the famous Italian scientist on hydrodynamics, recognized in his fundamentally new work "Hyperaviation and Superaviation" published in 1931,[4] that the classical theory of a ramjet engine was first developed by Professor B.S. Stechkin in the USSR.[5]

In autumn 1967, at the first symposium on the history of astronautics, held in Belgrade, Yugoslavia, I presented a report (see Paper 16) on "Early Experiments with Ramjet Engines in Flight," which gave the results of experiments with ramjet models installed in a 3-inch projectile for a field gun.

Flight tests of supersonic ramjets installed in an artillery-type projectile proved in practice that under certain conditions engines of this type could develop a reaction force, and that, due to this, a ramjet-type projectile had a greater range than that of a standard projectile.

Ramjet Test in a Rocket

Having confirmed the performance capability of the ramjet, the experimental investigations carried out also showed that these ramjets developed extra thrust of a comparatively small value. Then there arose a question of the possible creation of a ramjet developing thrust much higher than the drag experienced by the ramjet body within a suitable streamlined fairing.

To create this, I.A. Merkulov, an engineer, started investigating the thermodynamic cycle of a ramjet, and his first conclusion was that a ramjet operating on the proper Brayton cycle, that is, with combustion at $\rho =$ constant, where $\rho =$ velocity of air, could not develop thrust substantially above the drag experienced by the ramjet body, and, in fact, the engine could not thrust even itself, much less impart a positive acceleration to any vehicle. This results from the fact that to develop as great a thrust as possible, the air within the ramjet combustion chamber must be heated to a high temperature. But to keep the pressure constant while raising the gas temperature it is necessary to increase the com-

bustion-chamber cross-section in proportion to the temperature increase. Thrust augmentation therefore requires increasing simultaneously the ramjet dimensions and, hence, the value of its drag.

However, this unfavorable circumstance did not stop our work. It was proved that if the thermal efficiency of the cycle was deliberately decreased by burning the fuel at a decreased pressure; the ramjet dimensions could then be greatly reduced and, hence, the drag could be decreased at the expense of losing some thrust. The question naturally arose as to what extent the radial dimensions of the ramjet combustion chamber should be reduced.

It was necessary to choose ramjet dimensions such that they would allow the greatest free thrust (i.e., the difference between the ramjet thrust and the drag).

Having analyzed the results of the aerojet engine thermal cycles, Merkulov determined for the engine the optimal parameters which permitted it to develop thrust greatly exceeding its drag. Based on the theoretical investigations carried out by the Osoaviakhim Central-Council Stratospheric-Committee Jet Section, some ramjet engine test models were designed in 1936. All investigations and design of ramjet engines were performed by space technology enthusiasts of the Stratospheric Committee without compensation. These engines were designed by A.F. Nistratov, O.S. Oganesov, B.R. Pastukhovskiy, L.E. Bryukker, M.A. Merkulova, B.I. Romanenko, L.K. Bayev, and others. Many computations in theoretical investigations of ramjet cycles were made by A.D. Merkulova.

Then it was necessary to test the efficiency of the ramjet during flight tests and to show that this ramjet was able to impart a positive acceleration to the vehicle on which it was installed. It was decided that it would be tested first in a rocket.

The rocket equipped with a ramjet naturally could be tested only as the second stage. As the first stage, it was desirable to use a rocket with a different engine (e.g., a liquid-fueled one) or a powder rocket. For simplicity and reliability in performing the tests it was decided to use a powder rocket as the first stage, and a two-stage rocket was designed that consisted of a powder rocket as the first stage and a ramjet rocket as the second stage. This project drew on the experience of GIRD. The second stage also used solid fuel placed within the combustion chamber as a grain.

The rocket project was approved by scientists. For example, professor V.P. Vetchinkin, also one of the closest pupils of N. Ye. Zhukovskiy, rated highly the plan for the ramjet rocket. The support of the ramjet rocket project by famous scientists and foremost specialists in space technology allowed this project to be put into effect. In 1937 a special design department (headed by A. Ya. Shcherbakov) of an aircraft plant started constructing ramjet rockets. First, two ramjet models were designed there for performing systematic investigations of processes occurring in subsonic ramjets. To solve as quickly as possible the basic problem, i.e., to prove the possibility of creating a ramjet engine that could develop a thrust exceeding the drag and impart an acceleration to a vehicle, the P-3 rocket was designed. This engine was to use solid grains consisting of aluminum and magnesium powders mixed with other substances. Cylindrical grains with a through channel grains were placed in the engine chamber.

Two types of grains were used in rockets. The type manufactured by V.A. Abramov, a chemist from the Moscow State University, consisted of aluminium and magnesium powders bonded with an organic filler. These grains were very stable and burned uniformly in the engine chamber. The heat-producing capability of the grain equalled 4200 kg-cal/kg. The rocket propellant charge contained two grains of equal outer diameters, while the diameters of the central perforations used for introducing air into the combustion chamber from the engine diffuser were different.

The grain was ignited with black powder which, in turn, was ignited by means of a "stopin" fuse. The total grain weight was 2.1 kg, burning time being 8 sec.

Grains of another type were manufactured at the D.I. Mendeleyev Moscow Chemical-Engineering Institute. The work was directed by scientific staff worker Dergunov. The grains were made by compressing aluminium and magnesium powders under high pressure. To intensify the burning process and increase the engine thrust some oxidizer (potassium chlorate) was added to those grains.

Three series of ramjet rockets (16 in all) were manufactured for testing in flight.

The ramjet rocket of the first series had the following specifications: the first stage weighed 3.8 kg and the powder it contained weighed 1.4 kg, its total impulse was 260 kg/sec, maximum thrust was 450 kg, average thrust was 118 kg. and powder burning time was 2.24 sec; the ramjet rocket (second stage) weighed 4.5 kg and its diameter was 121 mm; and total initial weight of the two-stage rocket was 8.3 kg.

The next versions of the P-3 rockets had a somewhat lighter structure compared with the rockets of the first series.

While testing the P-3-2B rockets, powder rockets of 82-mm missiles were used as the first stages, and they had the following characteristics: total rocket weight was 3.510 kg, the "H" ballistite powder weight ranged from 1.050 to 1.079 kg, and the powder-gas exhaust velocity was 1860 m/sec.

The first step of experimentation included investigations of rockets in a wind tunnel. A score or two of ramjet rocket blowdowns were made throughout 1938 and at the beginning of 1939. These investigations permitted a determination of the rocket's coefficients of drag and selection of aerodynamic brakes to achieve quick separation of the first and the second stages. At the same time the burning process in a ramjet chamber was studied.

In February 1939, flight tests of the ramjet began at the airfield near the Planernaya Station, near Moscow (Figures 1 and 2). The rocket was launched vertically upwards using a launching device. During the first tests the rocket take-off, stage separation, and fuel ignition in a ramjet were developed. The first successful flight, which took place on 5 March 1939, clearly showed the increase of the rocket velocity due to the ramjet operation. Two rockets tested on that day contained grains manufactured by V.A. Abramov. These tests convincingly showed a reliable operation of the whole system. It was therefore decided to conduct official tests. To determine precisely the flight velocities and rocket altitudes, a group of astronomers was invited; they used the methods of meteorite observations for this purpose.

Official tests of the ramjet rocket, which took place on 19 May 1939, were performed at night to permit the rocket motion to be followed against the background of the dark sky by watching the trace of exhaust gases. The grain used in the rocket was made at the D.I. Mendeleyev Chemical-Engineering Institute. After the powder was ignited the rocket left the launching device and went upward. The first stage having separated, the second stage of the

FIGURE 1.—Two-stage ramjet rocket being prepared on launching rack, showing first-stage solid
propellant rocket below fins.

ramjet rocket climbed with increasing velocity. Those present at the tests could see distinctly that the rocket flight was successful.

The observations made by the group of astronomers established the following pattern of the rocket flight:

The first stage having burned out, the rocket acquired a velocity of 200 m/sec and reached a height of 250 m. After the burnout, the first stage was separated from the second one by its aerodynamic brake. The interval between powder burnout and ignition of the ramjet engine was about 2.5 sec. During this period the rocket traversed 375 m and attained a height of 625 m, at which point the rocket velocity had decreased to 105 m/sec. At this velocity the ramjet cut in, and it burned for 5.12 sec. By the end of the engine burn, the rocket reached 1317 m and acquired a velocity of 224 m/sec. After burnout of the ramjet, the rocket coasted upward for 6.06 sec, climbing to a height of 1808 m. By the end of the engine burn, the value of extra thrust, that is, the difference between thrust

and drag, was equal to 20 kg, the coefficient of thrust being 0.7. During the entire rocket flight with the ramjet cut in, the average acceleration was 23 m/sec².

Test results of these world's first ramjet rocket launches were set down in a statement worthy of being quoted in full:

Statement on ramjet engine test:

On May 19, 1939, the ramjet engine constructed by I. A. Merkulov was tested at an airfield near the Planernaya Station (near Moscow).

The test object was a wingless torpedo with a ramjet engine.

The fuel blend for this engine was prepared at the Mendeleyev Chemical-Engineering Institute.

For boosting the torpedo a conventional powder rocket was used.

Ignition of the fuel composition and the powder rocket was performed with electric plugs fed from a battery. To delay the ignition of the fuel for 1 sec after the powder rocket ignition, a stopin fuse was placed between the fuel and the electric plug. The torpedo flight height and velocity were determined by the group of astronomers.

FIGURE 2.—Second stage of ramjet-rocket vehicle being lowered onto launching rack.

For launching the torpedo into the air, it was installed in a launching ramp.

The launch took place at 22.40.

The torpedo tests yielded the following results.

The torpedo left the launching device and rose vertically. A second later, due to the aerodynamic brake, the powder rocket separated from the torpedo and fell. At that moment the ramjet engine cut in. A trace of hot exhaust products directed downward followed the exhaust nozzle. The engine burn was smooth and steady, and lasted 5.5 sec (according to the fuel available). The engine cut-in resulted in a great increase in flight velocity, the torpedo moving upwards with an increasing velocity during the entire period of the engine burn. The fuel having been consumed, the torpedo went on coasting. The whole flight was stable and precisely vertical.

The rocket flight allowed us to establish the fact that the operation of the ramjet engine was reliable and the flight velocity increased owing to this engine operation.

The rocket tests clearly demonstrated the fact of an accelerated vertical flight upward of the ramjet vehicle.

These tests proved in practice the possibility of creating a ramjet that can develop at subsonic velocities a positive thrust that will exceed the drag and even the sum of drag forces and weight.[6]

That was the end of the second phase of the efforts by Soviet scientists and designers to create ramjets.

Ramjet Flight Tests in Aircraft

The creation of a ramjet engine for aircraft was also of great importance. It opened the way for the development of those engines and their subsequent use in rockets. Aircraft could serve as excellent flying laboratories for carrying out thorough investigations of ramjets in flight.

On 3 July 1939, Merkulov presented to a meeting of the Technical Council of the Aircraft Industry Peoples' Commissariat a report that gave the experimental results on ramjets used in rockets and set forth further objectives for ramjet investigations, including improvement of its structure, and its application in aviation.

He proposed to use the ramjet in combination with the engine of a propeller-driven aircraft. The ramjets were to be used as auxiliary engines to increase maximum flight velocity. At that time the internal-combustion unit was the only powerplant applicable in aircraft in practice. It provided a high take-off and cruise economy plus good maneuverability of the aircraft in flight. At the same time a lightweight ramjet could allow the pilot to increase greatly the maximum flight velocity at a re-quired moment. Besides, it was advantageous to use the ramjet as an auxiliary engine because it did not require special fuel supplies such as were necessary, for example, for a liquid rocket engine, but could use the same gasoline as the main engine did.

In August 1939, a prototype airborne ramjet (auxiliary engine DM-1, intended for ground tests) was designed and manufactured. The engine diameter was 240 mm. Bench tests of this engine were performed in September 1939.

A successful testing of the DM-1 permitted its manufacture to be undertaken for on-board installation, and in September 1939, three DM-2 auxiliary engines were built.

Burnout of the thrust chamber of the auxiliary engine was prevented by a special cooling system, the gasoline entering the engine being used as a cooling liquid. Burning stability of the gasoline in the combustion chamber was achieved by a special device, the so-called protective ring, within the chamber. These protective rings formed small regions within the chamber in which the air flow had low velocities. In these protected regions (pre-combustion chambers) the ignition and smooth burning of a small quantity of gasoline took place. The flame that escaped the protective rings propagated burning through the main mass of the air-gasoline mixture. To assure ignition within the temperature range from $-60°$ to $+60°C$ and multiple starts in flight at any velocities, a special electrical ignition device was designed which was used throughout all flights.

DM-2 engines were very compact. Their length was 1500 mm, maximum diameter was 400 mm, nozzle exit diameter was 300 mm, and the weight of one engine without the engine frame was 12 kg and with the frame, 19 kg.

To investigate operation of the ramjet before flight tests the AT-1 special tunnel was built (after some modification it was designated the AT-2). Maximum air-flow velocity within its working section was 75 m/sec. The test of the auxiliary engines first in the AT-1 tunnel and then in the AT-2 verified their safe operation, and permitted the development of an ignition device and a smooth burning process, as well as the determination of the main ramjet parameters. These tests were carried out throughout the whole period of the DM development, both to check the structural improvements

made during the tests and to monitor the engine operation and its condition.

Test of two DM-2 models began in October, 1939, and on 22 October 1939, official tests of the DM-2 in a tunnel were performed. The results of these tests were summarized in a statement which said:

During the tests the engine was started three times. The controls functioned well. The engine appeared to be completely reliable and explosion-proof.

During the engine tunnel test the air flow developed a velocity of 120 km/hr. At this velocity the engine thrust was about 10 kg which corresponded to designed values.[7]

After successful wind tunnel tests of the ramjet engines, they were installed in the aircraft shown in Figure 3 for testing in flight.

During these first ramjet engine tests the aircraft where those engines were installed was essentially a flying laboratory for the investigation of ramjet operation.

To protect the fuselage and the tail from the possible effect of DM engine combustion products, the I-15-bis tail was covered with sheet duralumin before the tests.

Flight tests of the I-15-bis aircraft with two ramjets as auxiliary engines installed under the wings began in December 1939. The first ramjet aircraft was tested by test-pilot Petr Yermolayevich Loginov.

The flights performed by P.Ye. Loginov in December 1939, were the world's first made in a ramjet aircraft. It is interesting to note that the first flight of a foreign semijet aircraft, constructed by the Italian Caproni Company's Campini project and widely publicized by the press abroad, did not take place until August. This was seven months later than the flight of the I-15-bis ramjet aircraft.

Pilot Loginov's conclusions about the operation of jets constructed by I.A. Merkulov:

1. The engines provide some marked velocity increment of the I-152 aircraft.
2. The engine operation control is simple and readily done (one handle with a switch).
3. The engine operation is smooth at any speed and with a protective metal sheathing on the underside of the aircraft's wing, it is fireproof.

In all, the I-15-bis aircraft with the DM-2-type ramjets, piloted by different airmen, made 54 flights. Cut-in of the DM-2 increased the aircraft velocity an average of 18–20 km/hr. Tests were performed at flight velocities of 320–340 km/hr. The DM-2 had

FIGURE 3.—DM-2 ramjet engines suspended beneath wings of N. N. Polikarpov aircraft I-15-bis
(I-152), No. 5942.

the following parameters: the length, was 1.5 m, maximum diameter was 400 mm, nozzle exit diameter was 300 mm, engine weight was 12 kg, and supporting frame-suspension weight was 7 kg.

Then new aircraft appeared which had ramjets of improved characteristics, the DM–4, etc., for example. The installation of DM-4 auxiliary engines in the I-153 aircraft resulted in a velocity increment of 51 km/hr at a flight velocity of 389 km/hr, with a resulting velocity of 440 km/hr. During the Great Patriotic War (World War II) DM-4C engines were installed in the Yak-7b aircraft (Figure 4) and in other combat aircraft.

Conclusion

The examples given here show how extensively the work on creation of ramjets and their flight

FIGURE 4.—DM-4 ramjet engines mounted beneath wings of A. S. Yanovlev aircraft Yak-7b to
supplement performance.

tests was carried out in our country, even many decades ago. The main result of bench and flight tests made in those years was that they confirmed the correctness of the theory and computation methods developed earlier, and showed in practice the performance capability and reliability of engines of a new type. They also allowed more precise choices to be made concerning the trend of further research and development.

Concurrently with the flight tests, our country carried out theoretical and experimental investigations of the processes in ramjets, and undertook the study and development of separate ramjet elements as well as engines as integral units. All this work was begun at GIRD. Particular attention was paid to the study of the fuel-burning process and the development of the combustion chamber, the investigation of air intakes for supersonic ramjets, and the development of control methods and systems.

Comparison of the results of ramjet flight tests carried out in 1939–42 and analogous tests made in 1948 indicates convincingly what great successes Soviet science and engineering achieved in creating ramjets during those years.

A rather valuable work on investigating and developing ramjets was performed at the Moscow Aviation Institute 1942–43.

The achievements of Soviet scientists in creating theoretical and experimental principles of ramjets are exemplified in the scientific work, "The Ramjets" by Doctor of Technical Sciences, Professor Mikhail Makarovich Bondaryuk and Doctor of Technical Sciences Sergei Mikhailovich Il'yashchenko.

NOTES

1. K. E. Tsiolkovskiy, "Issledovaniye mirovykh prostranstv reaktivnymi priborami" [Investigation of Outer Space by Means of Reactive Devices], *Nauchnoye Obozreniye* [Science Review], no. 5, May 1903. An English version of this paper appears on pp. 24–59 of *Works on Rocket Technology, by K. E. Tsiolkovskiy,* NASA TT F-243, November 1965, which is a translation of *Trudy po raketnoi tekhnike,* M. K. Tikhonravov, ed. (Moscow: Oborongiz, 1947).—Ed.

2. F. A. Tsander, *Problema poleta pri pomoshchi reaktivnykh apparatov: mezhplanetnyye polety* [Problems of Flight by Jet Propulsion: Interplanetary Flights] (Moscow, 1932). Available in English as NASA TT F-147.—Ed.

3. René Lorin, "Une Expérience simple relative au propulseur á réaction directe," *L'Aerophile,* vol. 21, 15 November 1913, p. 514.—Ed.

4. G. Arturo Crocco, "Iperavmazione e superaviazione" [Hyperaviation and Superaviation], *L'Aerotecnica,* vol. 11, October 1931, pp. 1173–1220.—Ed.

5. B. S. Stechkin, "Teoriya vozdushnogo reaktivnogo dvigatelya" [Theory of the Air-Breathing Jet Engine], *Tekhnika Vozdushnogo Flota* [Air Force Technology] no. 2, 1929.—Ed.

6. In those years there was no fixed terminology. Therefore a two-stage ramjet rocket was called a "wingless torpedo with an air jet engine."

7. "A Brief Report of Airborne Air Jet Engine Tests to Increase the Maximum Flight Velocity," p. 74 (in the Scientific Archives of the Natural Science and Engineering History Institute, USSR Academy of Sciences).

18

On Some Work Done in Rocket Techniques, 1931-38

A. I. POLYARNY, *Soviet Union*

Beginning of Studies (1931-34)

Development in 1931 of a meteorological rocket for systematic sounding of the atmosphere was the first attempt of the author of this paper to work independently in the field of rocketry. During that period the author worked at the Scientific Research Institute of the Civil Air Force. For meteorological purposes, sounding of the atmosphere with a meteorological rocket could, to some extent, replace such soundings with the help of a plane, which was a common practice at that time.

It was envisaged by the design (Figure 1) that after the rocket's ascent to a prescribed height (6000 m), a telemetry device would become activated. As a result, there would occur a separation of the rocket's lower part from the upper, and the release of a parachute. During descent, a meteorograph would record the atmospheric data. Plans called for the subsequent radio transmission of these data earthward.

The engine was of a solid-propellant (powder) type. The optimum pressure in the engine was determined by taking into consideration the change in specific thrust and engine weight depending on the engine pressure and resultant altitude change. The optimum pressure was within the range of 30–40 atm. The diameter of the rocket was 60 mm and the length, 1000 mm. The requirements for an end-burning charge were determined. But the design was not put into effect, because I moved to the Institute of Aircraft Engine Construction (IAM), to the group headed by F.A. Tsander. Later, nevertheless, along with my other work, attempts were made to develop a charge with end-burning for solid-propellant engines (with increased rate of burning). One might expect that the porous charge with retarded surface of small channels evenly spaced in the charge would burn at a constant pressure with stable and increased linear rate as compared with a standard charge. Fixed volume burning would not change to explosive burning and detonation.

Aluminum powder was used as the retarding

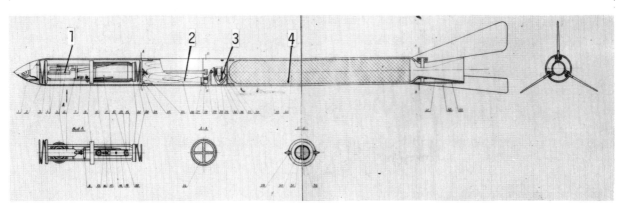

FIGURE 1.—Meteorological rocket with solid-propellant engine: 1, meteorograph; 2, parachute; 3, remote-controlled unit for opening the parachute; 4, solid-propellant engine.

agent. Small chips of smokeless powder were mixed with aluminum powder. Grains of that mixture, 15 mm in diameter and about the same length, were compressed. A special bomb fitted with a diaphragm pressure transmitter and photorecorder registering the pressure data on a rotating cylinder was employed to determine the linear rate of burning of these grains. The burning rate of the grains in the bomb (at the pressure of 50 atm) was constant. The linear rate of burning could be changed from 2 to 600 mm/sec, depending on the percentage of aluminum powder (0.5–8.0%), temperature of the mixture while compressing it (from 0° to 44°C) and pressure used (not more than 100 atm). Reproducibility of the results proved satisfactory.

At the close of 1931 I received an invitation to take part in the organization meeting of the Group for Study of Jet Propulsion (GIRD). I met F.A. Tsander at that meeting and after we had a talk he proposed that I work with him. I consented. At the beginning we worked at the IAM. Under the guidance of F.A. Tsander I made thermodynamic calculations for a rocket engine, did some development work, and carried out experiments with a OR-1 engine, which was the prototype of a liquid-propellant rocket engine.

After a short period in the IAM, the group, which was given the name of a team, moved to the premises of GIRD. S.P. Korolyev was appointed chief of the GIRD. One of the projects of the team headed by F.A. Tsander was to develop the OR-2 liquid-propellant rocket engine for the RP-1 rocket glider. In addition to development of a liquid-propellant rocket engine, their task was to accumulate experience in relation to control of a liquid-propellant rocket engine under flight conditions and to investigate future possibility of developing a composite space aircraft, with the last stage entering outer space (that was the idea of F.A. Tsander). Another aspect of their work concerned creation of the liquid-oxygen rocket which later came to be known as the GIRD-Kh rocket. The design of the OR-2 engine and the GIRD-Kh rocket was published in the collection of works by Tsander edited by L.K. Korneyev in 1961.

I had to make calculations, perform developmental work, and conduct experiments on the OR-2 engine and the GIRD-Kh rocket. The engine was first started on 18 March 1933. It operated for

several seconds and then was shut down because the nozzle burned out.

To add to the service life of the OR-2 engine we used refractory coatings for the nozzle and the chamber (corundum, magnesite, natural and artificial graphite, etc.). At the same time we tried to improve the external cooling system (see Figure 2). For the chamber, the corundum coating proved quite suitable, but the nozzle coated with this material soon disintegrated.

By the middle of August the tests showed that best results were achieved when natural graphite was used without any traces of other minerals. The engine thus lined with graphite operated for 30–40 seconds with only slight erosion of the nozzle throat. Soon after F.A. Tsander died, on 28 March 1933, L.K. Korneyev was appointed chief of the team. The GIRD-Kh rocket was launched on 25 November 1933 (see Figure 3).

By the end of August 1934 L.K. Korneyev, A.Y.

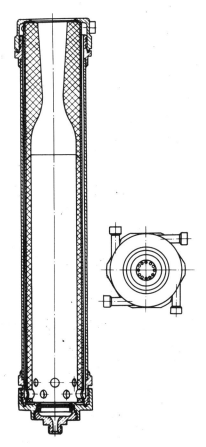

FIGURE 2.—Combustion chamber with graphite lining of OR-2 engine.

FIGURE 3.—Launching of GIRD-Kh rocket.

out of the tank with the help of gaseous oxygen formed from a partial evaporation of the lox. A heat exchanger, which was essentially a coil of pipe in the interior of the oxygen tank, was employed to intensify evaporation of the liquid oxygen. In passing through the combustion chamber jacket the oxygen was heated, and flowed back through the coil. That rocket was never used, due to lack of money.

The Osoaviakhim Rocket (1934-35)

In the period 1934–35, the Association for Promoting Aerochemical Defense (Osoaviakhim) undertook the task of developing a very simple liquid-fuel rocket which could be utilized in meteorology. In cooperation with E.P. Sheptitskiy, I developed such a rocket functioning on liquid oxygen (lox) and ethyl alcohol, the fuel feed from the tank being achieved by self-pressure through partial evaporation of the lox. The other fuel tank was filled one-third with alcohol and two-thirds with compressed air, which forced the alcohol into the combustion chamber when the valve was opened. The basic characteristics of the rocket (see Figures 5 and 6) were as follows: the rocket diameter was 126 mm; length with stabilizers, 1700 mm; launching weight, 10 kg; payload, 0.5 kg; fuel weight, 2.4 kg; engine operation time, 14 sec; pressure in the alcohol tank varied from 25 to 16 atm and in the combustion chamber, from 13 to 10 atm; thrust varied from 40 to 25 kg; estimated rated vertical flight altitude was 5000 m and estimated inclined flight range, 650 m. The rocket descended with the help of a parachute.

With the participation of the Osoaviakhim and

Polyarny, L.S. Dushkin, and I worked out a draft project of a liquid oxygen KPD-1 rocket (see Figure 4). This development was performed independently from the Jet Propulsion Research Institute (RNII), having been created by them. The characteristics of the rocket were as follows: the launching weight was 220 kg; pay load, 50 kg; fuel weight, 75 kg; length, 3300 mm; diameter, 400 mm; thrust, 550 kg; and the estimated flight range, 12 km. Liquid oxygen was supplied to the engine by forcing it

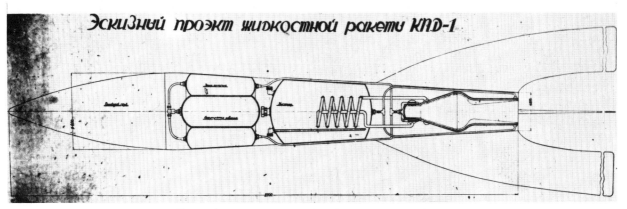

FIGURE 4.—KPD-1 lox and ethyl-alcohol powered rocket.

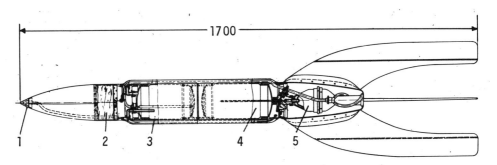

FIGURE 5.—Osaviakhim rocket, operating on lox and ethyl alcohol: 1, setup for parachute opening; 2, parachute; 3, oxidizer tank; 4, fuel tank; 5, engine.

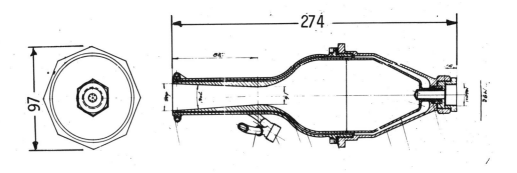

FIGURE 6.—Osoaviakhim all-metal engine.

its active members, (V.A. Sytin, I.A. Merkulov, K.K. Fedorov, N.N. Krasnukhin, and others), a rocket was made ready and a test stand was built. Initially the engine was checked out on the stand and by mid-1935 the entire rocket as a unit was brought to the prescribed parameters.

During the engine test procedure, consumption of liquid oxygen could be varied by means of a device (Figure 7) developed for the purpose. A specially designed float-type recording instrument was used to measure the lox flow rate during the rocket-engine testing. One of its basic parts was a float with a rod and disk on the end. On the oxygen tank cover, there was a pipe closed at the top; through an opening in the cover, the float's rod entered the pipe. Against the pipe's inner wall a spring pressed a plate equipped with a smoked paper tape rotating around a vertical axis; the plate's length equalled the float's depth of lowering. At specific times during the test an electromagnet fixed to the outside surface of the tube turned the plate with the smoked tape and pressed it against the float disc. In so doing, the disc made a mark

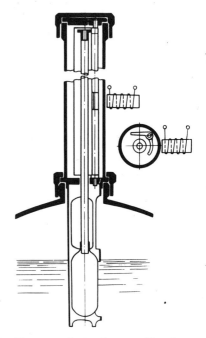

FIGURE 7.—Float-type device for recording lox consumption rate.

on the smoked tape. After the test was completed, the tape with the marks on it was treated with a shellac and alcohol solution to fix the recordings so they could later be read.

The R-03 and R-06 Rockets

In August 1935, I began working as deputy director at the recently organized Design Bureau No. 7 (KB-7) dealing with liquid-propellant rockets; L.K. Korneyev had been appointed its director. E.P. Sheptitskiy who had headed up a design subdivision, P.I. Ivanov (director of the aerodynamic group), the highly skilled mechanics M.G. Vorob'yev and A.S. Rayetskiy, plus a number of other specialists, transferred to the KB-7.

The first task of KB-7 (apart from organization of the design and production sections) was to set up a station for testing rocket units and rockets, taking into consideration the latest achievements in measuring techniques in allied fields.

The test station (Figure 8) was comprised of the following: a reinforced concrete tower for static firing tests, compartments for tanks with propellants, air pressure cylinders, a compressor and other equipment, a control room, a rocket assembly room, electrotechnical and ceramics laboratories (to be set up later), and some utility rooms. It was designed by the Kuibyshev Military Engineering Academy and its construction was completed in six months.

In addition to visual measurement of rocket parameters by means of instruments, photographs were taken and data were recorded by means of an oscillograph. A number of instruments were designed by KB-7 in collaboration with scientific research institutes. Four examples are given below:

1. A dynamometer with a capacitance pickup for thrust measurement was designed at KB-7 jointly with the Moscow N.E. Bauman Higher Technical School.

2. KB-7 developed and constructed capacitance pressure pickups (Figure 9) and dynamometers (Figure 10) to measure a change in the weight of the oxygen tanks during the test procedure.

3. Assisted by the All-Union Power Engineering Institute, KB-7 developed and constructed a "rotameter" (Figure 11) for remote measurement of fuel consumption. As a float moved it moved a plunger of Armco iron fixed to the float. The plunger was

located in a tube closed from the bottom, the tube being an extension of the rotameter casing. The tube was placed in three successively mounted tripe-phase coils. As the float moved, the plunger caused a phase shift that was indicated by the instrument mounted on the control panel and recorded by means of an oscillograph.

4. For direct observation of the engine's operation a special PER-1 periscope was designed, manufactured, and assembled on the test stand of the KB-7 by the Leningrad Optical Institute in 1938. Three people could simultaneously make observations from the control room. Magnification was up to ± 2.5. The periscope was provided with a scale for determining the size of the flame, and with a device for the measurement of angles. The plan of the test stand is shown in Figure 12 and the control and instrumentation panel in Figure 13.

The test station was furnished with equipment and instruments at such a rapid pace that we could start carrying out tests on the stand in the second half of 1936. Before KB-7 was set up, L.K. Korneyev was engaged in development of the R-03 rocket and I worked on a rocket which later came to be known as the R-06 rocket.

The attempt in spring 1936 to launch the R-06 rocket, which had passed tests in Osoaviakhim, showed normal operation of the power plant and satisfactory interaction of all rocket parts. At the same time the mechanism used for separation of the rocket from the hand device employed to open fuel values was unreliable when the speed of the rocket movement in the launch device was great.

The first task of KB-7 was to perform adjustment operations on R-03 and R-06 rockets for flight test. Direct-action (Figure 14) and breakdown (Figure 15) explosive valves served to ensure reliable conditions for the launching of rockets. Using breakdown explosive valves precluded the possibility of high-temperature gases penetrating the pipeline filled with a highly explosive mixture. A current of 0.08 ampere was sufficient to ignite the squib. Before the rocket was launched the squib had to be checked by way of remote control.

The engine was started in two stages: first the engine operated with low propellant consumption and then, after a certain period of time, it changed over to the main power rating. For pressurization of the fuel system, diaphragms calibrated for a preset bursting pressure were used.

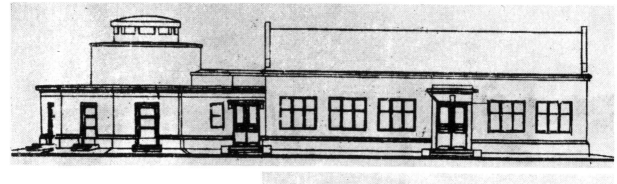

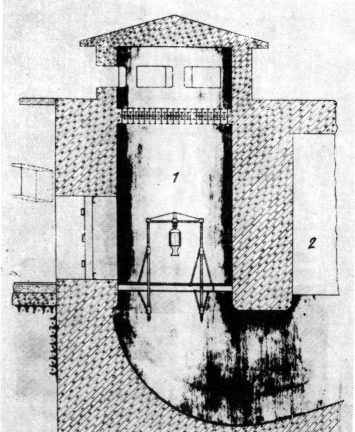

FIGURE 8.—General view of KB-7 test station (top) and section of firing bay: 1, firing bay; 2, shaft for escape of spent gases.

For remote observation of pressure change in the propellant tanks during starting, and for automatic switching of separate rocket elements, miniature pressure gauges (Figure 16) of the contact and rheostat type, which at the same time functioned as time relays, were used. These instruments and also the squibs for explosive valves were manu-factured in the electrotechnical laboratory of KB-7 (Ye. M. Kurilov).

Utilization of the system of explosive valves, calibrated bursting diaphragms, pressure and time relays, switched into a united electric system, made launching of the rocket fully automatic.

A mobile field shop on a truck and a mobile

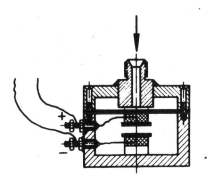

FIGURE 9.—Indicating sensor for remote pickup of pressure.

control panel on a trailer were organized on the launching range for preparation of rockets for starting and for effecting launching.

After these measures had been undertaken, within a short time drawings for manufacturing R-03 and R-06 rockets were issued, the models underwent wind-tunnel tests in the Central Institute of Aerohydrodynamics (TSAGI), a series of the rockets were manufactured, and required tests were carried out on the test stand. A general view of the final version of the R-03 rocket, and of the M-3 engine for this rocket, is given in Figure 17. The main characteristics of the rocket were: diameter, 200 mm; length, 2600 mm; launching weight, 34 kg; fuel weight, 12.5 kg; thrust, 120 kg; time of engine operation, 21 sec; flight range, 8500 m.

Those of the R-06 rocket did not differ much from the parameters established in Osoaviakhim. Changes made in the design of this R-06 rocket, when a series was manufactured, were limited to replacement of starting equipment and introduction of two-step starting of the engine, instead of a prolonged one-step starting.

From early 1937 to February 1938, ten R-03 rockets and nine R-06 rockets were launched (see Figure 18) at different angles to the horizon. In-flight stability of the rocket depended greatly on the speed and direction of the wind. Maximum inclined flight range reached by the R-03 was about 6 km, by the R-06, about 5 km.

Work on Improving the Rocket Design

Beginning in 1936, together with work on the R-03 and R-06 rockets at KB-7, research and development was undertaken on (1) engines and fuel, and (2) providing in-flight stability for rockets.

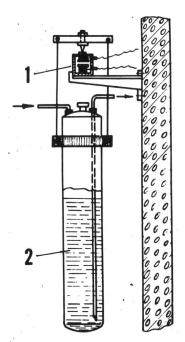

FIGURE 10.—Tank suspension on dynamometer (pressure pickup) for remote determination of lox weight in tank during engine testing: 1, load cell; 2, tank containing lox.

ENGINES AND FUEL

Study of different ignition systems for combustible mixtures proved that the most reliable system was to use a multispark plug mounted on a pipe through which hydrogen was supplied to the chamber during launching. This device was inserted into the chamber from the side of the nozzle.

Experiments on finding thermal-protective coatings for nozzle and chamber were carried out in cooperation with the Kharkov Refractory Insti-

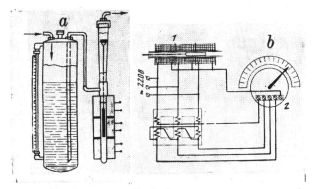

FIGURE 11.—Rotameter circuit for remote measurement of fuel flow rate, showing (right) connection of unit for telemetry transmission of rotameter readings: 1, pickup; 2, selsyn.

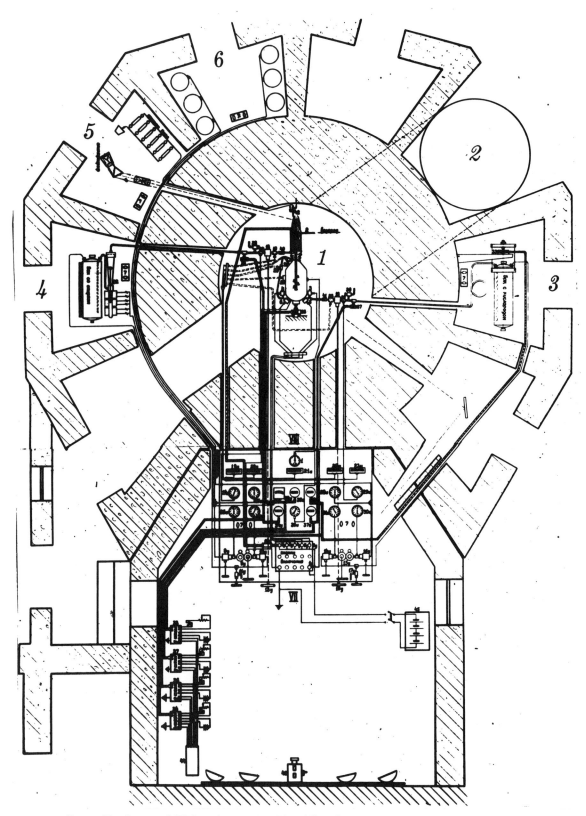

FIGURE 12.—Layout of KB-7 engine test stand in 1937, prior to installation of periscope: 1, firing bay; 2 shaft for escape of spent gases; 3, lox bay; 4, alcohol bay; 5, bay for spectrographic measurement; 6, bay for compressed nitrogen and air.

FIGURE 13.—Control and instrument panel for visual measurement and making motion picture records at KB-7 test stand.

tute. In 1937 a ceramic laboratory (chief of the laboratory was M.Yu. Gollender) was organized. A ceramic developed for the nozzle was manufactured of chemically purified electrically molten magnesium oxide with prolonged calcination carried out according to a special program. During operation of the engine for 60–90 sec the throat diameter of these nozzles increased by 0.5–1.5 mm.

Together with utilization of ceramics in the engine all-metal cooled structures of the engine were partly developed, the nozzle mainly was manufactured with a multiple thread from the side of the cooling liquid (see, for example, Figure 26).

An experimental engine was designed, built, and

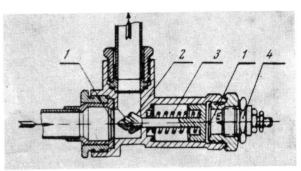

FIGURE 15.—Breakdown explosive valve: 1, diaphragm; 2, punch; 3, spring; 4, explosive valve.

tested in which the casing of the nozzle was made of welded coils of square tubing. All-metal engines with smooth wall surface from the side of cooling liquid (F. L. Yakaytis) were designed.

To obtain more accurately the characteristics of the combustion products of different types of fuels, a method of calculation of I-S diagrams for combustion products of fuels, taking into consideration the latest data on dissociation, was worked out for KB-7 by the Institute of Chemical Physics (Ya.B. Zeldovich and D.A. Frank-Kamenetskiy). Investigations of complete fuel combustion in the engine by the method of chemical analysis, carried out at KB-7 in cooperation with the Institute, showed that with accepted volumes of combustion chambers, completeness of combustion at first increased (this may be related to the influence of the walls) and then became constant and maintained a comparatively high level. The test results proved the balanced exhausting of the combustion products of alcohol with oxygen.

Research into special problems involved in mixture formation and combustion in a rocket engine required a more profound knowledge of changes developing in the composition of combustion products and temperature in different sections of the

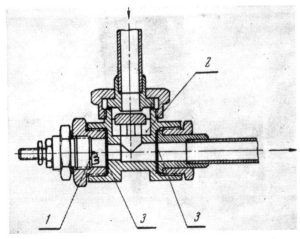

FIGURE 14.—Direct-action explosive valve: 1, electric primer; 2, non-return valve; and 3, diaphragms.

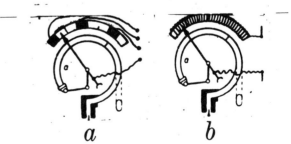

FIGURE 16.—On-board remote-reading manometers: a, Contact-type; b, Rheostat-type.

194

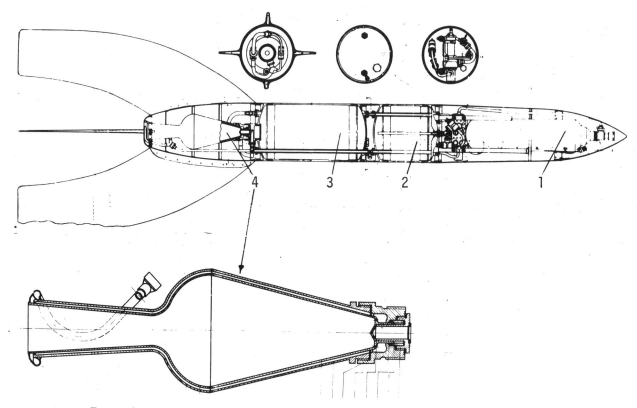

FIGURE 17.—R-03 lox and ethyl-alcohol rocket: 1, air pressure tank; 2, fuel tank; 3, oxidizer tank; 4, M-3 engine.

chamber. For this purpose, at the behest of KB-7, the Ukrainian Physicotechnical Institute (UFTI) worked out a method of determining the temperature and composition of combustion products in different sections of the combustion chamber with the help of spectral analysis. The problem was assumed to be solved by measuring the strength of the free radical spectral line C–C, C–H, CH–O, O–H and also CO_2, H_2O, CO and different nitrogen oxides in the spectrum range from 2811 Angstroms (A) for free hydroxyl to 147,800 A for CO_2. Temperature was hypothetically determined by the 3064-A band, belonging to free hydroxyl, the force factors of which were known precisely.

After preliminary spectrographic investigations of combustion products in the engine with quartz windows were carried out at KB-7, spectrographs were ordered from the Leningrad Optical Institute: a quartz spectrograph capable of photographing the spectrum from 2100 A to 7000 A, with dispersion in the range of 3000 A not more than 5 A/mm; and a spectrograph for the infrared section of the spectrum, with fluorite optics.

At the request of KB-7, UFTI investigated the possibility of obtaining fuel with concentrated hydrogen through saturating the fuel with hydrogen in liquid state at ultra-high pressures (from 5000 atm and up), with further freezing and cooling of fuel to low temperatures. It was assumed that a subsequent reduction in pressure at low fuel temperature would not greatly influence the separation of hydrogen from the fuel.

During this period more than 25 different types of engines, many of which underwent tests that gave positive results, were designed for the above-mentioned investigations and for various types of rockets.

IN-FLIGHT STABILITY

A version of an R-04 spinning liquid-propellant rocket (Figure 19) was investigated. Diameter of the rocket was 160 mm; length, 1100 mm; thrust, 45 kg. Pressurization of supply system components was with oxygen vapor.

Before launching, the rocket was spun up to

FIGURE 18.—R-06 rocket in flight.

2000 rpm by rotating the launching device. Four grains mounted in the nose cone of the rocket made it possible to spin the rocket additionally in flight. The rocket was manufactured and underwent stand tests.

Investigations to ensure in-flight stability of the rocket with the help of a gyroscope rigidly bound to the rocket body (suggestion of P.I. Ivanov) were carried out in consultation with Academician A.N. Krylov. The R-06 rocket, in which a gyroscope was mounted, was used for this purpose. Correspondingly, stabilizers were modified appropriately. The code name of this rocket (Figure 20) was ANIR-5.

Before launching, the gyroscope was rotated up to 19,000 rpm. In seven minutes the speed of rotation had decreased to 4500 rpm. The length of the

launching device was equal to the length of the rocket. To check vertical in-flight stability, six rockets were manufactured. Later flight tests of the ANIR-5 rocket showed that under proper conditions utilization of a gyroscope rigidly bound to the rocket body could provide satisfactory in-flight stability of the rocket. However, calculations showed that this method of ensuring stability of the rocket, when the size of the rocket was increased, became less profitable than ensuring stability with the help of a gyroscope linked to aerodynamic control surfaces. Experiments in this direction were made under the ANIR-5 project. Calculations were made and drawings of a model were prepared for wind-tunnel tests in TSAGI.

The AR-07 solid-propellant rocket with different

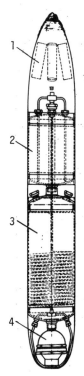

FIGURE 19.—R-04 liquid-propellant spinning rocket: 1, powder charges for additional spinning of rocket during flight; 2, fuel tank; 3, oxidizer tank; 4, engine.

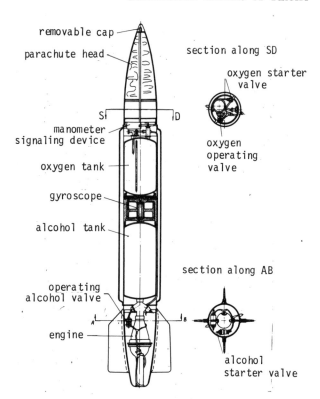

FIGURE 20.—ANIR-5 rocket (with gyroscope rigidly connected to rocket frame).

empennage was designed and developed to provide in-flight stability by imparting high speeds to the rocket on escape from the launching frame. At the same time various techniques of parachute opening were tested. Six vertical launchings of the R-07 rocket were effected. These showed that, with adequate selection of the empennage, when the rocket left the launching frame at a speed not less than 40–50 m/sec it was possible to ensure satisfactory in-flight stability of the rocket.

The following methods of parachute opening were tested at the same time on the R-07m rocket: 1, By firing a Bickford fuse with an incandescent filament at launching (opening mechanism activated after a fixed time lapse); 2, by firing Bickford fuse from a firing pin with a blasting cap when the rocket was boosted during launching (parachute opened after a fired time lapse); and 3, by means of a gyroscope which closed the fuse igniter contact when the rocket deflected 50° from the vertical (the opening depended on the position of the rocket). The last method proved to be the most reliable for opening the parachute after the rocket reached the maximum altitude.

A rocket with a combine engine (suggested by V.S. Zuyev) was one of the variants of a liquid-propellant-engine rocket having increased speeds on emergence from the launching device. The M-17 engine (Figure 21) was designed in KB-7 and developed on the test stand. First a powder grain burned out in the engine. At the same time plugs covering the outlet of the atomizers burned out. On completion of the powder-grain burning, when the supply pressure of liquid propellants exceeded the pressure in the chamber, the engine changed from solid-propellant to liquid-propellant operation. The wooden grid which earlier supported the powder grain burned out during the liquid-propellant phase.

One project to ensure in-flight stability of the rocket involved monitoring the rocket by means of a projected infrared beam. Stability was effected by means of a photoelectric device (as a sensor) mounted on the rocket and an actuating mechanism consisted of four microthrusters creating the required thrust in response to operation of the photoelectric device (named ENIR-7).

Under an assignment from DB-7, UFTI (R.N.

Lubricant

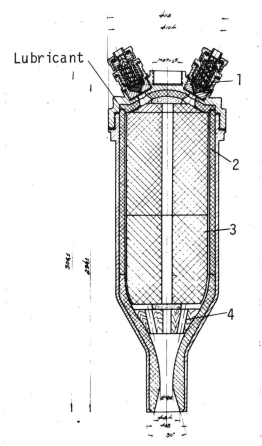

FIGURE 21.—Combined (solid- liquid-propellant) M-17 engine: 1, oxidizer and fuel nozzles; 2, ceramic lining; 3, solid-propellant charge; 4, wooden diaphragm.

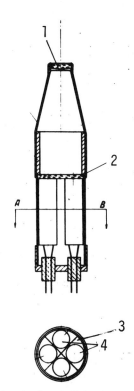

FIGURE 22.—Directional relay: 1, lines; 2, matte glass; 3, cross of thin sheet brass; 4, photocells at section A–B.

Garber) developed a photoelectric device reacting to the rocket's position vis-à-vis the projector beam direction and preventing the rocket's deflection. Also included were an amplifier, a spark discharger, and a current source.

The experimental direction relay, shown in Figure 22, had a diameter of 18 mm and a length of 60 mm. The lens (1) of the direction relay focused light on a frosted glass, (2), lying over a crosspiece of thin sheet brass, in each of the four quadrants of which a photoelement (4) was located. If the direction of the light beam coincided with the direction of the relay axis, the focal point of the beam coincided with the point intersection of the crosspiece blades, and the same amount of light would fall on all four photo-elements. When the direction-relay axis deviated from the direction of the light beam, the focus would shift to one of the photo-elements and actuate the mechanism.

The device limiting escape from the infrared beam consisted of four photo-cells located at the ends of the stabilizers. Photo-resistances (thallofide cells) were used as photo-elements. The inner resistance of these was 10 megohms in the darkness and with illumination 2 lux the resistance decreased to 5 megohms. A one-stage amplifier was used for photo current amplification. Each of four units of control had its own independent anode circuit, to which a spark gap was connected.

The spark gap and the combustion chamber of the microengine are shown in Figure 23. The combustion chamber was made of material with low magnetic permeability. Gaseous oxygen and hydrogen were used as propellants. This mixture was readily inflammable from a spark in a wide range of mixture ratio.

Propellants were supplied to the combustion through tubes (2 and 3). Combustion products emerged through channel (1) of the gas exhaust. The combustion chamber had two molybdenum electrodes (5) and (6) which were soldered in the plug made of molybdenum glass. A sleeve nut (10) connected the plug (4) with the combustion chamber. A spring (7) provided with an armature of soft

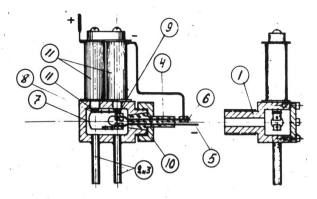

FIGURE 23.—Mockup of combustion chamber in micromotor with spark gap.

iron (8) and platinum contact (9) was fixed to electrode (5). The second platinum contact was fixed to the electrode (6). The iron tips of an electromagnet (11) were inserted into the plug case from the side. This electromagnet was connected to the anode circuit in series with the contact (9) and was shunted with a 2-mfd electrolytic condenser. When an electric impulse activated the electric fuel inlet valves, the electromagnet attracted the core, opening the contact, and simultaneously a spark ignited the fuel mixture. By means of this circuit (without transformer, inductor, etc.) the ignition of fuel was assured. The lamps were fed from the 160-v, 5-ma anode battery.

R-05 Rocket with Altitude of 50 km

Without waiting for the results of all the above-mentioned research and development, a stratospheric variant of a rocket with 50-km altitude was designed for the Geophysical Institute of the Academy of Sciences of the USSR. Its director, Academician O. Yu. Shmidt, showed keen interest in the

R-05 rocket. With direct participation on his part, such questions were discussed as the rocket's parameters, the instruments installed on board and their characteristics, the pattern of performing the tasks in developing the item, and so on. In this R-05 rocket (Figure 24), reduction in design weight was achieved by delivering the fuel components (alcohol and liquid oxygen) with the aid of a solid-reactant gas generator.

In the first launches, the rocket's in-flight stability was hypothetically assured by increasing its initial emergence velocity from the ramp to 40–50 m/sec by the additional operation, during takeoff, of two solid-propellant launching engines which separated from the rocket after completion of their work. Its characteristics were: diameter, 200 mm; length, 2250 mm; initial weight without boosters, 55 kg; payload (with parachute), 4 kg; weight of propellants (alcohol and lox), 30 kg; thrust, 175 kg; time of operation, 37 sec; full impulse of the two launching boosters, 1250 kg/sec.

Equipment mounted on the rocket included the FTI-5 unit, the DTU-1 aggregate, and other instruments. The FTI-5 was a miniature camera for automatically photographing the earth's surface during descent at specific time intervals. It had been designed and manufactured by the Leningrad Optical Institute on the order of KB-7.

The DTU-1 was a complex instrument assembly consisting of two barometers (registering from 769-15 and 15-0.5 mm/hg, respectively), a noninertial thermometer, and accelerometer, a pressure gauge for measuring pressure in the engine, a coding and distributing device, a timepiece, an electrical supply, and a miniature radio-transmitter. Readings of the measuring instruments were coded with the help of special mechanisms for periodic transmission

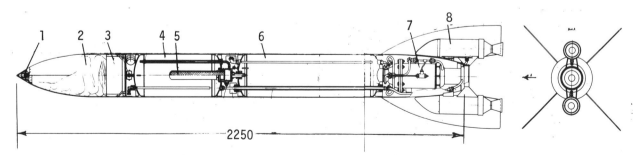

FIGURE 24.—R-05 rocket, designed to reach altitudes of 50 km: 1, device for opening the parachute; 2, parachute; 3, instruments; 4, fuel tank; 5, PAD; 6, oxidizer tank; 7, engine; 8, powder launching rocket engines (can be jettisoned).

of radio signals to the earth. Weight of the instrument assembly was 1.5 kg.

To receive signals from DTU-1, a receiving-decoding unit was used which consisted of a radio-receiver, a "shorinophon" and a decoding unit. The shorinophon recorded sound signals from the DTU-1 on a tape. This instrument, which weighed 1.5 kg, was developed on the order of KB-7 in the Main Geophysical Observatory of the Hydrometeorological Service (Professor P.A. Molchanow). A photo range-finder, for determining the flight path and defining the impact place of the rocket (in night flights with utilization of powder, leaving a trace when burning) was worked out in KB-7 with participation of the P. K. Shternberg Astronomical Institute.

The photo range-finder consisted of four blocks of cameras, located at points marked by geodesic layout. The flight trajectory was defined by recording the luminous trail of burning grains mounted on the rocket, on photographic plates which were later developed.

The M-29e rocket engine (Figure 25) was developed for the R-05 rocket. It operated at rated parameters not less than 50 sec. The solid-propellant hot-gas generator (PAD) with an operation time of 40–42 sec was developed by A.B. Ionov. Extensive tests of the engine with the PAD, and with tanks, the design of which was the same as for those of the rocket, but smaller, were carried out in 1939. They showed that the characteristics of the engine in the main rating (thrust, pressure in the

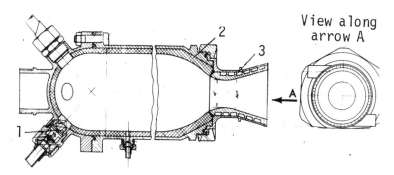

FIGURE 25.—M-29e engine for R-05 rocket: 1, injector; 2, lining; 3, nozzle which is being cooled.

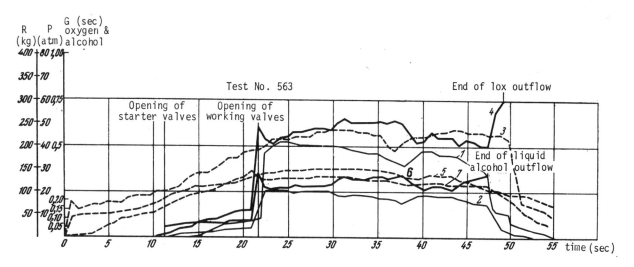

FIGURE 26.—Graph reflecting variation in parameters of R-05 rocket with PAD during complex stand tests: 1, thrust; 2, chamber pressure; 3, pressure in powder cell; 4, per-second use of lox; 5, pressure in oxygen tank; 6, per-second use of alcohol; 7, alcohol tank pressure; 8, powder launching-rocket engine (can be jettisoned).

PAD, tanks and chamber, and also propellant consumption per second) were close to design characteristics (Figure 26).

A variant of the R-05 rocket (the R-05g) was also designed in KB-7 for flight at an angle to the horizon.

R-10 Rocket with Altitude of 100 km

To increase further the rocket altitude (as there was no possibility of constructing large-scale rockets in KB-7) the R-10 composite rocket with an initial weight of 100 kg, was designed in 1938–39 to attain an altitude of 100 km. This rocket was powered by liquid-propellant first and the second stages, with two coupled solid-propellant boosters. Figure 27 shows the R-10 rocket without boosters.

To reduce the weight of the rocket structure of the first and second stage, liquid propellants were supplied with the help of the PAD.

To choose the method of ensuring in-flight stability for the R-10 rocket, it was necessary to obtain data on: launching of the R-05 rocket with solid propellant boosters, tests of automatic gyro control linked with aerodynamic stabilizers (ANIR-6), and tests of rocket monitoring by the projected infrared beam, with utilization of a photoelectric device (ANIR-7).

Characteristics of the R-10 rocket first stage were: diameter, 320 mm; total weight, 88 kg; weight of propellants (alcohol with oxygen), 45 kg; thrust, 160 kg; speed at end of operation of boosters (together with liquid propellant engine), 250 m/sec; time of operation of liquid propellant engine, 60 sec; speed of rocket at end of operation of the first stage, 560 m/sec; altitude of the rocket at separation of first and second stages, 21.2 km.

Characteristics of the R-10 rocket second stage were: diameter, 126 mm; total weight, 12 kg; weight of liquid propellants (alcohol and liquid oxygen), 4.2 kg; weight of powder grain in combined engine, 1.3 kg; payload, 0.5 kg; firing time of powder grain, 2.58 sec; thrust of the engine when operating on liquid propellants, 35 kg; firing time on liquid propellants, 24 sec; burnout velocity of the rocket, 1113 m/sec; burnout altitude of the rocket, 39.6 km. This rocket was launched with the objectives of (1) attaining a maximum altitude at comparatively low expense; (2) discovering the most effective method of ensuring in-flight stability of the rocket at altitudes up to 100 km; and (3) separating the rocket first and second stages and recovering the rocket from high altitudes by parachute.

Conclusion

The aforementioned facts show that after a series of launching of the R-05 and R-10 rockets we could start designing large-scale rockets with flight ranges greater than those mentioned above, and with a large payload.

REFERENCES

Under the title *O nekotorykh rabotakh po raketnoy tekhnike v SSSR v period 1931–1938*, this paper appeared on pages 122–44 of *Iz istorii astronavtiki i raketnoi tekhniki: Materialy XVIII mezhdunarodnogo astronavticheskogo kongressa, Belgrad, 25–29 Sentyavrya 1967* [From the History of Rockets and Astronautics: Materials of the 18th International Astronautical Congress, Belgrade, 25–29 September 1967], Moscow: Nauka, 1970.

The following sources, all in the Archives of the USSR Academy of Sciences, were listed at the end of this paper there (p. 144).

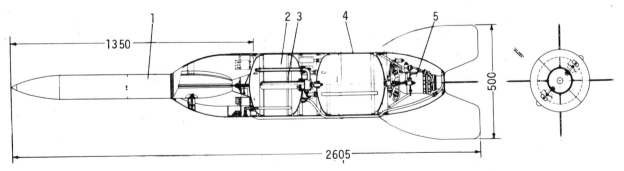

FIGURE 27.—R-10 composite rocket designed to reach 100-km altitude: 1, second rocket stage; 2, fuel tank; 3, PAD (high-pressure storage vessel); 4, oxidizer tank; 5, rocket engine. (2–5 are first-stage units).

1. Register of experiments on OR-2 motor, 1932–34 (razr. 4, op. 14, d. 2).

2. Correspondence and calculations about the KPD-1 rocket, 1934 (razr. 4, op. 14, d. 52).

3. Rocket according to L. K. Korneyev system. Calculations and correspondence, photographs, 1935 (razr. 4, op. 14, d. 55).

4. Testing of individual components of R-06, 1936 (razr. 4, op. 14, d. 58).

5. Register of experiments on R-03 (of separate components and parts). Register of the summer experiments. General view of R-03, 1937 (razr. 4, op. 14, d. 59).

6. Designs of R-07 Rocket, 1937 (razr. 4, op. 14, d. 60).

7. Reports and data of summer experiments on R-06 and R-03 in Leningrad and Pavlograd, 1937–38 (razr. 4, op. 14, d. 61).

8. Designs of R-05 rocket, 1938 (razr. 4, op. 14, d. 62).

9. Designs of R-05 rocket, 1938 (razr. 4, op. 14, d. 63).

10. Designs of R-05 rocket, 1938–39 (razr. 4, op. 14, d. 64).

11. Register of summer experiments of ANIR-5 rocket, 1938–39 (razr. 4, op. 14, d. 65).

12. Design of composite R-10 rocket, 1938–39 (razr. 4, op. 14, d. 66).

13. Design of R-05 rocket, 1939 (razr. 4, op. 14, d. 67).

14. Technical conditions for R-05 rocket (item 602), 1939 (razr. 4, op. 14, d. 69).

15. Rocket R-04, designs, general appearance, 1937 (razr. 4, op. 14, d. 70).

16. Correspondence about apparatus at KB-7, 1939 (razr. 4, op. 14, d. 119).

17. Various correspondence about apparatus (razr. 4, op. 14, d. 120).

18. Correspondence about apparatus at KB-7, 1936–39, (razr. 4, op. 14, d. 150).

19. Technical report about work at KB-7, 1938 (razr. 4, op. 14, d. 153).

20. Designs based on experimental station KB-7 1937 (razr. 4, op. 14, d. 174).

21. Maps, plans, and timetable for KB-7, 1939 (razr. 4, op. 14, d. 176).

22. Maps, plans, and timetable for Design Office No. 7 (KB-7), 1939 (razr. 4, op. 14, d. 177).

23. List of components for KB-7, 1939 (razr. 4, op. 14, d. 178).

24. Work plan for KB-7, 1938–39 (razr. 4, op. 4, d. 179).

25. Minutes of the technical meetings of NKB, 1939 (razr. 4, op. 14, d. 180).

26. Balancing data of KB-7 (razr. 4, op. 14, d. 181).

27. Archives material (copies of newspaper articles and journal articles) about actions of TSGIRD and TSS (Osoviakhim) in the 1930s in the field of rocket technology (razr. 4, op. 14, d. 222).

28. Archival material of actions taken by stratosphere committee Aviavnito and Moscow conference, 1935 (razr. 4, op. 14, d. 235).

29. Recollections of Merkulov about the work of Osoaviakhim, 1961–62 (razr. 4, op. 14, d. 237).

30. Material on KB-7, 1937 (razr. 4, op. 14, d. 244).

31. Work plan UVI for 1935 (1934) (razr. 4, op. 14, d. 246).

32. Benzine-oxygen liquid rocket motor, GIRD and RNII, 1933–34 (razr. 4, op. 14, d. 255).

33. Motors at KB-7, 1936–39 (razr. 4, op. 14, d. 256).

34. Archives (razr. 4, op. 14, d. 262).

35. Experimental Station KB-7, 1935–38 (razr. 4, op. 14, d. 267).

36. Rocket R-06 (razr. 4, op. 14, d. 271).

37. Rocket R-03 (razr. 4, op. 14, d. 272).

38. General views of rockets (razr. 4, op. 4, d. 278).

39. Starting stand for R-06, PS (razr. 4, op. 14, d. 279).

40. Mobile launching ramp for R-06, PS (razr. 4, op. 14, d. 279).

41. Motor M-29 (razr. 4, op. 14, d. 280).

42. Recollections of the employees of the enterprise KB-7 (razr. 4, op. 14, d. 291).

43. F. A. Tsander, *Problema poleta pri pomoshchi reaktivnykh apparatov: mezhplanetnyye polety* [Problems of Flight by Jet Propulsion: Interplanetary Flights] Moscow, 1961.

19

S.P. Korolyev and the Development of Soviet Rocket Engineering to 1939

B. V. Raushenbakh and Yu. V. Biryukov, *Soviet Union*

At the turn of this century K.E. Tsiolkovskiy formulated the basic principles of exploring space by means of rockets, but these ideas were propagated and developed in the course of the next 20–30 years mainly within a theoretical context by enthusiasts who considered them realizable only in the distant future. To translate these ideas from the sphere of theory and scientific fiction into practicable reality required people who could perceive in contemporary technology those elements which might be extended to space flight.

Sergei Pavlovitch Korolyev, a pioneer rocket-builder, was a man of that caliber. He became active in rocket engineering in the early 1930s.

Tsiolkovskiy's ideas on space conquest were impressive in the grandeur of perspectives they opened up before mankind, they captured bold and talented people with the alluring opportunity of contributing to a romantic cause, they suggested the feasibility in principle of space flights, and they laid out courses to follow; but they failed to answer whether space flight itself could be achieved immediately or must be left for the future. This question confronted everyone dealing with problems of space flight. Quite a group of young fledglings in the scientific community during the early 1920s insisted on immediate space flights, but most of them failed to see the difficulties implicit in the proposal, and gave up when the task became hard. That was how the Society for the Study of Interplanetary Communication came to its end in 1924, to be followed in its fate by the Interplanetary Section of Inventors in 1927, and by other space-oriented circles and groups. The development of rocket technology required funds—indeed appreciable amounts. It was only natural that the country at that time could only afford realistic, short-term projects, but by no means projects of interplanetary flights. It was a vicious circle: the idea of a rocket flight needed support which could come about through public recognition, but on the other hand, public recognition could best be won only by a real rocket flight.

Korolyev broke the cycle, and thus asserted himself as a leading scientist. He understood that the huge problem of space exploration must be solved by stages, rockets being used first for low-altitude flights, then in the stratosphere, and only later, when sufficient experience was acquired, outside the atmosphere. Having met F.A. Tsander and seen how much the man's aspirations and aims coincided with his own, and how far his scholarship and experience of 20 years in the field exceeded his own, Korolyev was quick to direct his efforts to the realization of Tsander's projects. Studying the design of an OR-2 engine he understood it to be the missing link for his projected rocket aircraft and a realistic basis for a wide-scale assault on the realization of a rocket flight. So he proposed to start on a simple flying machine incorporating that engine.

This project he undertook on an unpaid basis, a way followed at that time by many young designers of gliders and light airplanes. It became the rallying idea for the establishment in late 1931 of the Group for Study of Jet Propulsion (GIRD), the first Soviet team to seek ways of constructing a piloted liquid-fuel jet airplane. The group was under the scientific direction of F.A. Tsander, but the work on the rocket glider was controlled by S.P. Korolyev.

The new tailless airplane (BICh-11) of B.I. Cheranovsky, built according to the same delta-wing pattern as the preceding BICh-8 glider, formed the basis of the rocket aircraft. Korolyev, who was also a pilot, had shortly before made some

203

test flights in that glider.[1] The BICh-11 airplane was turned over to GIRD in February 1932, but the OR-2 engine could not be developed within so short a term. Both funds and skilled workers were lacking, and the seemingly simple task of creating a liquid-fuel jet engine and installing it in the glider, grew, in the process, into an aggregation of most complicated scientific and research problems. Wanted were new people not merely interested in space flights but capable of contributing to the practical development of rocket engineering.

That was how practical activities revealed the deficiency of personnel and special knowledge. The orientation of technical training also had to be changed in favor of the practical aspects of rocket engineering and its importance for the country's progress, rather than theoretical ideas, the feasibility of space flights, etc. The personnel training problem was especially acute. Korolyev had been an experienced exponent of practical knowledge in aviation and technology ever since his school days and in this respect, therefore, also took a leading role in GIRD.

He was quick to understand that both aviation and especially rocketry require the effort of large teams of subject specialists, and had therefore attached a very great importance to personnel training and selection. The result was that GIRD offered the world's first courses on jet motion and the whole character of training was revised. This change was described in Korolyev's letter of 31 July 1932 to an advocate of cosmonautics, writer Ya.I. Perel'man:

Though extremely busy with experimentation, we are very much concerned about the development of our mass work . . . . No time is to be lost. The immense local initiative is to be received and digested in such a manner as to create a positive public opinion around the problem of reactive motion, stratospheric flights and (in the future) interplanetary travels. The need to develop a body of literature is also very urgent, for it is practically absent, except for two or three books, and these are not generally available.

We think the time is right for publishing a series (10–15 items) of semitechnical booklets on jet motion, each one clarifying a single problem, such as "What is jet motion?" "Fuel for jet motion," "Applications of jet motion," etc. These may later be replaced by more specialized literature. . . .[2]

In this context Korolyev paid much attention to the training department of GIRD. He delivered lectures, wrote papers, advocated a new journal *Sovetskaya Raketa* (Soviet Rocket), and finally,

wrote the book "Rocket Flight in the Stratosphere."[3] This, although meant to popularize science, proved to be an important contribution to the rocket engineering of that time. Tsiolkovskiy found it to be a "clever, informative and useful book."[4]

Attaching high value to "group work," Korolyev was no less active in the personal selection of specialists, thus turning GIRD into a strong, viable team of engineers, designers, and mechanics, who had come from the aircraft industry, many of them Korolyev's long-time colleagues. To GIRD, and then to the whole Soviet rocket industry, it brought high technological standards.

Korolyev's part was highly esteemed from the very beginning. Thus, the secretary of GIRD wrote to Tsiolkovskiy:

Our experimental work on the GIRD-RP-1 rocket aircraft, is nearing its completion . . . . Many highly qualified engineers work with us, and best of them all is the chairman of our Technical Council S. P. Korolyev. He has already done more than a lot for all of us. He is also going to pilot the first rocket aircraft.[5]

The emphasis, in the technical training, on immediate practical targets of rocket technology and on the solution of urgent problems of the philosophy and technology of flights brought recognition to GIRD, and this was further enhanced by the weighty argument it had advanced in the form of a virtually completed (as it seemed at the time) RP-1 rocket aircraft. As a result, considerable support for GIRD had been developed, and the Central Council of Osoaviakhim, a voluntary society responsible, among other things, for aviation and technical sports and for supporting the construction of gliders and sports aeroplanes, in April 1932 decided to organize an industrial support facility to be known as the GIRD experimental plant. S.P. Korolyev became Director of both the plant and the whole GIRD. Thus a center was created, quite large for the time, possessing impressive design, research, and production facilities. Korolyev's organizing talent played a decisive role in the whole affair.

Speaking on the emphasis of GIRD's promotional and production activities on immediate practical goals, one question is to be answered: what was, at that time, Korolyev's actual attitude towards interplanetary flights? From official documents and his own papers it appears that Korolyev tried in those years to attract general attention to practical, down-to-earth use of rockets, insisting that "this very thing must command the attention of all those interested in the field, rather than as yet unsubstantiated fancies about lunar flights and record speeds of non-existing airplanes." [6]

This quotation seems to conflict with the aura of a great enthusiast and champion of cosmonautics that history has given him. When properly interpreted, however, the statement only reflects the complexity of conditions under which the pioneers in cosmonautics started their work. Alert to the fact that fancy talk of space flights at that stage would only compromise rocketry in the eyes of those lacking foresight, Korolyev chose not to discuss problems of cosmonautics but to put all his efforts to developing it in practice. His attitude towards the problem is explicitly stated in his letter of 18 April 1936 to Perel'man:

I would only like that you, an expert in rocket engineering and an author of excellent books, pay more attention not to interplanetary problems but to the rocket engine itself, to the stratospheric rocket, etc., since all this is closer, clearer, and more urgent for us now. . . .

I would very much like to see your excellent books among those which champion the cause of rocket-building and which teach and struggle for its flowering. Should it be so, the time will come for the first terrestrial ship to leave the Earth. We probably will not live to see it, and are destined to spend out life pottering about here below, yet successes are also attainable on this earth.[7]

Nevertheless, Korolyev did all he could to bring that time closer. He was a real champion of the cause. Workers at GIRD testify that he was as enthusiastic as Tsander about the concept of interplanetary flights. A lunar flight was his cherished dream. The work program of GIRD provides a most convincing evidence of his devotion to this idea. It had three goals: first and most immediate—practical proof of the feasibility of jet flight and its expediency; second and basic—extensive research for optimal solutions and for a substantial practical output in terms of new flying machine; third and long range—primary attention to those research problems which would clearly contribute to making space flight practical. These research problems included use of liquid oxygen as the most promising rocket fuel; the technological, medical, and biological factors associated with manned flight; and, finally, the use of metal fuel and development of an air-breathing jet engine for acceleration in the atmosphere.

The purposeful efforts of GIRD's Director S.P. Korolyev, its brigade leaders F.A. Tsander, M.K. Tikhonravov, Y.A. Pobedonostsev, and the whole staff put the "GIRD plant" to work. Prototypes of engines, rockets, experimental installation were turned out in metal, field and flight tested, and improved. Although work on the RP-1 rocket aircraft was slowed down and then stalemated because of difficulties connected mostly with the OR-2 engine (designed as a liquid-fuel jet engine with sophisticated controls) this did not affect the other activities of GIRD, for the RP-1 was by that time only one point of the challenging program, which was otherwise successfully fulfilled. The first Soviet liquid-fuel rocket, GIRD-09, was successfully launched on 17 August 1933, followed by the liquid-fuel rocket GIRD-10 on 23 November of the same year.

The Jet Propulsion Research Institute (RNII), established in 1934 as the world's first state-owned research facility for rocketry, was a product of the government's support of promising branches of science and technology, of the country's industrial progress, and of the combined efforts of GIRD and the former Gas Dynamics Laboratory (GDL), of Leningrad, both of which became the nucleus of the Institute. In the Institute, fairly large for that time, S.P. Korolyev concentrated exclusively on tasks of fundamental and applied nature, heading research on rocket planes.

Following the experience of GIRD, Korolyev, in his initial period in the Institute, saw a reliable engine as the immediate goal. In his book he wrote:

Each researcher, each worker in this field must concentrate on the motor. Other problems, complicated as they might be, will undoubtedly find solution in the course of work on models of flying objects and the objects themselves (which certainly will fly, provided there is a reliable engine).[8]

Korolyev himself did not become a designer of rocket engines, however, and still continued research on rocket-propelled vehicles, concentrating on complex problems. Such an attitude is explained by the fact that by 1936–37 the RNII had developed rocket engines meeting existing requirements, among them the ORM-65 nitric-acid liquid-fuel jet engine with a thrust of 150 kg, and the 12/K oxygen liquid-fuel jet engine with thrust of 300 kg and adequate operational time. The engine problem was therefore less acute. Korolyev told his colleagues that problems of flight dynamics and stability were becoming imperative. Main efforts therefore had to be directed towards the development of experimental rocket-propelled craft with stabilization and control systems on different principles. Engines could be further improved on test benches, whereas problems of flight dynamics could only be solved by way of flight tests. In Korolyev's opinion, the flight of piloted rocket craft continued to be the main prospective task. At the 1934 All-Union conference on atmosphere studies, under sponsorship of the Academy of Sciences of the USSR, he read a paper devoted to manned rocket flight problems.[9]

In March 1935 the RNII and the Aviation Department of the All-Union Engineering Society on Korolyev's initiative convened the All-Union Conference on the Use of Jet-Propelled Aircraft in the Exploration of the Stratosphere. There Korolyev delivered a detailed report entitled "Winged Rocket for Manned Flight," in which he summarized the results of his investigations and for the first time described unique features and possible designs of the rocket plane, its calculated weight analysis, and its flight characteristics. The report proposed the development of a rocket-plane laboratory for purely experimental flights at low altitudes. It would thus be "possible to make a systematic study of the operation of rocket elements in flight. When secured at a required altitude, it might be used for experiments with an air-breathing jet engine and a whole series of other experiments." [10]

Korolyev's preference for rocket gliders rather than ballistic missiles originated not by virtue of his profession as an aircraft designer but by the limitations of the engine industry in those years. The characteristics of the already existing liquid-fuel jet engines and those under design (thrusts of the order of 100–300 kg and specific thrusts of about 210–230 sec—rather modest from today's point of view), were useful only in comparatively small wingless rockets for experimentation purposes (such rockets were actually built, including those for the stratosphere studies). Thus, winged rockets were the only possibility to airlift weighty objects, including man. The development and flight tests of such rockets were well within the frame of Korolyev's idea of the time-spaced development of rocketry. In the process of developing piloted winged rockets, various problems were to be solved involving superlight structures; sophisticated, safe, and reliable engines (including fuel tanks and feed systems); cabin sealing; the aerodynamics of high (supersonic) speeds; and the flight dynamics and other problems also of importance for carrier missiles and space ships.

Korolyev understood that unmanned rocket craft are good enough for solving certain technical problems, and he therefore organized in the RNII tests of numerous small-size winged rockets. The first such rocket started on 5 May 1934.

The 212 rocket with the previously mentioned ORM-65 engine and a gyroscopic automatic stabilizer was the best known of that type. Its estimated range was 80 km. It was started from a rocket-powered sled by a powerful accelerator. The 212 was flight tested in 1938–1939.

The most complicated problem involved in designing unmanned winged rockets had long been flight stability, and Korolyev turned for help to specialists in mechanics and mathematics. In 1936 he made a detailed progress report on winged rockets at a session at the Mechanics Research Institute of the Moscow State University, where he posed the task of investigating the motion of uncontrolled and controlled winged rockets and solving the flight stability problem. Such a study, undertaken on a contract basis by a group of young mechanics and mathematicians, was the first case of pure science put to solve causal problems of rocketry.

Korolyev not only had Moscow University undertake the solution of prospective problems in mechanics, he also employed prominent scientists for advisory service, in addition to similar work carried on in RNII itself.

He organized a special department for the development, production, and adjustment of gyroscopic control instruments; for the enormous role to be played in rocketry by automatic flight-control systems was clear to him. His people had to solve a new and, for that time, difficult problem of bringing the characteristics of these instruments into accord with dynamic properties of the rocket. It is worth mentioning that the level at which some dynamics problems connected with rocket-propelled aircraft were treated in his department was higher than in the aviation industry.

Having accumulated the necessary experience and having developed suitable engines, RNII could proceed with the rocket plane. In contrast to extensive activities on smaller unmanned rockets, all efforts on a manned flying machine with a rocket engine, which was a far more expensive and labor-consuming project, were focused on the rocket-plane laboratory. The experience obtained while working on the RP-1 rocket glider and testing unmanned rocket gliders became useful here. Korolyev came to the conclusion that the "flying-wing" scheme should not necessarily be used for a rocket-engine flight, that all attempts to adjust the existing gliders to liquid-fuel jet engines made the task unnecessarily cumbersome, and that, therefore, a normal glider specially designed for the purpose was wanted.

In his step-by-step approach to the problem, Korolyev designed, on his own initiative, the double-seated SK-9 glider, which was presented in 1935 to the All-Union Conference of Glider Builders in the Crimea. Unaware of the designer's plans, the delegates were puzzled by the glider: it seemed too sturdy, the wing surface was comparatively small, the second pilot's seat was uncomfortable. All these apparent drawbacks turned to advantage when rocket-fuel tanks replaced the second seat and the increased sturdiness allowed for speeds during a rocket flight unattainable by conventional gliders.

While in the Crimea, during prolonged aircraft-towed flights and in the course of extensive summer tests performed mostly by himself, Korolyev managed to solve all the problems he considered to be the first stage in the development of a rocket glider.

The SK-9 having passed all-around tests, the Technical Council of the RNII, on the basis of this glider and the work program for the future, discussed Korolyev's design of an experimental rocket plane. It was decided to put the rocket plane on a priority basis for 1937.[11] In that year the SK-9 was brought to the Institute, and a propeling installation with an ORM-65 rocket engine was mounted on it. The machine, designated RP-318, had to serve as an experimental laboratory for testing and elaborating ideas to be put into the design of a future high-altitude rocket plane. Firing tests of the propelling plant, mounted on the glider, started toward the end of the year. There were dozens of them.

In February 1938, in a paper written jointly with Ye.S. Shchetnikov and entitled "Research Work on a Rocket Plane," Korolyev for the first time defined the purpose of rocket aircraft, delineated optimal regions of their use, and formulated the major goals for the future. The principles of a fighter-interceptor and an experimental aircraft for studying the stratosphere and the aerodynamics of high speeds were scientifically expounded. A four-stage project for such an aircraft was proposed: 1, The initial variant, to utilize the results obtained in the RNII earlier (when starting from the earth, it was to reach an altitude of 9 km, and starting from a height of 8 km, an altitude of 25 km); 2, a modified variant, designed for a more prolonged flight; 3, a record variant; and 4, a prospective variant. The fourth rocket plane, when carried by a mother aircraft, was to reach in the rocket flight an altitude of 53 km. The project had many features common to the experimental aircraft of today.

In 1939 the SK-9 got a new rocket engine, the RDA-1-150, and on 28 February 1940 pilot V.P. Fyedorov performed the first flight in a rocket plane.

After successful flights of the RP-318, the Institute's primary attention turned to studies on the rocket plane. They also drew the attention of other research agencies, and by 1942 the first rocket fighter BI-1, a joint undertaking of the RNII and the aviation industry under the guidance of V.F. Bolkhovitinov, performed its first successful flight.

Thus it follows that S.P. Korolyev's part in starting and developing Soviet rocketry, which is the avant-garde of world rocket engineering, is very great. Great also is his contribution to the development and popularization of rocket engineering, to the education of rocketeers. He was a distinguished organizer and manager, research worker, and designer—in fact the leading specialist in the development of rocket-propelled aircraft. All these qualities predetermined his outstanding role in the development of rocketry in its decisive stage, i.e., in the 1950s and 1960s, and Sergei Pavlovitch Korolyev performed his part brilliantly. In the history of the progress of humanity, his name stands as a founder of practical cosmonautics.

NOTES

1. *Samolyet* [Aircraft], 1931, no. 11–12, p. 36.

2. Arkhiv AN SSSR [Archives, USSR Academy of Sciences], f. 796, op. 3, d. 36, l. 271.

3. S. P. Korolyev. *Raketniy polet v stratosfere.* Moscow, 1934.

4. Arkhiv AN SSSR, f. 555, op. 3, d. 152, l. 10–11 ob.

5. Arkhiv AN SSSR f. 555, op. 4, d. 652, l. 15–15 ob.

6. See note 3.

7. Arkhiv AN SSSR f. 796, op. 3, d. 36, 1. 234–235.

8. See note 3.

9. *Trudy Vsesoyusnoy Konferentsii po izucheniyu stratosfery. 31 Marta – 6 Aprelya 1934 g.* [Transactions of the All-Union Conference on Study of the Stratosphere, 31 March–6 April 1934], Leningrad, Moscow, 1935, pp. 849–55.

10. "Air Engineering," 1935, no. 7, pp. 35–56.

11. Arkhiv AN SSSR razr. 4, op. 14, d. 105, 1. 9.

12. *Vestnik vozdushnogo flota* [Herald of the Air Force], 1957, no. 9, pp. 68–73.

13. Arkhiv AN SSSR, razr. 4, op. 14, d. 103, 1. 83–95.

20

The British Interplanetary Society's Astronautical Studies, 1937-39

H. E. Ross, F.B.I.S., *United Kingdom*

The British Interplanetary Society was founded by Mr. Philip E. Cleator, a contracting engineer, in October 1933.[1] A *Journal* and a *Bulletin* were published from Liverpool, lectures were given, and articles written to stimulate interest whenever opportunities arose. Membership (though never more than about one hundred until after 1945) soon became international, attracting such well-known pioneers and personalities as Ing. Baron Guido von Pirquet (Austria), Robert Esnault-Pelterie (France), Willy Ley, Dr. Otto Steinitz, and the Count and Countess von Zeppelin (Germany), G. Edward Pendray (USA), and Dr. Yakov Perelman and Professor Nikolai Rynin (USSR). Correspondence with other astronautically-minded societies was maintained, and during 1934 Cleator visited Germany and contacted members of the then disbanded VfR.[2] In 1936 Cleator's *Rockets Through Space* awakened general interest in Britain, and paved the way to a better understanding of astronautical possibilities.[3]

By 1936, however, the numerically strong London branch of the Society dominated affairs.[4] As a result, headquarters were officially transferred to the metropolis early in 1937, and Professor A. M. Low was elected the new president.[5] A Technical Committee then began work under the direction of J. Happian Edwards.[6] Members of this committee, with their nominal assignments, were: H. Bramhill (draftsman), A. C. Clarke (astronomer), A. V. Cleaver (aircraft engineer), M. K. Hanson (mathematician), Arthur Janser (chemist), S. Klemantaski (biologist), H. E. Ross (electrical engineer), and R. A. Smith (turbine engineer). Aid was also provided from time to time by Richard Cox Abel, J. G. Strong, and C. S. Cowper-Essex. An Experimental Committee was formed a little later to develop

certain concepts.[7] Most active in this capacity were Smith, Edwards, and Cowper-Essex. A number of the members are shown in Figure 1, a photo I took in July 1938 during the visit of, then, Midshipman Robert C. Truax.

The main project undertaken by the Technical Committee was a feasibility study of a manned vehicle designed for a round trip to the Moon, projected in terms of then-existing techniques and materials, or reasonable extrapolations of them. In other words, the requirements of such a mission would be surveyed, outstanding problems exposed, and solutions attempted. The function of the Experimental Committee was to deal in a practical way with such proposed solutions as might be developed within the limit of a minute research fund which had been established.

Credit for rapid progress in overall design must be given chiefly to Edwards and Smith, who had been close friends and interested in the possibility of space travel since schooldays. In fact, the idea of cellular-step construction was Edwards' and the engineering embodiment Smith's.[8] It will be convenient to describe the vessel after recounting certain supporting work done by members of the two Committees.

Since the feasibility of space flight rests primarily with a sufficiently powerful means of propulsion, a survey of between 80 and 120 possible propellant combinations was made by Janser (an Austrian research chemist) and Edwards, working in collaboration.[9] It is interesting to note that the possibilities considered included colloids with metallic additives, and that evidence was given for the development of solid propellants competing, systemwise, with liquid combinations. A small rocket proving stand was later designed and made by Smith to conduct

FIGURE 1.—Members of the British Interplanetary Society and R. C. Truax in July 1938. From left: J. H. Edwards, Research Director, British Interplanetary Society; Eric Burgess, Founder and President, Manchester Interplanetary Society; H. E. Turner, Editor, Manchester Interplanetary Society *Journal;* Midshipman Robert C. Truax, USN, holding liquid propellant rocket motor of his design; R. A. Smith, engineer and well-known illustrator of space subjects; M. K. Hanson; and Arthur C. Clarke.

motor and propellant tests, but experimentation was arrested by lack of money and facilities. Suitable materials for spacecraft construction, including plastics, were considered and reported upon by Janser.

Though in prewar days it was known that short-wavelength radio would be a possible means of communication across space, the efficacy had not been explored. And radar as a navigational aid was then a secret military art. Because of this lack of information, the Technical Committee preferred to suggest transit navigation principally by optical observations of the planets and stars. However, navigation during main thrust periods was to be done automatically by inertial instruments—a principle since commonly used in complex guidance and control systems of rockets and spacecraft. An inertial altimeter, a speedometer, an impulse meter, and an accelerometer were listed for development, but only the altimeter was worked on.[10] This consisted in essence of a weight, a spring, and a flywheel. The idea was that when the spaceship accelerated there would be a charge in the internal "gravitation" putting the spring-weight combina-

tion out of balance by an amount proportional to the acceleration. The double integral was effected by setting the out-of-balance force to operate a flywheel, the revolutions of the flywheel then giving a reading of the altitude reached by the vessel. This was not the best kind of mechanism for the job, but the cost was small. Unfortunately, lack of engineering facilities and intervention of other activities aborted progress. Similarly, development of a high-energy lightweight primary battery, based on a magnesium reaction, intended to avoid heavy conventional batteries, had to be abandoned.[11]

In prewar days nothing certain was known about the physiological effects of zero gravity. Some people believed that derangement would be complete or persistently severe; others thought that there would be some derangement but fairly rapid acclimatization; few maintained that no ill-effects would occur. In any case, it was generally accepted that work involving motion would be rendered difficult. Faced with uncertainty (and with rather unaccustomed deference to prevailing pessimism), the Technical Committee decided that the ship would have to rotate in order to furnish a gravitational datum—

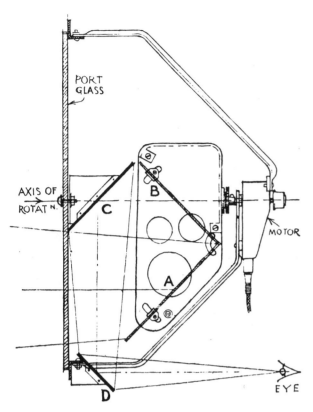

FIGURE 2.—Principal features of the Coelostat.

FIGURE 3.—Mock-up of the Coelostat as demonstrated at the Science Museum, London.

with the extra advantage that stability at launch from Earth and during flight would be improved. Only at lunar touchdown, when spin must be annulled, need a condition of zero gravity exist momentarily. It was obvious that spin could either be annulled during observations, or television used. But cessation of spin, even for short periods, would be a retrograde step to be avoided if possible, while viewing by television entailed heavy gear and would in any case, unless much refined, be incapable of showing stars. However a neat solution was provided by Edwards in the form of a light and simple optical device which in essence is a slow-motion stroboscope. Briefly, the "Coelostat," as it was named (see Figure 2), consisted of two mirrors (A and B) placed at 90° to each other and revolving together. Two more mirrors (C and D) formed a stationary periscope into which the observer looked. Light falling on mirror B from the scene was reflected on to A, C, and D in turn and then passed via a suitable eyepiece to the eye of the observer. When the mirror-pair A/B was revolved at half the speed at which the ship was rotating the exterior scene would appear stationary to an observer. A

working model of this instrument is shown in Figure 3. Probably the first ever produced solely for use in a spaceship, it was made by Smith,[12] and was demonstrated, immobilizing a rotating disc, at a meeting of the Society held in the Science Museum, South Kensington, London, on 7 March 1939. Another type of coelostat for radial viewing was discussed but not developed.

We may now pass on to examine the "Moonship" evolved by the Technical Committee and integrated by R. A. Smith, whose drawings are reproduced in Figure 4. In the drawings each of six main "Steps" consisted of a hexagonal honeycomb formation of individually complete solid propellant rockets. This novel constructional approach originated with Edwards, who maintained that solid systems competing with liquid complexes could be developed, and who in any case was disposed to inventive heterodoxy. Certainly, solid units, lacking complicated pumps, valves and plumbing, were far simpler and more compact affairs than liquid propellant systems. Moreover, with the proposed cellular construction it would be possible to keep dead weight at a minimum by jettisoning used units piecemeal instead of as whole steps, with a consequently much improved overall performance. It will also be apparent that the thrust would be controllable simply by regulating the frequency at which units are ignited. Indeed, this battery system seems to have been the first practical scheme for controlling the thrust of large solid propellant rockets. The design also differed from all its contemporaries, and presaged modern practice, in be-

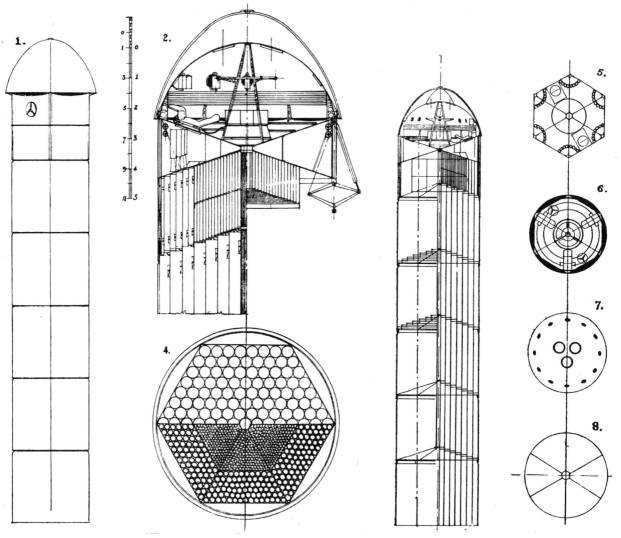

FIGURE 4.—Design for the British Interplanetary Society lunar spaceship.

ing unstreamlined and devoid of aerodynamic fins.[13]

With overall dimensions of about 32 m by 6 m, the ship was calculated to weigh 1,000,000 kg. Of this, 900,000 kg would be propellant graded to yield an exhaust velocity of 3.4 km/sec with the largest rockets and 3.7 km/sec with the smaller. Burning times would also differ. The biggest rockets were nearly 4.6 m long and 38 cm diameter—small by modern standards but incredibly enormous at that time to anyone not astronautically minded. There were 168 in each of the first five Steps and Step six held 450 of medium size and two tiers each of 600 small units, making a total of 2490 solid propellant units. A central conduit down the ship carried the electrical wiring.

The conically stacked units comprising a Step were held in position by light transverse webs and interlinked release bolts. A light hexagonal sheath encased each Step, serving as a heat shield as well as contributing to strength. Webs and sheath would fall away when all the units of a Step had fired and jettisoned.

The corners of the hexagonal compartment between the sixth Step and cabin contained six groups of liquid propellant motors pointing rearwards. These hydrogen-peroxide units were for the fine control of velocity and for tilting the ship before directional corrections. They were also for balancing the ship at lunar touchdown. Just under the cabin were six sets of liquid-propellant opposed tangential jets. These controlled spin as required in furnishing a gravitational datum during flight; they were also used to stop rotation prior to lunar touchdown. This compartment also had two airlock vestibules; the rest was storage space. One of six liquid-buffered landing legs is shown in Figure 4. These were to be retracted close to the ship at launch from Earth and would be spread for lunar landing.

A blunt, radially segmented, reinforced ceramic carapace covered the plastic-domed cabin to protect it from heating during ascent through Earth's atmosphere, after which it would be jettisoned. Although this amount of protection revealed unwarranted fear of high temperature during ascent, it is worth remarking that the carapace was visualized as functioning partly by acting as a heat sink and partly by ablation.

The cabin contained three radial couches for the crew—notably, form-fitting, as is current practice. Motor ignition and other flight controls were on the arms of the couches to afford fingertip manipulation. The couches were hinged for automatic response to the prevailing gravitational datum if desired, and mounted on rails to permit change of radial position. A circumferential walkway was provided for crew movement, with a handrail above attached to the central supporting frame. Three forward-view windows are shown in Figure 4 and there were six rear-view lunettes where the circular cabin juts beyond the ship's hexagonal body. Coelostats of the type described gave views in these two directions with the ship spinning. In addition, portholes just above the walkway permitted observation in twelve radial directions—which multiplicity might be useful while at rest on the Moon. Coelostats of the second, undeveloped, type afforded a stationary view from these portholes with the ship in flight and rotating. All the windows were double-glazed, and were to be covered when not in us as additional safeguard against meteor puncture. The cabin dome was depicted as having a single wall. However, in fact, it was to be double-walled to improve thermal insulation and to act as a "meteor-bumper." Unfortunately the drawings do not show this feature, as they were completed before all details had been settled. Unfortunately, too, I forgot to mention this innovation in my original article.[14] My recollection of Technical Committee discussions on the utility of double-walling is how-

ever confirmed by A. V. Cleaver.[15] The cabinet at the base of the dome support was to contain the flight programmer and electrical power-pack for all purposes. The flight programmer (Figure 5) was designed around selector switches of the automatic telephone exchange type.[16] The system is too complex to detail here, but a few points may be mentioned: In association with the inertial altimeter, accelerometer, etc., and a pendulum stabilizer and gyro destabilizer, the programmer was (in intention at least), capable of stabilizing the ship, holding a course, regulating acceleration, and ceasing operation when the required flight-stage velocity had been achieved. In short, it was a complete robot pilot. There was, however, provision for overriding manual operation and corrections by any one of the three crew members, should necessity arise. Moreover, the liquid propellant motors were available for fine control. The ascent acceleration, starting at 1 g, was to be limited to a modest 3 g at cut-off. It was calculated that at lunar touchdown all but the top 600 small rocket units would have been used and jettisoned. Before ascent from the Moon, and with the object of lightening the ship as much as possible, everything not needed during the return flight would be removed from the cabin and cached. And the landing legs would be unbolted so that they simply support the ship, forming a launching cradle left behind on ascent. Finally, a parachute would be fitted atop the cabin. It was calculated that the remaining 600 solid propellant rockets plus remaining liquid propellant would suffice to carry the ship back to Earth and provide terminal braking down to a safe parachuting velocity, after some air braking.

The ship's payload was discussed by M. K. Hanson in the January 1939 *Journal*.[17] Consumable stores sufficient for three men for twenty days would be carried. Air and water would be obtained by catalysis of 227 kg of concentrated hydrogen peroxide, but a little liquid oxygen would also be taken for emergency and spacesuit use. Soda lime or other suitable chemical means would be used to remove carbon dioxide and water vapor from the cabin's atmosphere. Food would be chosen for energy yield rather than protein content, with attention to vitamin and salt needs. It was suggested that perishable stores might be kept in a container outside the ship, where refrigeration could be obtained. Cocoa and coffee were to be the main beverages. A general re-

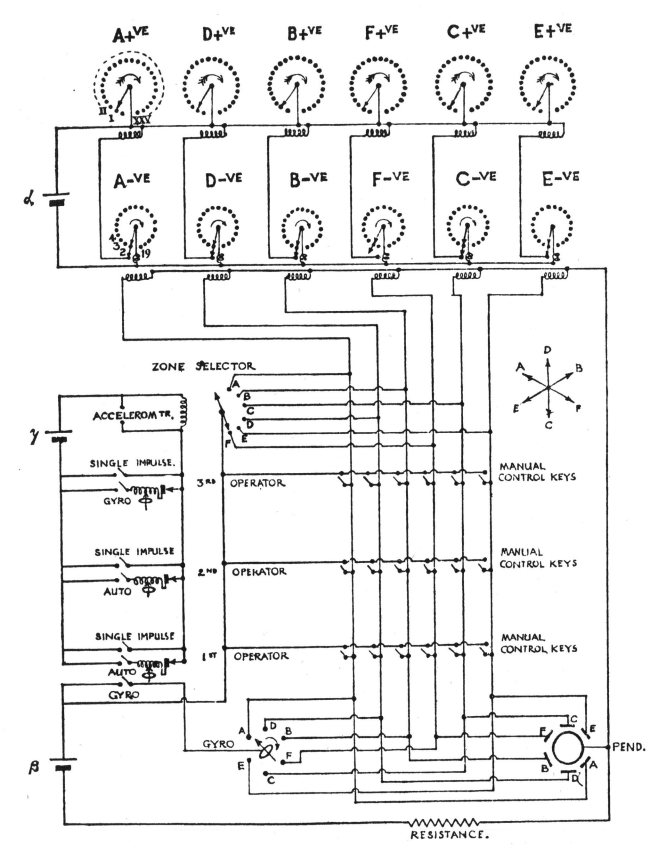

FIGURE 5.—Diagram of the flight programmer for the lunar spaceship.

pair kit and medicine chest would be carried—the latter containing a little alcohol which might be raided to celebrate the lunar landing. The imperative need to minimize dead weight is humorously reflected in the spartan culinary outfitting. There was to be only one electrically-heated pan for boiling and frying, one cup, one spoon and one plate for each of the crew—and only one knife and fork, passed hand to hand, between all three. Power for cooking, lighting and heating was to be obtained from the main battery. All waste products would be disposed of through one of the airlocks.

Since the ship was to be self-reliant as regards navigation, various necessities were mentioned, such as geometrical instruments, mathematical tables, almanacs, etc. With weight-saving always in mind, indelible balsa-wood pencils would be supplied and light rice-paper used for printed and written matter. A rangefinder, small telescope, sextants, and a chronometer were to be carried to obtain star-fixes while in transit and also for use on the Moon.

Four spacesuits were to be taken—that is, one spare in reserve. The helmets were to be roomy, oxygen in liquid form probably used, and arrangements would be made for heating. Dark goggles and sunburn lotion would guard against the Sun's actinic rays. It was suggested that rubber membranes might be provided which could be inflated balloonwise over the head and arms, inside the atmosphere of which the astronauts might eat and drink while on a long exploratory trek. (This idea might be extended, with several obvious advantages, to use of a gas-proof membrane, attached to a thermally-insulating base, to contain the whole spacesuited individual.)

A light canvas tent and light camp beds were to be carried by the party to improve thermal insulation during rest periods while abroad on the Moon. Contact with the ship would be maintained either by signal rockets or light flashes. It was also remarked that reports and commentaries might be transmitted to Earth as signals or speech via a light beam. Today, xenon flashers and lasers are proposed possibilities for this purpose.

The program of exploration was visualized as including checking the Moon's gravitation with a spring-balance and gravity pendulum, geological surveying, photographing and mineralogical sampling. The field and laboratory equipment proposed for this work was given.

The main article on the British Interplanetary Society spaceship concluded with a note that a "launching device" for the vessel would be discussed in a subsequent issue of the *Journal*. But war intervened and the article was not written. A few details were however given in the July 1939 *Journal*.[18] These, slightly augmented by remarks elsewhere and the present writer's recollections, are as follows:

The ship was imagined as being launched almost vertically from a flooded rotating caisson submerged in water. Said Smith, this floatation would have "distributed the load over a greater area." High pressure steam was to be injected into the caisson to start the vessel upwards, and almost immediately afterwards 126 of the first Step rockets would be ignited by impulse from a running dynamo situated in the conduit at the bottom of the Step. This was intended to avoid excessive instantaneous load on the ship's power-pack.

Launching was to take place from a high-altitude lake situated as near the Equator as possible. Reasons for this choice were: maximum advantage from Earth's rotation, minimum air-resistance loss, minimization of launch weight, a range-head more easily sequestered and patrolled than one on land, and less damage to surroundings in event of explosion. Most favoured location was the Andean Lake Titicaca, 3800 m high, partly in Bolivia and partly in Peru, centered on about 16° south latitude, and with access by railroad from the Pacific Coast.[19]

Upon outbreak of war, further concerted work became impossible, and the Society's activities were suspended. However, some leading members maintained contact, and work was still done, the fruits of which are found in post-war publications.

I think I am justified in saying that the foregoing much abridged account of the work of the pre-war British Interplanetary Society's Technical and Experimental Committees reveals original and sound technical thinking on many of the problems involved. Indeed, at the time of publication, the British Interplanetary Society spaceship was in overall conception and detail by far the most realistic and competent embodiment existing. At this later and technically more potent date, we may perhaps sum its virtues and failings by saying: "If not true, it was well invented."

NOTES

Under the title *Astronavti'eskie issledovaniya Britanskogo mezhplanetnogo obshchestva v 1937–1938,* this paper appeared on pages 145–53 of *Iz istorii astronavtiki i raketnoi tekhniki: Materialy XVIII mezhdunarodnogo astronavticheskogo kongressa, Belgrad, 25–29 Sentyavrya 1967* [From the History of Rockets and Astronautics: Materials of the 18th International Astronautical Congress, Belgrade, 25–29 September 1967], Moscow: Nauka, 1970.

1. P. E. Cleator, "Retrospect and Prospect," *Journal of the British Interplanetary Society,* vol. 1, no. 1 (January 1934), pp. 2–4.—Ed.

2. Cleator, "Editorial," *Journal of the British Interplanetary Society,* vol. 1, no. 2 (April 1934), pp. 13–15.—Ed.

3. A Review by E. F. Russell of *Rockets Through Space,* by P. E. Cleator (London: George Allen & Unwin, Ltd., 1936) appeared in "For the Astronautical Library," *Journal of the British Interplanetary Society,* vol. 4, no. 1 (no. IX, February 1937), pp. 11–12.—Ed.

4. J. H. Edwards, "A London Section?" *Journal of the British Interplanetary Society,* vol. 3. no. 2 (no. VIII, June 1936), p. 32; and "The London Branch of the Society, Proceedings," ibid., vol. 4, no. 1 (no. IX, February 1937), pp. 18, ff.—Ed.

5. Edward J. Carnell, "Editorial," *Journal of the British Interplanetary Society,* vol. 4, no. 2 (no. X, December 1937), p. 3; and same issue, p. 3, A. M. Low, "Pioneering" (President's Message), and pp. 5–8, R. A. Smith, "Policy of The British Interplanetary Society."—Ed.

6. "Technicalities" (Being the Report of the Technical Committee up to October 1937. Compiled by R. A. Smith, A. Janser, H. E. Ross, H. Bramhill, and A. C. Clarke, under the direction of J. H. Edwards), *Journal of the British Inter-* *planetary Society,* vol. 4, no. 2 (no. X, December 1937), pp. 8–15.—Ed.

7. J. Happian Edwards, "The British Interplanetary Society Technical Report," *The Journal of the British Interplanetary Society,* vol. 5, no. 1 (no. XI, January 1939), pp. 17–23.—Ed.

8. See note 6.

9. Arthur Janser, "A Contribution to the Fuel Problem," *The Journal of the British Interplanetary Society,* vol. 4, no. 2 (no. X, December 1937), pp. 18–20; and A. Janser, "Fuels and Motors," ibid., vol. 5, no. 1 (no. XI, January 1939), pp. 23–25.—Ed.

10. See note 6 above, and J. H. Edwards, "Report of the Technical Committee," *Journal of the British Interplanetary Society,* vol. 5, no. 2 (no. XII, July 1939), pp. 17–21.—Ed.

11. See note 10.

12. R. A. Smith, "The British Interplanetary Society Coelostat," *Journal of the British Interplanetary Society,* vol. 5, no. 2 (no. XII, July 1939), pp. 22–27.—Ed.

13. H. E. Ross, "The British Interplanetary Society Spaceship," *Journal of the British Interplanetary Society,* vol. 5, no. 1 (no. XI, January 1939), cover and pp. 4–9.—Ed.

14. See note 13.

15. H. E. Ross, "The Pre-War Contribution of the British Interplanetary Society," *Spaceflight,* vol. 3, no. 5 (September 1961), pp. 164–168.—Ed.

16. J. H. Edwards and H. E. Ross, "The Firing Control of the British Interplanetary Society Lunar Spaceship," *Journal of the British Interplanetary Society,* vol. 5, no. 2 (no. XII, July 1939), cover and pp. 4–12.—Ed.

17. Maurice K. Hanson, "The Payload of the Lunar Trip," *Journal of the British Interplanetary Society,* vol. 5, no. 1 (no. XI, January 1939), pp. 10–16.—Ed.

18. See note 10.

19. See note 15.

21

The Development of Regeneratively Cooled Liquid Rocket Engines in Austria and Germany, 1926-42

Irene Sänger-Bredt and Rolf Engel, *German Federal Republic*

Introduction

With the ultimate goal of conquering the vastness of space outside the earth's atmosphere, the technical development of a suitable propulsion system, the liquid-propellant rocket engine, began during the mid-twenties of this century at two different places within the boundaries of the German speaking countries. Both developments were carried out independently of each other and almost simultaneously, but with slightly different technical objectives.

In northern Germany, in Reinickendorf on the outskirts of Berlin, a group of young enthusiasts from the "Verein für Raumschiffahrt" (Society for Space Travel) under the direction of Rudolf Nebel and Klaus Riedel tried to implement man's first step into space by developing a wingless liquid-propellant rocket based on the Oberth concept and designed to take off vertically. Among others in this group were Wernher von Braun, Rolf Engel, and Willy Ley.

In Austria, Eugen Sänger, a young civil engineering candidate at the Technical University in Vienna, tried to pursue the same goal by developing a manned spacecraft with liquid propulsion. During most of his experimental work on propulsion systems, carried out in a shed of the old "Bauhof" building on Dreihufengasse, he was assisted only by two other students, the brothers Friedrich and Stefan Sztatecsny.

Both groups had been encouraged in their efforts by the publications of Hermann Oberth, especially by his book *Die Rakete zu den Planetenräumen* (The Rocket into Interplanetary Space), brought out in 1923 by the publishing firm of Oldenbourg

in Munich. The work of the German group received additional stimulation by direct co-operation with Hermann Oberth during the years 1929 and 1930. Members of both groups also indicated, however, that Kurd Lasswitz' science-fiction novel *Auf zwei Planeten* (On Two Planets) published in 1897, had been the very first stimulus to setting their technical goals.

Both groups also had in common that they worked on their own, without public funds, financed only by small donations from a few industrialists and private associations, and that sometimes their efforts were barely tolerated or even met with opposition from their contemporaries. It is well known that some of them who were less well off, and their families, went hungry in order to be able to go on with their work; and they even had to pay for the printing of their publications that later were to attract world fame. Also, with the exception of one person, none of them ever got a penny in license fees for the patents which opened a new era for mankind and are still being used by the major aerospace companies all over the world. Rudolf Nebel was the one exception: upon disbandment of the Rakentenflugplatz Berlin (Rocket Field Berlin) in 1934, he received 75,000 reichsmarks from the Third Reich as a one-time indemnification.

As to their technical approach, both groups chose as energy source for their propulsion system the combustion heat of various hydrocarbons in oxygen. The two propellants were fed separately, either by compressed gas or pumps, into the injection system of the combustion chamber formed by metal walls leading, in most cases, into a Laval-type nozzle.

While the work of the German group clearly aimed at launch and ballistic flight tests, Sänger in

Vienna—because his goal was to develop an aircraft engine—limited his efforts to testing propulsion units, but he proceeded very systematically and obtained valuable test data.

Though Sänger started his tests later than the German group and worked mainly by himself, he was in a more advantageous position: from the very beginning, because of his different objective, he devoted more attention to the problem of cooling his rocket engine than the German group did. The latter, when not simply relying on the heat capacity of the combustion chamber walls, placed the engine into a container filled with a stagnant coolant, although Oberth had already proposed in his book a regenerative cooling process. Since Sänger wanted to develop a rocket engine for a manned aircraft and not a ballistic projectile to be launched vertically, he had to build his engine so carefully and so safe that it would be reusable many times. Thus, he initially concentrated on the development of the engine itself, without facing the complex problems of producing a flightworthy overall system. Consequently, he could devote more attention to the so-called "braking tests" in a ground test facility than other researchers did who were interested in reporting as fast as possible on flight altitudes and ranges obtained by their ballistic rocket models. (He called these "braking tests" in analogy with tests of internal combustion engines, in which torque is braked and measured, whereas in his tests the thrust was being sustained and measured.) Sänger prepared his tests in a most systematic and logical way and, especially in studying cooling problems, took advantage of tapwater available from a stationary source. From the very beginning, Sänger's tests aimed at obtaining high exhaust velocities which are accompanied by high combustion temperatures and chamber wall stresses, whereas Oberth and his followers tried to achieve first of all simply a "functioning" of the rocket engine and artificially lowered the combustion temperatures by water injection.

To aid in understanding the development approaches taken in the early German and Austrian rocket projects described herein, a systematic synopsis of possible and so far known cooling methods for rocket engines is being attempted. In principle, two methods can be distinguished for cooling rocket engine parts exposed to combustion gases— capacity (capacitance, or heat-soak) and dynamic cooling.

Capacitance cooling is a static process whereby heat flowing from the combustion chamber is stored by the solid chamber walls and—if they are present—also by the walls of a cooling jacket surrounding the thrust chamber. The heat thus received is continually collected within the coolant material, but this method does not result in an equilibrium condition and is useful for a limited time only, i.e., until the heat storage capacity is exhausted. A limit case of capacity cooling is represented by ablation cooling; here heat is dissipated by successive melting or subliming of a suitable protective layer (e.g., nylon, phenolic resin, or graphite) covering parts endangered by heat.

The term dynamic cooling covers any method using conduction, convection, or radiation to dissipate from the endangered zone that amount of heat which cannot be stored by the combustion chamber walls. There are two ways to accomplish this:

1. To minimize heat transfer from the combustion gas into the heated wall side either by reducing the temperature difference between both (high wall temperatures with refractory wall materials, artificial reduction of combustion temperature by water injection, etc.) or by influencing the boundary layer (coolant mist, optically reflective wall surfaces, electrical fields for sufficiently ionized combustion gases, etc.).

2. To dissipate as rapidly as possible the heat contained in the chamber wall by maximizing heat transfer from the cooled chamber-wall side into an adjoining suitable and efficiently ducted coolant.

Gartmann proposed the terms "internal," and "external" cooling for these two methods.

Film cooling, invented by Oberth and achieved by injecting water into the boundary layer, is an example of internal dynamic cooling. In the case of external dynamic cooling—where the amount of heat from the hot combustion gases, passing to and across the combustion chamber wall and then into a flowing coolant, is carried off with the coolant—a state of equilibrium can be obtained if the coolant can be ducted in such a way that the heat amount received by the heated chamber wall side equals that dissipated into the coolant from the cooled wall side.

Two more alternate dynamic cooling methods can be distinguished: (1) surface area cooling or forced flow cooling, respectively, and (2) supplementary cooling or regenerative cooling. Both methods are independent of each other and permit all combinations between them, e.g., regenerative surface area cooling or forced flow supplemental cooling, etc.

Surface area cooling, in the case of external cooling, denotes a process in which the flowing coolant circulates with two degrees of freedom within a non-subdivided jacket around the combustion chamber. Adequate flow velocity and heat dissipation are not assured at every point. An example for internal surface cooling is the continuous liquid coolant mist injected into the boundary layer of the combustion gases. Under forced-flow cooling, in the case of external cooling, the coolant is one-dimensionally ducted through tubes which completely cover the surface areas of the combustion chamber and nozzle so that flow velocity and thermodynamic state of the coolant can be determined for any flow path point. Any defined, one-dimensional guiding of ionized combustion gases within the combustion chamber core by a field of electromagnetic forces would exemplify internal forced cooling.

Supplemental cooling, as its name implies, instead of propellants, catalysts, or working fluids contained within the propulsion system, uses supplemental coolants.

In a regenerative cooling scheme, however, the coolant is a propellant or working fluid and part of the propulsive energy supply system. The heated coolants fed into the combustion chamber, together with the energy carried by them, are not wasted; they aid in processing for combustion. A special type of regenerative surface cooling, e.g., the mist, or film cooling, method, was mentioned earlier; a propellant component, not water, is injected into the combustion chamber in such a way that a protective layer of film is being formed between wall and combustion gas or circumferentially around an intermediate wall. Furthermore, there is the transpiration cooling method in which a cool propellant forced into the combustion chamber through a permeable material keeps the hot combustion gases off the wall.

Regenerative cooling combined with propellant feeding improves simple regenerative cooling; the heat received by the propellant coolant preheats this propellant and with it directly enters the combustion chamber. The heat extracted from the combustion chamber walls during the cooling process not only warms up, but even evaporates, the coolant; then the heat powers an auxiliary vapor-driven prime mover which in turn drives the propellant feed pumps. Two variations of this combined regenerative cooling exist: either a propellant or a non-propellant intermediate coolant can be used. In the first case, the coolant passes through the turbine into a condenser and, after being reliquefied on the cold propellant tank walls, finally enters the combustion chamber; in the second case, the coolant returns to the inlet side of the cooling channels.

Work of the Berlin Team

Among other contemporaries, Willy Ley, Rudolf Nebel, and Alexander Scherschevsky reported in the 1930s on the development of liquid-propellant rockets in Germany. Also, records of the experiments conducted on the Raketenflugplatz Berlin (Berlin Rocket Field) still exist in Rolf Engel's archives.

In Ley's *Grundriss einer Geschichte der Rakete* (Outline History of Rocketry),[1] published in November 1932, the following list of important milestones is given:

1923. Professor H. Oberth publishes his fundamental work *Die Rakete zu den Planetenräumen* (The Rocket into Interplanetary Space).

1926. On 24 November, Heinrich Schreiner, Graz is granted the German patent DRP 484,064, entitled "Mit fluessigen Betriebsstoffen betriebene Gasrakete" (Liquid-Propellant Gas Rocket). The liquid or liquefied propellant is fed into the combustion chamber by piston or other pumps.

1927. In June, the Verein für Raumschiffahrt e.V. (Society for Space Travel) is founded in Breslau by Max Valier and Johannes Winkler. Its monthly magazine *Die Rakete* (The Rocket) appears until the end of 1929. In 1930, the Society transfers its activities to Berlin.

1929. On 10 April, Dr. W. Sander launches a rocket using liquid propellants. However, this is not a true liquid-propellant rocket, i.e., a rocket using liquid fuel and liquid oxygen, but some sort of a pyrotechnical rocket using liquid substances.

1930. On 19 April, the first test run of a liquid-propellant rocket automobile built by Valier and the Heylandtwerke takes place.

1930.   In May, a 14-day exhibition of liquid-propellant rockets and experimental equipment is held by the Society for Space Travel in Berlin on the Potsdamer Platz and afterwards in the Wertheim department store.

1930.   On 17 May, Max Valier is killed by an exploding liquid-propellant rocket.

1930.   On 27 September, the Raketenflugplatz Berlin (Berlin Rocket Field) is founded by Rudolf Nebel.

1931.   On 14 March, near Dessau, Johannes Winkler launches a rocket using methane and oxygen. Altitude about 600 meters. The second Winkler rocket explodes during launch on 6 October 1932, on the Frische Nehrung near Pillau.

1931.   On 11 April, at the Berlin Central Airport, Chief Engineer Pietsch of the Heylandtwerke demonstrates an improved Valier rocket automobile. Propellants: alcohol and oxygen.

1931.   On 14 May, at the Berlin Rocket Field, a 1-liter liquid-propellant rocket (Double-Stick Repulsor) is launched to a height of 60 meters.

1931.   On 23 May, at the Berlin Rocket Field after completion of the workshops and static test run of the engine, a Riedel Repulsor, using gasoline and oxygen, attains a distance of more than 600 meters. A fortnight before, the same device had already reached an altitude of 100 meters. Meanwhile, improved repulsors of the same dimensions have reached distances of 5 kilometers and altitudes of about 1.5 kilometers. Thus, the technical development of the liquid-propellant rocket has begun.

One very important date is missing in this list, namely 23 July 1930, the day when Hermann Oberth together with Rudolf Nebel, Klaus Riedel, Rolf Engel, and Wernher von Braun (who had just received his high school diploma) demonstrated his "Kegeldüse" (cone-shaped nozzle) to Dr. Ritter, the director of the Chemisch-Technische Reichsanstalt (Government Institute for Chemistry and Technology with functions similar to the U.S. Bureau of Standards). On a rudimentary test rack of the Institute, the Kegeldüse produced about 7.7 kg maximum thrust for a total combustion time of 96 sec. and a nearly constant thrust of 7 kg for 50.8 sec with a sub-stoichiometric composition of liquid oxygen and gasoline. The demonstration proved so successful that Dr. Ritter recommended further work on this rocket engine as worthy of support by the Deutsche Notgemeinschaft (German Foundation providing funds for selected projects).

The rocket projects suggested by Oberth in 1923 that influenced the overall development of liquid rockets in Germany and Austria, had already included combustion chambers with inner dynamic regenerative surface cooling. For example, Oberth had proposed a two-stage high-altitude probe, Model B, and a manned spacecraft, Model E, with the first stage in both cases burning an alcohol-water mixture and liquid oxygen, and the second stage burning liquid hydrogen instead of the alcohol-water mixture. As proposed, the thrust chamber of the second stage would be fitted into the liquid hydrogen tank and use the heat capacity of the propellant for cooling; for the first stage, a novel dynamic cooling process was proposed. Necessary cooling was to be achieved by varying the mixture ratio of the propellants,[2] thus reducing the combustion temperature, and by insulating the combustion chamber walls by a dynamic cooling film of evaporating fuel which is the simplest method of regenerative cooling. The absorbed heat was to pre-heat the fuel, while the film of evaporating fuel would protect the chamber walls from the hot combustion gases. Oberth described this as follows:

The combustion chamber does not join directly with the jacket surfaces. In between, there is a thin wall connected to the jacket by metallic braces and thus held in the correct position. Liquid from the atomizer flows between this thin wall and the jacket, vaporizes, and thus protects the chamber walls from burning. The vapor discharges between atomizer and jacket into the chamber. Within the chamber, the vapor remains near the walls; thus, with high vaporization, the walls are being insulated from the hot gas . . . . This arrangement allows the dry weight of the rocket to be much less than it would be if chamber and nozzle were lined with fireproof materials on the inside, and this is a considerable advantage. It also permits the gases to pass along the metallic surfaces which retard the flow less than asbestos or chamotte.[3]

In this description, the coolant is simply called a "liquid" and no indication exists where a supplemental cooling system or regenerative cooling is considered. In a different paragraph additional information is given:

Nevertheless, in order to obtain lower combustion chamber temperatures for the Model B, I considered weaker compositions; i.e., for the alcohol rocket, instead of rectified alcohol, a 13.4 percent dilute alcohol, which only gives a combustion chamber temperature of about 1400°C and an exhaust velocity of about 1700 m/sec . . . .

An additional feature of Models B and E is the insulation of the wall by the vapor of the coolants . . . so that burning of the chamber wall is definitely avoided . . . . With Models B and E, this dynamic cooling can become very effective by letting gas, of the same chemical composition as the forming gas, flow along the walls. According to Kirchhoff, this absorbs almost completely the heat radiated from the inner chamber.[4]

Actually, the technology of the A-4 rocket, which became operational 19 years later, included all essential details of Oberth's suggestions for the first stage of his Models B and E that he made in 1923. But still, there was a long way to go. As to the cooling method, the first rocket engines developed after 1923 used much more primitive processes.

In his *Wege zur Raumschiffahrt* [5] Oberth still suggested a simple sounding rocket, Model A, with the liquid-propellant engine encased by the fuel tank in the lower part and the liquid oxygen tank in the upper part. Capacitive cooling was to be applied; the pre-heated oxygen was to be fed into the combustion chamber by its own vapor pressure and the fuel by a pressurizing gas.

Oberth's first rocket engine test model, the "cone-shaped nozzle," built in the same year according to the specifications of the German patent DRP 549,222, had capacitive cooling only—even without a cooling jacket—but with oxygen-rich combustion resulting in low combustion-gas temperatures. For example, during the famous demonstration at the Chemisch-Technische Reichsanstalt, the amount of oxygen injected was 1.9 times the stoichiometric value. According to Willy Ley's notes, one of the combustion chambers of this series was lined with a ceramic material (steatite magnesium). The text of the patent did not include any details regarding the cooling system, only the somewhat vague phrase: "The inner lining can be of clay, asbestos, mineral wool, platinum sponge, or similar materials. It can also be omitted entirely, for example, when using copper sheets adequately cooled from the outside." Actually, the combustion tests with the lined combustion chamber proved unfavorable. In his publication Rakentenflug,[6] Nebel commented on the tests with Oberth's combustion chamber models that "Use of fireproof material did not prove to be successful, either, and in many tests the material burnt up." Still, this led to the development of the so-called "Spaltduese" (slot nozzle) providing a thrust of 2.5 kg. After the slot nozzle, the cone-shaped nozzle was developed with a thrust of 7.5 kg. Soon, this conical nozzle attained a constant thrust of 7.5 kg over a combustion time of 100 sec. Because of the rudimentary equipment, the tests progressed very slowly. Materials problems were especially hard to solve because all "fireproof" materials burned up at these high temperatures.

The German patent 484,064, mentioned in Ley's chronicle, was held by Heinrich Schneider, a former Austrian Marine officer, with whom Hermann Oberth had corresponded for a short while in 1924. The patent was based on an earlier Austrian patent of 25 November 1925, and referred only to suggestions for propellant flow, not to any cooling systems. Entitled "Mit flüssigen Betriebsstoffen betriebene Gasrakete" (Gas Rocket Using Liquid Propellants), it contained no less than 16 claims. According to the then existing state of the art in rocketry, the sketch of the overall design of the rocket thrust chamber, attached to the patent specifications, showed a static liquid cooling system. The combustion chamber and the first quarter of the nozzle were surrounded by a jacket filled with non-circulating liquid; the rest of the exhaust nozzle was uncooled. The descriptive test simply mentioned that "the space around the nozzle and the combustion chamber may be filled by a coolant."

Ley also reported briefly on the firing of a liquid-propellant rocket by Friedrich Wilhelm Sander, the owner of a factory in Wesermuende, which produced rescue and signal rockets, and since early 1928, solid-propellant rocket motors for the first Opel-Rak test runs by Max Valier. In his book *Raketenfahrt*, Valier himself wrote in 1929:

In the field of liquid-fuel rockets, Sander must be mentioned as the most successful research engineer of the year. On 10 April 1929, he was the first who succeeded in launching such a rocket on a free-ascent trajectory. According to his specifications, the rocket was 21 cm in diameter, 74 cm long, and weighed 7 kg without and 16 kg with propellants. The burning time was 132 sec, maximum thrust 45 to 50 kg. The propellant, which Sander keeps secret, had a combustion heat of 2380 k cal/kg. It seems that he used gasoline and a suitable oxidizer under special burning conditions. As construction materials, steel and light metals were used.

This first liquid-propellant rocket took off so rapidly that it was impossible to track its flight or to recover it. Sander therefore repeated the experiment two days later, attaching 4000 m of 3-mm rope to the rocket and applied all precautions known to him from his marine rescue rocket operations. In spite of its heavy load, the rocket took off like a bullet, taking with it 2000 m of rope, and disappeared forever with the torn-off part.

After this success, Sander concentrated again on rocket propulsion for manned aircraft. By May 1929, he had succeeded in producing a thrust of 200 kg for a period of more than 15 minutes, and in July, at the Opel plant in Rüsselsheim, he attained combustion times of more than 30 minutes with a thrust of 300 kg. Sander was most concerned with achieving operational safety and using low-priced fuels. Using a waste product of the chemical industry, he succeeded in reducing the price for one kilogram of fuel to 20 pfennige.

Considering this state of development, economical rocket flight operations over distances of several thousand miles may be possible in the foreseeable future, as soon as the remaining deficiencies in Sander's rocket engines can be eliminated.[7]

Afterwards, however, no one ever heard again of Sander's liquid-propellant rockets, and it has remained unknown whether the reasons were personal or due to actual deficiencies in his liquid-rocket engines. As far as the co-author remembers, Sander's liquid rockets had capacitive cooling only and oxygen-rich combustion.

At least from 1924 on, Max Valier had dreamed of a spacecraft with rocket propulsion as the ultimate goal of his work, but had never put into writing any details regarding the proposed propulsion system. Thus, for a long time, the question remained open whether he envisaged a turbo-engine or a solid- or liquid-propellant rocket as the final solution. Only in January 1930 did he begin to develop his own liquid-propellant rocket engine after having received, at the end of 1929, some support for his project from the Heylandtwerke in Berlin-Britz. After preliminary combustion tests with alcohol and gaseous oxygen, he ran his engine, called "Einheitsofen" (standard combustion chamber), for the first time on 26 March 1930, with liquid oxygen. With this combustion chamber, weighing about 4 kg, Valier made the first successful test runs of the RAK-7 automobile on 17 and 19 April 1930. The fuel and liquid-oxygen tanks were completely separated from each other, one located in front and the other in back of the driver's seat. As to the cooling problem, the Einheitsofen did not show any fundamental improvement over the conical nozzle. The combustion gas temperature was kept low by adding water to the alcohol, so that capacitive cooling was sufficient. One of Valier's associates, Walter J. H. Riedel, wrote about the Einheitsofen:

The chamber was made of standard steel tubing. At one end was the expansion nozzle and at the other the propellant injection system. Oxygen was fed through a number of small bore holes from the pre-mix chamber into the combustion chamber. The fuel was injected into the chamber against the flow of the oxygen gas. A drag disk reduced the velocity of the oxygen gas flow by producing vortex fields.[8]

Valier had planned to continue the development of his combustion chamber with the aid of the Shell Oil Company, and thus had to commit himself to using Shell oil (kerosene) instead of alcohol. Of course, this increased the cooling problem. Riedel reported on this as follows:

Instead of using alcohol, as before, Shell oil had to be used. Alcohol is a fuel that can be mixed with water in any desired proportion, allowing reduction and determination of the combustion temperature. With kerosene, this is not that easily done. By adding water to kerosene and shaking it, an emulsion forms for a short while, during which kerosene and water mix; afterwards, they quickly separate again. In order to maintain the integrity of the combustion chamber walls, the gas temperature had to be kept within certain limits. The problem was solved by feeding the kerosene, prior to entry into the combustion chamber, through a so-called emulsion chamber.[9]

On 17 May 1930, Valier was killed during preliminary tests with this emulsion chamber. Less than a year later, on 11 April and 3 May 1931, Alfons Pietsch, a senior engineer of the Heylandtwerke, made another test run of the RAK-7 with an improved rocket engine weighing about 18 kg. According to Willy Ley[10] this engine must have yielded a thrust of 160 kg and been cooled by the fuel, but no proofs or any further data on the type of cooling used were ever found.

At the end of 1929, Johannes Winkler, in the journal *Die Rakete,* suggested the construction of long cylindrical combustion chambers for methane-liquid oxygen with ceramic lining of the nozzles near the throat area. In summer 1930, he began to build his first liquid-propellant rocket engine, which he called a Strahlmotor (jet engine), and at the end of the year he started to run his first ground tests. The first firing attempt, on 21 February 1931, was a failure; but the second firing of the complete aggregate HW-1 (Hückel-Winkler-Astris 1), at Gross-Kuehnau near Dessau on 14 March 1931 has been recorded in the annals as the first flight of a liquid-propellant rocket in Europe. The rocket—about 60 cm long, its main structure made of aluminum sheet, and with a launch weight of about 5 kg—consisted of a triangular arrangement of three tube-like containers for methane, liquid oxygen and compressed nitrogen for pressurization. The engine, 45 cm long, was made of seamless steel tubing and positioned approximately along the centerline of the assembly.

In October 1931, in a rented room of the Berlin Rocket Field, Winkler and his first assistant, Rolf Engel, began construction of the HW-2, bigger and with a length of 1.50 m and take-off weight of 50 kg. This rocket—with spherical propellant tanks arranged one above the other, a parachute in its nose, engine in the aft part, stabilizer fins, and a stream-lined hull of very thin Electron sheet metal—had a mass ratio of 4.8, which was superior to the mass ratio of the later V-2. After its completion in summer 1932, the first launching was scheduled for autumn after only one ground test, in which major parts of the expansion nozzle had melted. During the first launch attempt on 29 September 1932, in Pillau, the propellant valves froze, blocking the flow of the propellants into the combustion chamber. During the second launch attempt, on 6 October 1932, propellant leaking through the valves formed a flammable mixture outside the combustion chamber so that the rocket exploded immediately after ignition. All of Winkler's rockets had capacitive cooling and operated with oxygen-rich combustion.

The Berlin Rocket Field, founded on 27 September 1930, may be considered the true center of German liquid-fueled rocket development before World War II. Its somewhat pretentious name—like Sänger's German Rocket Flight Yard (Deutsche Raketenflugwerft) in Vienna—was born out of the highspirited and romantic mood of the space pioneers of the early 1930s; they were a mixture of clear-thinking engineers and hopelessly idealistic universalists who were closer to the sky than all the perfectionist but demystified super-rocket and satellite teams of today. The dedication took place after a visit to Berlin by Henry Ford, whose attention they had hoped to capture with this name. A fine but—in view of their different goals—meaningful distinction exists between the names chosen by Nebel and Sänger: a "rocket field" is a place from which to launch rockets, whereas a "rocket yard" denotes a place where rockets are built.

The site covered about 4 km² and was rented from the city of Berlin for a symbolic fee of 10 reichsmarks per year, but with some restrictions concerning the buildings and facilities, which belonged to the German War Department. Jointly in charge of the test facilities were the engineers Klaus Riedel and Rudolf Nebel, the latter of whom enthusiastically described the facilities in 1932:

The workshop building includes the workshop with two lathes, one milling machine, and two drill presses, plus work benches, an assembly room with welding equipment, a forge and ancillary equipment, living quarters, and a big storage room for materials of all kinds. The workshop is protected against explosions by high earth walls, and behind these walls, in a deep hollow, is situated the newly erected static test stand. In the administration building there are two rooms used as living quarters, an office, a drafting room, a reception room, etc. Three more dwellings at other locations of the site complete the complex. Far away from the living quarters and the workshop is the firing shed, the historical site where the launchings of the first liquid-fuel rockets took place.[11]

About fourteen years later, in his book *Rockets and Space Travel,* Willy Ley wrote a bit less enthusiastically, but with humor:

The place itself was suitable for practically nothing. Half of it was hilly and covered with trees, and some of the depressions between the hills were swampy.

To make it worse from a businessman's point of view, the jurisdiction was somewhat doubtful. During the First World War, when the police garrison had been an army garrison, the place had been used to store ammunition and the War Ministry had erected storage buildings. These were massive concrete barracks with walls a foot thick, surrounded by blast guards in the form of earth walls, 40 feet high and about 60 feet thick at the base. . . .

We had to make an enormous number of promises. We were to use only one of the two gates, we were to occupy only two of the buildings and were not to enter any of the others . . . , we were not to make any changes in the two buildings we were permitted to use, and we were not to move in machinery and/or equipment which could not be moved out within forty-eight hours. We promised everything . . . .

The smaller building next to the gate, not surrounded by an earth wall, had only one story. . . . It had obviously been the guardhouse, with a rest room and an office for the officer in charge and a room for the soldiers of the guard. . . . During the interval between the time the guard had moved out and we had moved in, somebody had used it to store lumber which was afterwards forgotten. When we finally got the door open, we found a solid layer of thoroughly rotted wood, a yard thick. It was a full day's work to drag this wood out into the open, to burn it, and to clean the house.

After that, Nebel and Riedel set up a bachelor household in the two small rooms and used the larger room as temporary storage space for our equipment. . . .

This room was later used as a combination office, reception, conference, and board of directors' meeting room; I called it the *chambre à tout faire.* But during the winter it became an incredible jungle of machinery and raw materials. We wrote hundreds of letters to firms manufacturing things we could use. . . .[12]

Unfortunately, of the many tests conducted on the Berlin Rocket Field between 1930 and its forced abandonment in 1934, no official accurate records exist. As Walter Dornberger commented: "It was not, for instance, possible before the middle of 1932 to obtain from the 'Raketenflugplatz' in Berlin any sort of records showing performance and fuel consumption during experiments."[13]

Also, many of the personal documents of the various scientists working at the Berlin Rocket Field may have been confiscated during the purge in 1933 and 1934 when, among others, Rolf Engel and his associate Heinz Springer were arrested; the documents may have disappeared in some archives or been destroyed during the war.

The first tests on the Rocket Field were performed with the Minimum-Rakete (MIRAK), one of the first variations of which had been tested with little success in Bernstadt, Saxony, in August 1930. MIRAK-1, a concept of Rudolf Nebel's, still bore strong resemblance to a solid rocket. The guiding stick of the 30-cm-long rocket was an aluminum tube which served also as propellant tank and contained half a liter of gasoline to be fed into the combustion chamber by the pressure from a CO_2 cartridge. In the nose of the rocket, a 1-liter liquid-oxygen tank was mounted; by its own vapor pressure the contents was to be fed into the combustion chamber located under the tank. The cone-shaped engine, made of cast iron, had only capacitive cooling and was unlined. About 2 kg of thrust was achieved, which hardly surpassed the take-off weight of the rocket.

MIRAK-2, aside from having a larger diameter, did not differ much from its predecessor that had exploded during a static test early in September. Instead of the CO_2 cartridge, a tubelike compressed gas container was provided which also formed the second guiding stick of the rocket. This time, the rocket engine was not positioned below the liquid oxygen tank but protruded into it, thus accelerating through heat dissipation from the motor the vaporization of the fuel in the tank and the oxygen supply to the combustion chamber. The bottom of the aluminum rocket head was made of copper and formed in such a way that the cone-shaped nozzle protruded into the interior of the rocket head and thus into the lox tank. At the top, above the lox tank, a safety valve was mounted. But MIRAK-2 also proved to be too heavy for the thrust that it produced. In the spring of 1931 it exploded because the walls of the lox tank could not withstand the increasing gas pressure resulting from the rising heat of the tank's contents.

In Brügel's *Männer der Rakete* Ley wrote:

> Soon it was found that the main emphasis had to be placed on the development of the combustion chamber. A special testing stand for combustion chambers became necessary, where the engine itself, not the entire rocket, could be

tested. Used as raw material for the new "big test stand" . . . was the launch rack which originally had been constructed for the launching of Oberth's rocket near Horst on the Baltic Sea. And on this "big test stand" a breakthrough occurred. Someone had had the idea to test a new type of combustion chamber and no longer use iron and "fireproof materials"—which all burnt—but a light metal combustion chamber with cooling. No one knows whose idea this was; but I remember that months ago, Riedel had told me of such plans; thus, I am inclined to assume that he was the originator of this improvement.[14]

The German patent 633,667, dated 13 June 1931, was granted to the inventors Rudolf Nebel and Klaus Riedel for the new cooling process, using the heat capacity of a non-circulating liquid. It carried the title "Rückstossmotor für flüssige Treibstoffe" (Reaction Motor for Liquid Propellants) and listed the following claim:

> Reaction motor for liquid propellants, fuel and oxygen, which are fed separately into the combustion chamber where they are mixed and burn; the motor characterized by having a combustion chamber made of metal with high heat conductivity, with high pressure from an outside coolant exerted against the thin chamber walls to counteract the pressure of the combustion gases in the chamber, and injection nozzles with separate fuel supply control, positioned in such a way that the fuels injected in opposite direction to the exhaust of the combustion gases still mix in the upper part of the combustion chamber.

The new egg-shaped motor weighed only 250 g, in comparison to the 3 kg of the old conical nozzle. The walls were of aluminum. Rudolf Nebel described the new model of the rocket motor as follows:

> The now smallest rocket motor provided a maximum thrust of 32 kg. For reasons of greater safety, maximum performance was soon limited to 25 kg. With this type of motor, the first liquid-propellant rockets were built. The development took place in March 1931.[15]

Ley reported on the progress of this work:

> After this success, the second MIRAK, which also had exploded in the meantime, was to be replaced by a third and different looking MIRAK . . . . Of course, the new combustion chamber was to be used and placed, not into the bottom but under the bottom of the lox tank. But MIRAK-3 was never put together, only parts of it were completed. Riedel, meanwhile, had told me of another plan that he did not yet reveal to anyone else. . . . When the new device was ready, he showed it to Nebel and I suggested that we call this new device "Repulsor" in order to distinguish it from MIRAK on the one hand and a solid-propellant rocket on the other.[16]

The so-called "Zweistab-Repulsor" (two-stick thruster) was completed in early May 1931. After the first attempt failed on 10 May 1931, it was launched on 14 May 1931, and climbed to an altitude of 60 m. Thus, two months after Winkler's rocket had been launched, a second successful launch of a liquid rocket in Europe took place and demonstrated the flying capability of the Repulsor. As to the cooling, a few problems still remained. Ley described the situation in *Männer der Rakete*: ". . . The rocket took off well, but immediately hit some trouble . . . and made several loops in the air. The cooling water ran out of the container, which was open on top, and the engine burnt through."[17]

Up to June 1931, three models of the Zweistab-Repulsor were tested and launched; they did not differ much from one another.

In August 1931, the first launch of an improved model, the "Einstab-Repulsor" (one-stick thruster), took place. The rocket reached a height of 1000 m on the first launch. It resembled a four-pronged fork with prongs placed upward and the handle formed by the lox tank. Two of the prongs were propellant lines and the other two were braces. The fuel tank was arranged in line with and below the lox tank. Under it, near the tail fins, was the container for the parachute. Mounted on top and supported by the four prongs was the old engine surrounded by a jacket filled with non-circulating cooling water. The tests with the Einstab-Repulsor were extremely successful.

The May 1932 edition of the journal *Raketenflug* included the proud announcement: "Up to May 1932, the Berlin Rocket Field can claim 220 static tests and 85 launches of liquid-propellant rockets." In spite of these impressive figures, the activities on the Rocket Field had reached a climax with the deevlopment of the Repulsor; during 1932, the crew began to disperse. Johannes Winkler and his first assistant, Rudolf Engel, were the first to transfer to the newly founded Raketenforschungsinstitut-Dessau (Dessau Rocket Research Institute). A few months later, on 1 October 1932, Wernher von Braun accepted employment with the Heereswaffenamt (Army Ordnance Department) which asked him to carry out experimental work in their Sub-Office for Rocket Development under the direction of Walter Dornberger.

Work on the Rocket Field under Nebel and Riedel still continued. Besides flight tests of various Repulsor models, the design and development of a larger rocket engine with 64-kg thrust were started in April 1931. To distinguish it from the smaller egg-shaped Repulsor engine, Ley called it the "Aepyornis-Ei" (Giant Ostrich Egg). Tests of this engine, using 0.8 liter of gasoline and 3 liters of lox, were unsatisfactory with respect both to thrust and cooling. Again, static cooling had been applied, but was not sufficient for these much bigger engines.

The decision was made to develop an engine for 250–750 kg of thrust with regenerative cooling, using fuel as coolant. Also with respect to the fuels, variations were tested. In winter 1931 Riedel had already thought of using a water-alcohol mixture which Oberth had proposed. He hoped to maintain tolerable chamber temperatures without too greatly diminishing the performance, as is the case when gasoline is burned oxygen-rich. Preliminary tests were run between August 1932 and March 1933 with gasoline and also with alcohol-water mixtures of 40 to 90 percent alcohol. Construction of the engine began, according to a report by Herbert Schaefer, a colleague at the Rocket Field, about Christmas 1932.[18] On 9 March 1933 the new engine was tested for the first time on a provisional test rack. During March and April 1933, a new test stand for 1000-kg-thrust rocket engines was finished, and a series of tests with eight models was started. On March 25 and April 3, the first and second models, respectively, exploded immediately after ignition. During April about 20 additional tests were run and produced good results, providing thrusts of 150 to 200 kg.

In autumn 1933, Riedel and Nebel applied for a patent on their method of regenerative dynamic surface cooling. The application was declared secret and filed under the No. 32,827 I 46 g. It could not be determined whether national security, political, or objective reasons prevented their being granted a patent. But it is a fact that their inventive idea was not new when the application was filed. In 1928, Konstantin Eduardovitch Tsiolkovskiy had already published a proposal for such a method of dynamic regenerative cooling, and in Männer der Rakete (1933) Tsiolkovskiy reported: " . . . Figure 34 shows a rocket motor of my own design that was published in *Technische Rundschau* [Technical Review], 1928, no. 31. The principle of pre-heating the propellant in a cooling jacket surrounding the chamber was used for this motor."[19] Moreover, in 1929, Alexander Boris Scherschevsky, a Russian student and former assistant to Oberth and Nebel in Berlin during 1928–29, had published in his book a design sketch by Tsiolkovskiy and commented about it:

> Tsiolkovskiy's rocket engine consists of a spherical combustion chamber and a conical nozzle . . . . The cold propellants enter the combustion chamber at opposite sides at the top and, separated by a partition, flow from the inlet into a platelet grid. Each propellant after passing through its grid made of platelets inclined towards the center, mixes with the other. An electric glow plug initiates ignition at the grid until the latter starts glowing. The combustion chamber is cooled by a fuel (hydrocarbon) and this in turn by surrounding lox.[20]

The new engine with regenerative cooling was to have served as the propulsion system for a big demonstration rocket to be launched during the spring 1933 air show in Magdeburg. The rocket, referred to in the literature as the Magdeburg Startgerät, or 10-L Rocket, was a modest prototype of a projected manned rocket 10 m in height, called Piloten-Rakete (Piloted Rocket). The 10-L had been built simultaneously with the construction of the big test stand. After unsuccessful launch attempts in Magdeburg, the 10-L was modified for launchings from Lindwerder Island in Lake Tegel. Under the name Vierstab-Repulsor (Four-Stick Thruster) it made history. Details of its test launches, which were carried out between June and September 1933, with the propulsive energy provided by the combustion of gasoline and oxygen, were recorded in the following documents which belong to the few records still existing today:

10-liter rocket (Magdeburger Startgerät)

Built by: Rudolf Nebel, Klaus Riedel, Hans Hueter, Kurt Heinisch, and the mechanics Bermueller, Ehmeyer, and Zoike.

Date: 1933 (January–April).

Purpose: Rocket built for demonstration at air show in Magdeburg.

Coordinator: Mr. Mengering.

Ground tests: August 1932 to March 1933.

Launching rack: Vertical double rail, 12 m high.

Launch tests:

8 June 1933, 4 a.m.:
On the Mose estate near Magdeburg. Oxygen tank leaking; experiment stopped.

11 June 1933, 11 a.m.:
On the Mose estate near Magdeburg. Oxygen valve fails; experiment stopped.

13 June 1933, 6 p.m.:
On the Mose estate near Magdeburg. Oxygen valve fails; experiment stopped.

29 June 1933, 6:45 p.m.:

Thrust 185 kg. Guide roll jams in rack and breaks; rocket tilts. After reaching height of 30 m, rocket falls back, burns out on the ground.

14 July 1933, 5:45 a.m.:
Lindwerder Island in Lake Tegel. Rocket reaches height of 600 m, then makes 3 loops of about 30 m radius; parachute opens shortly before impact on water; probably failure of oxygen valve.

21 July 1933, 5:00 p.m.:
Lindwerder Island in Lake Tegel. Rocket reaches height of 100 m; burns out on the water.

5 August 1933, 8:00 a.m.:
Launch from raft in Lake Schwielow near Potsdam. Valve fails; rocket reaches height of 60 m, then burns out on the water.

11 August 1933, 12 noon:
Launch from raft in Lake Schwielow near Potsdam. Valve fails; rocket reaches height of 80 m, falls into the water with engine still burning; in spite of rescue efforts, could not be found again.

1 September 1933, 3 p.m.:
Launch from raft in Lake Schwielow near Potsdam. Rocket reaches height of 30 m, then starts to spin; submerges in water, then reappears with engine still burning, parachute opens too early and stops ascent.

9 September 1933.
Launch from raft in Lake Schwielow near Potsdam. Pipe breaks and parachute burns.

General details:

Pressurization: oxygen by self-evaporation, gasoline and nitrogen pressurant prior to lift-off.

Propellants: Liquid oxygen and gasoline.

Cooling: Forced fuel flow and excess O_2.

Measurements (slightly different for all types):

Length: 280 cm.

Max. diameter: 75 cm.

Configuration: 4 tanks in square formation. Magdeburg type with shroud (first launches without shroud). Lake Schwielow type in longitudinal formation, length about 4.5 m.

Stabilizer fins: In most cases none.

Weight and other data (Approximations):

Engine: 3.5 kg.

Tank, structural elements and valves: 60.0 kg.

Air frame: 6.5 kg.

Payload: 0 kg.

Dry weight (without payload): 70.0 kg.

Volume: 1.0 m³ per tank (Duralumin).

Combustion chamber: Duralumin and Pantal.

Tensile strength: 11–13 kg/mm².

Specific weight: 2.7 g/cm³.

Elongation: 20 to 25%.

Combustion chamber: Bondur.

Tensile strength: 40 to 45 kg/mm².

Elongation: 16 to 20%.

Length (total): 70 cm.

Length (Inside): 62 cm.

Configuration: Elongated ellipsoid.

Max. inner diameter: 16.8 cm.
Max. O.D. combustion chamber: 30.0 cm.
Throat diameter: 5.03 cm.
Nozzle exit diameter: 8.4 cm.
Injection element configuration: 3 counterflow systems.
Max propellant capacity: 34 kg O_2, 6 kg gasoline.
Stoichiometric propellant weights: 3.5 kg O_2 (includes 62%
   O_2 excess) + 1 kg gasoline = 4.5 kg.

Operational data:

Tank pressure 20 kg/cm² (gauge).
Combustion pressure 18 kg/cm² (gauge).
Burning time (full thrust) 32.5 sec.
Average thrust 250 kg.
Specific propellant consumption 6.8 kg/ton sec.
Propellant flow rate 1.7 kg/sec.

Propulsion system data:

Exhaust velocity: 805 m/sec.
Engine weight/impulse: 14.0 kg/ton sec.

Rocket stage data:

Tank and structural weight/impulse 240 kg/ton sec.
Air frame weight/impulse 26.0 kg/ton sec.

Seen historically, these tests with the 10-L rocket indicated progress, at least with regard to the engine development; but this did not suffice to maintain operations of the Rocket Field and the Verein für Raumschiffahrt. With the Magdeburg adventure, the people in charge had gone too far! Not only did they hurt their professional reputation by quackish advertisement of a manned rocket flight and lose the confidence of their contract partners because they did not fulfill their promises regarding schedules and performance for which they had been paid in advance; they also lost complete control over their finances by inadequate calculations and bookkeeping.

All this was sufficient reason for intervention by those who had assumed political power in Germany in the spring of 1933. Herbert Schaefer reported [21] that an inspector who supervised all activities was assigned to the Rocket Field and, a short time later, the Gestapo confiscated all journals and newspapers, books, and working papers. In 1934, the organization was dissolved and similar incorporations prohibited. The most competent technician and designer in the group was doubtlessly Klaus Riedel, who was hired by Walter Dornberger, Chief of the Sub-Office for Rocket Development in the German Ordnance Department. The talented organizer and *spiritus rector* of the group, Rudolf Nebel, received a good sum of money as indemnification payment.

From the military point of view, Walter Dornberger gave the following account:

This office, to which problems of rocket development had been transferred in 1929, was confronted at first by a muddle difficult to straighten out. Neither industry nor the technical colleges were paying any attention to the development of high-performance rocket propulsion. There were only individual inventors who played about without financial support, assisted by more or less able collaborators. . . . Until 1932, no solid scientific research or development work was done in this field in Germany . . . The Army Weapons Department was forced to get in touch with the individual inventors, support them financially, and await results. For two years, the department tried in vain to obtain something to go on. No progress was being made in the work. There was also the danger that thoughtless chatter might result in the department's becoming known as the financial backer of rocket development. We had therefore to take other steps. As we did not succeed in interesting heavy industry, there was nothing left to do but to set up our own experimental station for liquid-propellant rockets at the department's proving ground in Kummersdorf near Berlin. We wanted to have done once and for all with theory, unproved claims, and boastful fantasy, and to arrive at conclusions based on a sound scientific foundation.[22]

Among the first members of the experimental station—besides the then very young Wernher von Braun and the mechanic Heinrich Grünow—were two former employees of the Heylandtwerke, Walter Riedel, a close collaborator of Max Valier, and Arthur Rudolph, who, after Valier's death, had continued with Alphons Pietsch the development of Valier's "Standard Combustion Chamber."

The first engine, built at the end of 1932 by this group according to Walter Riedel's suggestions, had regenerative surface cooling, using fuel as coolant. Dornberger described the engine:

The combustion chamber, with its round head and tapering exhaust nozzle, was calculated to develop a thrust of 300 kg. On the right side of the measuring room . . . a spherical aluminum container with liquid oxygen was suspended. . . . A similar container hung on the left-hand side. It contained 75 percent alcohol. The alcohol duct forked into two branches, each connected to the bulbous edge of the exhaust nozzle. Thin piano wires from the tanks led over rollers through the concrete wall to instruments that would trace the graphs of fuel consumption during firing. The rocket motor itself had double walls. Between them rose cooling alcohol at a high rate of flow from bottom to top. The alcohol, warmed to 70° C, entered the inner chamber through small sievelike injection nozzles in the chamber head. It was met there by liquid oxygen ejected from a centrally placed brass sprayer shaped like an inverted mushroom and perforated with many small holes.[23]

The first test, on 21 December 1932, was a failure. The engine and test rack burnt out after a detonation.

A smaller version of the 300-kg combustion chamber had already been ordered in 1931 from the Heylandtwerke, according to Dornberger's account. Cylinder-shaped, it had been designed for a thrust of 20 kg, with double iron walls for cooling purposes; thus, most likely, the first combustion chamber with regenerative surface cooling was built in 1931 by Heylandt. Toward the end of 1933, after a series of significant modifications but without fundamental changes in the cooling system, the 300-kg engine finally operated and developed exhaust velocities up to 1800 m/sec in static testing.

For the rockets following the A-1 with its 16-sec burning time, engines with longer operation times, higher performance, and better cooling systems had to be built. The 1000 kg engine of the A-2 rocket, however, that reached altitudes of more than 2000 m during the first launches in December 1934, did not show any significant modifications compared to the A-1.

Subsequently, between the groundbreaking ceremony for the new test facilities in Peenemuende in August 1936 and the first test firing of the A-3 from the new test area in December 1937, the new A-3 rocket with a height of 6.5 m and take-off weight of 0.75 tons was developed; there also was developed by Wernher von Braun, Walter Dornberger, Walter Riedel, and Walter Thiel, in close cooperation, a new and considerably improved engine developing a thrust of 1500 kg. The modifications included an improved injection system with centrifugal injection nozzles, a mixing chamber between injection head and combustion zone, and improved gas flow through conical form of the lower part of the combustion chamber. But, again, cooling problems increased with improvements in performance and rise of combustion chamber temperature in the 1500-kg engine.

During the development and construction of the next prototype, a 4500-kg engine, using an assembly of three injection heads from the 1500-kg engine in one combustion chamber, one of Thiel's associates, Wilhelm Poehlmann, suggested a decisive innovation. Dornberger described this event as follows:

> Yet the motors still burned through, from time to time, at points along the wall or at the throat of the nozzle. Dr. Thiel's engineer colleague, Poehlmann, made a useful suggestion: How would it be if a sort of insulating layer were formed between the heat of the combustion gas and the wall? If we sprayed the inner wall of the chamber with alcohol, it would of course evaporate and burn, but the temperature of this layer could never equal that inside the chamber. Such was the origin of film-cooling. A large number of small perforations at the endangered sections admitted alcohol to the motor and especially to the exhaust nozzle under slight differential pressure. The holes in the wall were filled, after drilling, with Wood's metal, which melted as soon as the flame formed, thus allowing the cooling alcohol to enter.[24]

The first large 25-ton engines which were tested in spring 1939 on test stand 1 at Peenemuende, used this new cooling process. Thus, after 15 years, in 1938, an idea first proposed by Oberth in his famous book *Die Rakete zu den Planetenräumen*, had finally been realized. On 3 October 1942, the first successful launch of an A-4 rocket provided the climax of this development and represented an important milestone.

Work of Eugen Sänger in Vienna

In a curriculum vitae presented in 1934, Eugen Sänger wrote:

> During physics classes in high school we were at times introduced to the field of rocketry. After 1926, when the use of rocket propulsion for very fast stratosphere airplanes had been recognized as feasible, I began to study this problem more seriously.

In August 1931, Sänger started to summarize his occasional studies and their results in the form of a book published by R. Oldenbourg, Munich, in the spring of 1933 under the title *Raketenflugtechnik* (Technology of Rocket Flight). Having temporarily completed his preliminary theoretical studies, Sänger began in 1933 to conduct experiments at the Technische Versuchsanstalt (Technical Research Institute) regarding the selection of materials for a reaction motor. In autumn of 1933, he proposed to the Verband der Freunde der Technischen Hochschule Wien (Society of Friends of the Technical University of Vienna), a brief, well-defined program for "Model Tests with Uniform-Pressure Rocket Engines." In addition, a program for the practical development of rocket flights was set up and presented to the public. Actually, the true inspiration for Sänger's work in the field of spaceflight and rocketry had been a science fiction novel that he had received on 7 February 1919, at the age of 13, as a gift from his physics teacher, Dr. Gustav Schwarzer. It was the book *Auf zwei Planeten* (On Two

Planets) by Kurd Lasswitz, published in 1897, which Rudolf Nebel had also mentioned in his book *Raketenflug*[25] as one of his sources of inspiration.

On 28 January 1964, a few days before his death, Sänger said in an interview with a reporter from RIAS Berlin:

Indeed, my first contact with astronautics took place in high school when my physics teacher, whose favorite pupil I was because I had shown special interest in his experiments, presented me with the book *Auf zwei Planeten* by Kurd Lasswitz. . . . Of course, I read the novel with fascination and later dreamt that this would be a task for my whole life. But, of course, at that time, no one ever thought that this could really become a professional career. I started to study these questions seriously when I got hold of the first publication by Hermann Oberth. This happened while I was enrolled at the Technical University in Vienna. I was preparing myself for the tests in mechanical engineering and had studied these subjects very thoroughly. When I began to recalculate Oberth's formulae, I became convinced that there was much behind his writings which had to be taken seriously. From that moment on, I started to delve more and more into this area. An additional problem for me was that I had studied civil engineering at the Technical University . . . and that I had to change my major considerably toward the field of aviation and whatever might follow.

These historical aspects and Sänger's inclination toward a systematic approach may explain why he did not try, as the Berlin group did, to use Oberth's plans for developing and testing single- or multi-stage ballistic rockets, but rather followed in the Austrian tradition of von Hoefft and Valier and pursued the logical course from aeronautics via stratospheric flight to the gradual exploration of space. In the papers that Sänger left behind were several plans that he had made during different times of his life. In these he had formulated the goals of his various activities and carefully checked off the milestones already reached. One of the earliest plans dated back to about 1929 and 1931. Under the entry "constructions" he listed the following steps:

Stratosphere Plane—Space Ferry—Space Station—Planetary Spacecraft—Space Ship; and under the heading "Publications —Major Studies" the planned books: Stratospheric Flight— Cosmo-Technology—Biotechnology, and a philosophical novel "The Road to Thule."

From the very beginning, Eugen Sänger considered space travel as a manned flight venture. Thus, the realization of his first project, a stratosphere plane, simply seemed to him the very first step toward true space flight; and he did not want to skip this step (as it later actually happened). In line with his studies as a civil engineer, he began with the design of the airframe and the study of its aerodynamical flight behavior. During this time, the first direct meeting between Eugen Sänger and the two Austrian space flight pioneers, Guido von Pirquet and Franz von Hoefft, took place; but it did not lead to any technical cooperation. Guido von Pirquet wrote about it:

In 1927, Hoefft had the idea to have a rocket model tested in the wind tunnel of the Institute of Aerodynamics at the Technical University of Vienna. Based on the concepts of Hoefft, I built the test model. While the test results were satisfactory, they did not find any immediate technical application. But we learned at that time that a young assistant of the Institute was a great rocket enthusiast. Thus, for the first time, I heard of Eugen Sänger.

Somewhat later I learned that Sänger was looking for a place to test rockets. As I owned a vacant field near Vienna, 1 km in length and 140 m wide, which I considered suitable for such tests, I contacted him and he came to see me and my wife in Hirschstetten and we met personally for the first time. However, the tests were not made on my property after all and I also did not discuss with Sänger the possibility of testing my nozzle configurations.

Still existing today is a letter to Guido von Pirquet, then secretary of the Wissenschaftliche Gesellschaft für Höhenforschung (Scientific Society for High Altitude Research), dated 27 March 1928, in which Sänger applied for membership in the society and offered his assistance for Dr. Hoefft's preliminary experiments at the Institute for Aerodynamics.

Among the fragments of papers listed in Sänger's first "life plan" was a draft for Raketenflugtechnik (Technology of Rocket Flight). The cover page carries the additional inscription "Thesis to Obtain a Doctorate in the Engineering Sciences, Submitted to the Technical University Vienna in Summer 1929 by Eugen Sänger. Studies on the problems of high altitude flights of rocket airplanes." The draft is divided into four sections: (1) General Comments; (2) Ascent; (3) Free Flight; (4) Descent. It does not include studies on propulsion systems. Apparently, Eugen Sänger had prepared the draft for this thesis after he had passed his oral examinations for a doctor's degree on 27 June 1929. In his last interview with RIAS in 1964, he explained:

I wanted to write my doctoral thesis on a subject in the field of space flight. My very wise old teacher Katzmayr, however, under whom I was studying aeronautics, told me at that time: "Well, I believe it is more practical if you write your doctoral thesis on a more classical subject. Things will then go much smoother. If you try today to write your thesis on space flight, you may be an old man with a long beard before you get your degree."

Dutifully and successfully, Sänger wrote his thesis on "The statics of multi-spar truss wings with parallel webs, cantilevered and half-supported, directly and indirectly loaded," and was awarded a doctor's degree on 5 July 1929.

From February 1930 on, Sänger worked as assistant to Professor Rinagl at the Institute for Materials Research of the Technical University, in Vienna. His private work continued nevertheless. In the second chapter of a manuscript entitled "Cosmo-Technology" he listed under the heading "Ship Propulsion – The Rocket as Prime Mover" the following outline: (1) General Remarks; (2) Rocket Theory; (3) The Chemical Rocket; (4) The Radium Rocket; (5) The X-Ray Rocket. As "Radium Rocket" Sänger described what we would call today an isotope-heated propulsion system. In the chapter "X-Ray Rocket" he put on paper some preliminary studies on what many years later became known as his theory of the "Photon Rocket."

Up to mid-1931, Eugen Sänger still spent most of his time on wind-tunnel tests with three-dimensionally curved flight profiles. Apparently, no records are left, but the results were published by Sänger in an article, "Über Flügel hoher güte" (On High-Performance Wings), that appeared in the magazine *Flugsport* (Air Sports) on 24 June 1931.

Immediately following, he began to summarize the results of his fundamental studies on rocket flight, using many elements from his earlier drafts for "Stratospheric Flight" and "Cosmo-Technology." In May 1933, they were published under the title "Raketenflugtechnik." [26] The 222-page treatise with chapters on "Propulsive Forces, Aerodynamic Forces, Trajectories" was to be a fundamental theoretical textbook. In the introduction, Sänger specified that design details were intentionally omitted in all discussions. Yet, some comments on the cooling problems encountered with liquid rocket engines were included on page 53:

One of the significant physical properties of the propellants is their cooling capacity. . . . This cooling capacity is of importance because the propellants themselves must probably be used to cool the engine instead of having a special coolant dissipate heat across combustion chamber and nozzle walls to the outside air. As a rule, the cryogens (liquid hydrogen, liquid oxygen, liquid nitrogen) are unsuitable for wall cooling since they boil off under the pressure and temperature

conditions within the tank and do not absorb heat prior to evaporation.

According to the notes of his later Vienna log book, Sänger's first designs for a combustion chamber and his preliminary practical experiments date back to 1932, the year in which he also started to lecture on this subject at the Technical University in Vienna.

The oldest of Sänger's still-existing test logs dates from December 1932. With a welding torch Sänger spot heated the 3-mm-thick steel wall of a cylindrical container filled with water and recorded the following: "The wall becomes red hot; a layer of steam forms at the hot spot and displaces the water; afterwards, the wall melts very quickly."

In this Vienna log book one of the first sketches, dating from 3 January 1933 bears the designation "Basic Project." It depicts a simple conical nozzle with a small opening angle (about 8°), an extended exhaust, and double-path cooling. The portions of the engine steel jacket exposed to combustion gases are lined with magnesium oxide. Also provided is a jacket for dynamic cooling by means of a propellant which is pumped from the tank through the cooling jacket—in counter flow to the exhaust gases—into the injector. Altogether, the proposal combines capacity cooling by a ceramic liner with a high melting point and regenerative surface cooling.

Since his primary duties were as assistant at the Institute for Materials Research, it is understandable that in the beginning Sänger was preoccupied by materials testing, especially by screening potential structural and heat-resistant materials for the rocket engine. Up to February 1933, after his first test firings with chamber walls of steel and static water cooling had been unsatisfactory, he exposed plates, or pipes of electrode graphite, thorium oxide, tungsten, and magnesium oxide to flames of a welding torch. During all these tests he studied with special interest the effect of oxygen-rich combustion and the rate of dissociation of the welding flame.

For a few months after 3 February 1933, there are no notes in the log book, only blank but numbered pages. It is not clear whether the experiments were interrupted due to other commitments—such as the publication of *Raketenflugtechnik*—or whether test logs from this period were lost.

During this time, the only known direct contact between the Berlin and the Vienna group occurred.

Rudolf Nebel, who had somehow heard very quickly of the contract signed on 11 March 1933 between Sänger and the publishing house Oldenbourg, wrote Sänger on 25 March 1933:

Dear Dr. Sänger:

We heard that you are planning to complete your manuscript on rocket technology by April 1. Herewith, we are taking the liberty of forwarding you some informational data and asking whether you might need additional material for your book. We could also supply photographic material. We assume that you are interested in including in your book the latest research and are looking forward to hearing from you.

Sincerely yours,
Berlin Rocket Field, Nebel.

Attached to his letter was Nebel's paper "Rocket Flight" dating from the year 1932. Eugen Sänger, on April 5, sent the following thank-you letter:

Dear Mr. Nebel:

This is to thank you for your letter of March 25 and your paper "Rocket Flight" which I read with very great interest.

I am continuing with my work and would, of course, be glad to accept your kind offer, should you be able to relate to an outsider some of your apparently considerable experience. First of all, I would like to mention that my book "Technology of Rocket Flight" that has already gone to print, discusses in a purely theoretical manner the scientific aspects of the indicated subject. Structural details and photos of structural elements are not included. My studies are limited to liquid-propellant rockets. In comparison to your practical experiments a difference exists in that I have eliminated on the basis of my theoretical studies any static liquid cooling of the rocket because of the chill-down problems that would occur at high flight speeds. Partly, this is due to the fact that I have considered the rocket purely from the standpoint of a propulsion system for aircraft.

Thus, it would be of special interest for me to hear of the experience that you gained earlier when still using heat-blocking, highly refractory materials for nozzle walls, in particular I am interested in the type of materials used.

For lecture purposes I would appreciate receiving from you some technical slides and detail drawings showing the actual configuration, if these can be made public.

May I thank you again for your kind offer. With best regards,

Sincerely yours,
E. Sänger.

No reply to this letter was ever received from Berlin, perhaps because of the poltical changes occurring at that time.

On 10 October 1933, Sänger presented a comprehensive plan, "Testing Models of Constant-Pressure Rocket Engines," to Professor Rinagl, his superior and the director of the Technical Research Institute of the Technical University in Vienna; to Professor Katzmayr, chief of the Department of Aeronautics; and also to the Association of Friends of the Technical University in Vienna, asking for their support for his efforts. With regard to the cooling problem he mentioned in this paper:

A key problem in building a rocket thruster burning at constant pressure is the thermal design of the combustion-chamber wall. It essentially consists of a load-carrying outer shell, which has to withstand the very high combustion pressures, and of an inner liner, which has to meet the following requirements:

1. Adequate high-temperature service life, i.e., sufficient mechanical strength at temperatures around 3500° C. Because of low heat transfer and a very thin temperature boundary layer, the inner surfaces of the combustion chamber liner attain almost the same temperature as the combustion gases.

2. Adequate resistance against chemical reactions with high-temperature combustion products, thus assuring that a liner lasts at least for a maximum operating time of 20 minutes.

3. Adequate thermal insulation assuring that the penetrating heat can be absorbed by the propellants; the use of propellants as coolants is feasible if the heat flux through the liner is less than 1% of the liberated chemical propellant energy.

4. Minimum weight.

Because of the first requirement, from the currently known high-temperature resistant materials only a few metals, metallic oxides, carbides and pure carbon may be considered, mainly: thorium oxide, rhenium, zirconium carbide, titanium carbide, tungsten, tantalum carbide, niobium carbide, hafnium carbide, a mixture of hafnium and tantalum carbide, and carbon. A final selection from among these materials would have to be based on screening tests. . . . To cool the walls of the combustion chamber and nozzle directly by air stream during flight or by circulating a coolant around the combustion chamber wall and through an air-cooled heat exchanger, as used for internal combustion engines, is impossible. The huge amount of heat to be dissipated in a very short time approximates 150,000 kilowatts for an aircraft weighing only 10,000 kilograms at take-off. . . . Direct or indirect air-cooling must be ruled out because the air streaming past the aircraft is heated by stagnation and friction. . . . Consequently, the temperature difference between ambient air and cooled wall at first diminishes and at very high flight speeds turns zero or negative. . . . The walls exposed to the burning gases must be highly heat-insulating and without cooling withstand chemical reactions of high-temperature combustion gases. Cooling of the combustion chamber and heat flux across its walls is limited by the heat-ingesting capability of the propellants serving as coolants prior to their evaporation and injection into the combustion chamber. . . . The design considerations valid for the combustion chamber apply also to the structural and liner materials of the nozzle. . . . Of course, even the most careful precautions cannot prevent relatively rapid wear of the liner material of the combustion chamber and nozzle throat. For the initial development it would be satisfactory if the liner lasted for one flight (principle of ablation cooling) and be replaced each time thereafter. . . . A complete combustion chamber wall with graphite liner can be built according to the following scheme [a drawing showing a wall section]. The porous graphite liner can also be replaced by a porous carbon liner of higher mechanical strength and another high-temperature chemically resistant material, such as magnesium oxide, thorium oxide or the like. . . . One should also investigate whether the wear of the combustion chamber wall could be reduced by a fuel additive (perhaps iron carbonyl, *asphalt*, etc.) which burns and leaves deposits on the wall, as for example in internal combustion engines, and thus regenerates the chamber liner. . . . Finally, methods for cooling the chamber walls and nozzle throat have to be developed. From the previous discussions it follows that only the propellants qualify as coolants. Of these, liquid oxygen must initially be eliminated; prior to its evaporation it cannot absorb any additional heat, and evaporation must not occur since only as a liquid can it be fed into the combustion chamber at a tolerable power consumption. However, one could take advantage of the fact that an increase in pressure raises the saturation of the liquid oxygen and results in a temperature difference which would permit the liquid oxygen to absorb a certain amount of heat; the liquid oxygen, only after its discharge from the pumps, could be passed through the cooling jacket of the thrust chamber, but this method would necessitate extremely thick cooling-jacket walls. . . .

The report also proposes three test series, the first involving "small thrust devices producing 10 to 20 kilograms of thrust." Suggested test objectives of the first series are:

1. Find suitable high-temperature-resistant materials for lining combustion chamber and nozzle throat.
2. Determine magnitude of exhaust velocity and its dependence on combustion pressure and mixture ratio.
3. Determine allowable ratio of propellant mass flow to combustion chamber volume.
4. Find suitable configurations and structural materials for building the nozzle.
5. Gather experience on auxiliary equipment.

As to the hardware of the first test series, the following ground rules apply: weight does not matter; tapwater is used to cool the combustion chamber, thus the chamber material need not be a highly effective thermal insulator; external energy drives the propellant pumps, etc.—or briefly, let test objectives predominate.

In these initial proposals for methodical rocket propulsion research, Sänger suggested that details of the propellant coolant loop and the feed-pump drive system be clarified only during the second test series.

In December 1933, Sänger submitted to the Austrian Defense Department a revised version of his development plan, augmented by the preliminary design of a liquid-oxygen-cooled rocket propulsion system SR-2 which he described as follows:

The principle is that the diesel fuel flows from the tank through the pump into the combustion chamber as a liquid, whereas the oxygen passes as a liquid from the tank through the pump, is forced (while evaporating) through the cooling jacket passages, and enters the combustion chamber as a gas of approximately 100° C. Thus the thermal stresses across the injector elements are reduced and about 55% of the fuel caloric value can be absorbed by the coolant.

This concept combined cooling by storing heat in the liner with independent external cooling by tapwater and forced regenerative cooling (oxygen coolant channels).

By the way, shortly after the release of the development plan in October 1933, the Viennese journal *Radio-Welt* (Radio World), (No. 43, 22 October 1933) published for the first time for wide distribution a design sketch of a rocket engine by Sänger. The sketch did not contain any new items on cooling methods or propellant feeding beyond the original proposal of 5 January 1933, but instead of a conical chamber it showed a spherical combustion chamber with a Laval-type nozzle attached.

The first version of the research proposal prompted Professor Rinagl to make available for the first test runs some unoccupied buildings located in the old "Bauhof," on Dreihufeisengasse near the Electrotechnical Institute, which were modified in a makeshift fashion to provide a test area open to the outside and some sort of an adjoining operations and observation bunker. Sänger also gained the support of two of Rinagl's assistants, the Sztatecsny brothers Friedrich and Stefan. With them he founded a cooperative association which truly endured the upcoming tough and critical months. The trio proudly called the old shed in the Bauhof "Deutsche Raketenflugwerft" (German Rocket Flight Yard).

Less successful was Sänger's second version of the research proposal submitted to the Austrian Department of Defense, through Dr. Leitner, Superintendent General. In early February 1934, the manuscript was returned to Sänger with the following reply:

Concerning your letter of December 26, 1933, you are informed herewith that after evaluation of your rocket development proposal the Department of Defense does not intend to pursue this matter any further since the basic design concept (use of liquid hydrocarbons and liquid oxygen) appears non-feasible because of the unavoidable detonations connected with the combustion of the said propellants.

February 3, 1934   For the State Secretary
                                 Dr. Leitner, Superintendent General.

Not even was an effort made, prior to returning the manuscript, to erase the reviewer's vitriolic pencil notes from the submitted pages.

The youthful research team, however, could not be discouraged; from that time on they began to look more and more beyond the border, especially toward Germany, as the defiant name of a "German" Rocket Flight Yard demonstrated.

On 7 February 1934, preliminary tests were run again, of which the very first established the trend for future cooling methods. Sänger's log book reads:

Half-inch steel and copper tubing with a wall thickness of 1 to 2 millimeters is connected to a water line and water is passed through. An attempt is made to melt the tubing by heating it on the outside with a welding torch (largest available burner No 22–30). But as long as running water completely fills the tube, the torch can cut neither copper nor steel tubing.

At the end of the detailed test report it says: "The experiments are considered decisive for testing thrustor models with metallic combustion chamber walls cooled by fuel."

The next combustion chamber design, SR-3, was first hot-fired on 14 March 1934, after completion of the test set-up. It no longer had a liner, only bare steel walls which were still water-cooled during the first test series. Otherwise, SR-3 consisted of a cylindrical combustion chamber and an attached Laval nozzle with a 6° half-angle, a 1.2-mm throat diameter and a nozzle-area ratio of 10:1. A cylindrical cooling jacket surrounded chamber and nozzle. The total length of the thrustor was 180 mm and its outside diameter 57 mm. During Sänger's first test series, Shell diesel fuel from a three-cylinder, manually operated pump was burned with gaseous oxygen supplied from bottles with a volume of 6 m³ and under storage pressure of 150 atm. During the test the thrustor was suspended from the ceiling in a hinged frame which could move only in the direction of the horizontal thrustor axis. A horizontal spring dynamometer, firmly braced to the ground, accepted the full thrust. Also recorded, in addition to thrust, were chamber pressure, flow rate, and cooling-water temperature, fuel and oxygen consumption, total thrustor operating time, and overall test duration. By 6 April 1934, this type of thrustor was tested 60 times and combustion chamber pressures up to 45 atm, thrust levels up to 1 kg and exhaust velocities up to more than 830 m/sec were measured during test runs exceeding 26 min. Thereafter, for some tests, the throat diameter was varied between 1.2 and 2.5 mm—and correspondingly the nozzle area ratio—with the result that the exhaust velocities increased up to at least 1460 m/sec and the thrust levels up to 2.80 kg.

On 20 March 1934, while still running these tests, Sänger—drawing from his experience gained on February 7—conceived the first thrustor featuring forced regenerative cooling with the cooling coils wrapped around the smooth walls of the combustion chamber and nozzle. By 14 April 1934, this concept was incorporated into the design of SR-4. Copper tubing of 8/10 mm (id/od), tightly wound, with wall-to-wall contact, was to be brazed to the 3-mm-thick cylindrical combustion chamber shell and the adjoining nozzle. The total thrustor length was to be 283 mm and the maximum outside diameter 95 mm. For the first time, a short nozzle with an 8° half-angle, a 2.4-mm throat diameter and again an area ratio of 10:1 was proposed.

However, on 23 April 1934, based on analytical studies, Sänger terminated the work on SR-4 in favor of a new design (SR-5) with thrustor walls made up solely of coiled tubing welded on the outside; thus, the load-carrying shell portions were exposed to lower temperatures and the heat-dissipating surfaces enlarged in comparison to those of a smooth inner wall. The shell of the elongated cylindrical combustion chamber of SR-5 consisted of coiled double tubing with the coolant in counterflow so that both coolant inlet and outlet were close to the injector. The short nozzle with a 4° half-angle had a 2.3-mm throat diameter and a 4:1 area ratio. SR-5 tests were run between 7 and 14 May 1934. During a burning time of 260 sec at a chamber pressure of 47 atm this model realized an exhaust velocity of 1750 m/sec comparable to a theoretical value of 1913 m/sec.

During one of these firings Sänger, for the first time, thought about vapor as a potentially feasible coolant and on 9 May 1934, wrote about test run 83 in his log book:

For the time being, since a water pump is not available and cooling by vapor to be investigated, partial evaporation of cooling water is acceptable. . . . During the test run, strong evaporation at the cooling water outlet can be observed, and at times reading of the dynamometer is difficult. After 260 sec, at test cut-off, the nozzle is thrown out; at the top, water passages have been leaking slightly, but apparently, due to the manufacturing, the walls were already very thin and only kept leakproof by brazing them to the nozzle. In any case, cooling by coolant evaporation is feasible.

On May 12, he wrote:

The tests in Vienna aim at developing a rocket engine of 100-kg thrust with self-contained propellant feeding and self-contained cooling.

On May 13:

Since detonations cannot be eliminated whenever diesel fuel and liquid oxygen are burned, the rocket combustion chamber must be designed to permit reaction rates of 500 PS/cm³. Under these conditions the combustion chamber volume of the 100-kg thrust rocket engine shrinks to 7 cm³, thus making the project of 5 January 1933, important again. All the same time, detonations in such a thrustor are harmless! Heat transfer drops to a minimum! The operational limits of a cooling method using solely liquid oxygen can be determined on small scale thrustors. . . . One must try to obtain optimum atomization by forcing O_2 and fuel through many small orifices, with the propellants impinging on each other perpendicularly to the thrustor axis! One should also consider splash plates with concentric tube injector elements and short cylindrical combustion chambers!

Thus, according to the "Basic Project", the SR-6 was built without cylindrical combustion chamber as a purely conical thrust chamber with a half-angle of 3°, a throat diameter of 5.0 mm, a total nozzle length of 200 mm, and an area ratio of 9.6:1. It was made of 1-mm-thick Caro bronze. On May 21, Eugen Sänger wrote in his log book with regard to SR-6:

Design and construction of SR-6 will be based on experience gained by tests on

1. Liquid cooling of metallic combustion chamber walls (7 February 1934)
2. Total heat flux across chamber walls (22 April 1934)
3. Reaction rates of high pressure combustion chambers (13 May 1934 and 5 January 1933)
4. Nozzle efficiencies (20 May 1933)

For future designs the experience on

5. Liquid oxygen as high-pressure coolant (19 October 1933)
6. Steam as high-pressure coolant (9 May 1934)
7. Propellant feeding (26 April 1934)

will be applied.

Original plans called for operating SR-6 with liquid oxygen; but since delivery of adequate liquid oxygen pumps from Germany was delayed, it was decided to start testing the SR-6 with available gaseous oxygen and water as a coolant. After testing of the model was completed, Sänger wrote on 9 June 1934:

Summary of essential test results obtained to date:

A. Principal items:
   1. Liquid coolants for metallic combustion chamber walls
   2. Heat flux of about 0.3 PS/cm² independent of thrust
   3. Combustion and detonation speed (combustion chamber reaction rate)
   4. High efficiencies of nozzles with small half-angle
   5. High-pressure fuel as coolant
   6. High-pressure oxygen as potential supplemental coolant
B. Design:
   1. Patent on combustion chamber wall (5 June 1934)
   2. Thrustor without combustion chamber (5 January 1933)
   3. Propellant pumps (26 April 1934)
   4. Monolithic structure (partly SR-6, totally SR-7)
C. Performances achieved:
   1. Thrust of about 5.5 kg
   2. Exhaust velocity of about 1780 m/sec in spite of wrong nozzle area ratio.

Furthermore, during these tests Sänger was able to increase the combustion chamber pressure to 17 atm under entirely stable combustion with oxygen supplied at 50 atm pressure. He then decided to modify his test program and instead of the liquid oxygen firing tests to develop the high-pressure fuel cooling method conceived in 1932. For these tests—in contrast to the ones run at Berlin—he planned to feed liquid oxygen by pump through the cooling passages into the combustion chamber. On 4 June 1934, Sänger explained his decision as follows:

The Linde Corporation offers oxygen pumps of about 1500 PS with a weight of 1000 kg, which is still unacceptable; also, the high-pressure gasifiers operating above the critical pressure of 51 atm only furnish gaseous oxygen and they cannot be used either. Hence, the tests with gaseous oxygen in Vienna will be terminated. This is no problem, since self-contained cooling can be accomplished with fuel. At the same time, the specified combustion chamber pressure is reduced to 50 atm in order to obtain improved nozzle dimensions and reduce the residual oxygen in the storage bottles. When injecting liquid oxygen into the latest thrustor model built in Vienna, the operational characteristics are not expected to differ from the performances to be obtained with gaseous oxygen injection up to thrust levels of 50 kg.

The new test model, SR-7, used fuel as a coolant and provided for optional liquid or gaseous oxygen injection. The nozzle had a length of 110 mm, a half-angle of 6° and an area ratio of 5.3:1. It was made of non-scaling bronze and its top part of nickel steel. This time, instead of cooling passages of coiled tubing brazed to the chamber wall, a novel monolithic process was applied whereby integral circumferential grooves were milled into the chamber wall and welded tightly on the outside.

While the new nozzle was being built, Sänger worked again on the fuel problem. On 18 June, he recognized that even with Laval nozzles only a fraction of the theoretical exhaust velocity could be attained; for diesel fuel and oxygen burning at 100 atm the exhaust velocity would not be much higher than 3000 m/sec because of limited chamber pressures and losses caused by dissociation and friction. Thus, even before completion of SR-7, he conducted several preliminary tests on 22 July 1934, with light metal powder suspended in diesel fuel.

On 23 June 1934, the first test with a closed fuel-coolant loop was run. With pumps built by the Bosch Company, diesel fuel was forced at a pressure of 60 atm through the cooling channels of the rocket engine being fired; the diesel fuel was water-cooled and returned to the storage tank. During 15 tests, operating times up to 9 minutes and thrust levels up to 12 kg were demonstrated.

The following test models, SR-8 and SR-9, did not differ from SR-7 except for nozzle length, nozzle half-angle, and area ratio. On 24 July 1934, SR-8 produced a thrust of more than 27 kg, and on 31 July 1934, SR-8 delivered a thrust of 30 kg. However, on 1 August 1934, Sänger wrote:

It seems that the allowable combustion chamber reaction rate is being exceeded, as combustion partly occurs in the open.

During the last test series, increases in thrust reduced the temperatures of the fuel coolant, thus indicating that a larger and larger part of the nozzle was used for mixing instead of burning. This is in agreement with observations made on very short nozzles on 26 July 1934 (SR-8). Apparently, propellant, mixing was not completed entirely within, but partly outside the nozzle.

Therefore, the configuration of SR-10, SR-11, and SR-12 was again based on Sänger's design published in the October 1933 issue of the magazine *Radio-Welt* (Radio World); but it included forced coolant flow as proposed on 15 May 1934, and utilized previous test experience on allowable combustion chamber reaction rates. Model SR-11 delivered again an exhaust velocity of over 2700 m/sec. The coolant tubing could be separated at midlength for easier disassembly of a defective thrust chamber portion. Furthermore, for the first time, the fuel coolant of SR-12 could be chilled twice, as it was found that the fuel exiting from the cooling passages was critically close to its upper temperature limit.

Along with these tests for the development of a

regenerative cooling system with forced fuel flow as coolant, the investigations on burning and cooling effects of liquid oxygen progressed in spite of temporary disappointments. Sänger, unable to obtain a suitable oxygen pump, decided on 4 July 1934, to run his ground tests, for the time being, with pressure-fed liquid oxygen, and he designed a special set-up for it. The simple testing equipment consisted of the following components:

1. High-pressure gas supply system consisting of a 40-liter bottle under an initial pressure of 150 atm and suspended on a scale.
2. Liquid oxygen tank—a 6-liter bottle enclosed in a vacuum-tight jacket filled with about 100 kg of mineral wool; the bottle had a thin riser line connected with the supply line, also a port with a burst-diaphragm and a filler line branching off to the high-pressure gas tank.
3. Measuring system for consumables—a spring scale holding the high-pressure gas bottle and lox tank (together weighing about 200 kg) and clearly indicating weight changes of about 0.1 kg.
4. System of supply lines—lox supply lines of 5-mm-id copper tubing, thermally insulated with asbestos cardboard; a conventional oxygen bottle shut-off valve with hard-rubber gaskets replaced by copper gaskets; valve could be operated from the blockhouse.

This set-up allowed, over a limited but sufficient time, lox to be injected under high and constant pressure through an injector element mounted at the end of a 10-m-long copper line into the combustion chamber or into the open, and the oxygen to be measured consumption during this time. On 20 July 1934, the facility was ready for operation. Originally, tests were to be run with the SR-8 model burning lox and diesel fuel. But it turned out that the close spacing of lox and fuel injection elements, unavoidable in Sänger's model combustion chambers, caused the exiting lox to freeze up the fuel passages even when they were under full flow at a pressure of 200 atm. Therefore, testing was limited to firing in the open; fuel and lox impinged on each other and were ignited by a gas flame. The tests were run up to 20 minutes; lox and fuel injection pressures and impingement angles were varied. On 24 August 1934, Sänger concluded:

In summary, the open firings with lox have shown:

1. Under continuous ignition, a mixture of atomized lox and atomized diesel fuel burns very much like gaseous oxygen. The oxygen mist seems to ignite only after complete evaporation.
2. A mixture of lox and frozen fuel droplets does not detonate, but burns stably and quite rapidly.

In contrast to the comments from the Austrian Department of Defense, the test results prove the outstanding feasibility of the propellant combination. Future engine developemnt tests will be run alternately with gaseous and with liquid oxygen, the latter ones only as complementary tests.

In spite of fuel-rich combustion and correspondingly low combustion gas temperatures, the fuel coolant temperatures in the cooling passages of SR-11 and SR-12 went up to 450° C. To find the causes of this temperature rise, SR-13 was equipped with separate cooling passages for chamber and nozzle. The combustion chamber was made of 6/8 mm (id/od) copper tubing wound to shape for water and later for lox as coolant and the thrust chamber of 2/4 mm (id/od) copper tubing was wound to shape for fuel as coolant. The coolant velocities ranged from 10 to 15 m/sec. After eight tests with SR-13, Sänger wrote in his log book on 18 September 1934:

The current situation is as follows:

The combustion chamber made of carefully wound copper tubing, faultlessly connected at both ends and brazed tight on the outside with bronze wire, withstands all loads with both water and fuel as coolants.

However, the same thermal design does not work at the throat. Thrust chambers, whether cooled by fuel or water and whether made of copper or steel, are burning through near the inlet and in the throat area. Fuel-cooled copper nozzles behave best and water-cooled steel nozzles worst. But it seems that burn-through can be avoided by smooth surfaces inside the nozzle. Obviously, the rough surfaces in the throat area greatly increase the combustion gas-to-wall heat flux up to 1.7 PS/cm² as measured under oxygen-rich combustion. Convection heat transfer seems to be important. . . . The wall thickness, especially that of copper tubing, is less important for the required heat flow rates across the wall. Of decisive importance is the ratio of combustion-gas heat flow to wall and wall-to-coolant heat flow, as determined by the boundary layers on each side.

The hot-side heat transfer is determined by (1) radiation and (2) convection. Convective heat transfer peaks especially around the throat area because of gas velocity and density.

The coolant-side heat transfer is determined by convection and increases with coolant flow velocity and temperature difference between coolant boundary layer and coolant bulk.

Equilibrium between the heat flows on both wall sides must be obtained at wall temperatures compatible with the wall material.

During a number of previous thrust-chamber tests run within the allowable wall temperature range, the hot-side heat flow indeed exceeded that on the coolant side. . . .

In the first place one must try to keep the equilibrium wall temperature below the melting temperature of customary metals, such as copper or bronze.

A. The hot-side heat flux must be minimized.
  1. Eliminate all heat transfer caused by flow perpendicular to the wall (minimum turbulence, no perpendicular flow; walls as smooth as possible).
  2. Reject radiative heat by reflective surfaces.
  3. Minimize heat-exposed surface areas by avoiding protrusions, bends, etc.
  4. Maximize combustion-gas boundary-layer temperature to reduce temperature difference of combustion gas bulk and boundary layer (reduces radiative and convective heat flow).
  5. Reduce combustion-gas density (reduces convection).
B. The coolant-side heat flux must be maximized.
  1. Provide very high coolant flow velocities for better heat transfer.
  2. Increase the heat dissipating surface areas by cooling fins (for example, by internally grooved tubing, according to Sztatecsny).
  3. Provide for coolant flow mainly perpendicular to wall (direct impingement, highly turbulent).
  4. Increase coolant density (high pressure for gases, metallic powder added to diesel fuel).
  5. Increase temperature difference on coolant side by use of cryo-coolants (for example, lox).
  6. Increase coolant boundary-layer temperature for reasons identical to those on the hot side.

If these steps necessitate uneconomical efforts or fail to obtain wall equilibrium temperatures below 1000° C, then high-temperature-resistant nozzle materials have to be used.

Based on this knowledge, SR-14 was built and fired on 4 October 1934. During the second test, it produced a thrust of 2 kg and obtained an exhaust velocity of around 3000 m/sec for a chamber pressure of 16 atm and highly fuel rich combustion; the steady-state run-time, however, was not determined very accurately. During a later test, with 30% fuel-rich combustion, a chamber pressure of 22 atm and a steady-state run duration of 63 sec, a thrust of 4.5 kg and an exhaust velocity of 2760 m/sec were obtained. During both tests, the temperature of the fuel and water coolant stayed within allowable limits and the rocket engine was undamaged.

Regrettably, the testing of this model was limited to five runs. On 17 October 1934, Professor Rinagl forbade further testing because the noise allegedly annoyed the neighbors. The 135th and also the last test, on 23 October 1934, was a demonstration run for Count Max von Arco-Zinneberg; the test operation was smooth and no hardware was damaged. Based on his test experience, Sänger recorded the following notes as patent claims:

1. High-pressure combustion chamber characterized by ducting the propellants around the chamber in such a way that they enter it in a preheated condition and cool the chamber walls.

2. Use of metals as fuels, either in pure form or as additive to other fuels.
3. Use of rocket engine combustion gases to drive propellant feed pumps.
4. Special tubing for building thrust chambers; proper tubing profiles provide for a smooth inside wall and large surface areas for cooling.
5. High-speed lox pumps to prevent oxygen evaporation.
6. Manufacture of combustion and thrust chambers by winding tubes to proper shape.
7. Wall-cooled nozzles characterized by an average divergence angle larger than 25° and smaller than 27° (shortened nozzle).

Sänger, in December 1934, published a short report on his tests and their technical conclusions in a special edition of the magazine *Flug* (Flight). In the following months, he applied for an Austrian patent on some of his ideas including, on 9 February 1935, a claim for the regenerative forced-flow cooling of rocket engines. The Austrian patent 144,809, "Raketenmotor und Verfahren zu seinem Betrieb" (Rocket Engine and Method for its Operation), reads in part:

The coolant must be carefully ducted around the combustion chamber through a specially designed cooling jacket so that a prescribed coolant flow velocity is safely maintained over the entire combustion chamber wall in order to assure at all places the required heat transfer and avoid spot heating of the wall material beyond an allowable limit.

Twelve patent claims followed:

1. Rocket engine with essentially continuous combustion, characterized by forcing a coolant along walls exposed to the combustion so that a specified coolant flow velocity is safely maintained at any given spot of the combustion chamber wall; the ratio of useful combustion chamber volume to the throat cross-sectional area ranges from 50 to 5000 cm^3/cm^2.
2. Rocket engine according to claim no. 1, characterized by grooves machined into the combustion chamber wall, which serve as coolant passages and are properly covered to form a leakproof channel.
3. . . . by winding tubes of arbitrary cross-section around the combustion chamber wall to provide coolant passages.
4. . . . by joining together tubing of any chosen cross-section to form coolant passages with the combustion chamber wall; the tubes to be properly connected to each other.
5. . . . by providing for the combustion chamber wall tubes of such cross-section that joining them together results, without trouble, in a properly shaped, smooth wall surface on the combustion side.
6. . . . by ducting connections, injection passages, etc., into the combustion chamber between the cooling channels in such a way that no uncooled material concentrations occur.
7. . . . by keeping the coolant along its flow path entirely or partly under increased pressure.
8. . . . by reducing to a desired level the amount of combustion-gas heat radiation to the wall through properly heat-reflecting wall surfaces.
9. . . . by applying improved wear-resistant coatings to chamber wall areas subject to wear by impinging combustion gases.
10. . . . by exploiting the wall-to-coolant heat flux for preheating the propellant prior to injection into the combustion chamber.
11. . . . by actually using the propellants (i.e., fuel, lox, etc.) partly or entirely as coolants.
12. . . . by adding to the propellants suitable ingredients, such as catalysts, amylic nitrate, etc., to vary the speed of combustion.

In addition to this basic patent, many patents of addition in various countries were granted; among others, on 11 December 1941, the German patent DRP 716,175; the Italian patent 334,064; the French patent 792,596; the British patent 459,924; and in the United States, patent application USA Serial 33,516 was filed, but the patent was not granted, probably due to the war.

Effective 1 February 1936, Sänger accepted a contract with the Deutsche Versuchsaustalt für Luftfahrt (German Research Institute for Aeronautics) at Berlin-Adlershof that committed him to prepare plans for the establishment of a Raketentechnisches Forschungsinstitut (Rocket Research Institute) and a research program for liquid rocket propulsion systems. Construction of the institute began in February 1937 at Trauen near Lueneburg.

Sänger was able to continue his Viennese tests on a larger scale only after he had moved to Fassberg, near Trauen, on 25 August 1937, and after the "most vital" parts of his new test facility had been completed. This actually happened after the 1926–36 period that was to be covered by this report. Nevertheless, a short historical summary of the later investigations, as far as they concern the completion of his cooling method developed in Vienna, will be presented on the following pages.

On 25 October 1938, prior to resuming his test runs and based on his experience with vapor coolants dating from 9 May 1934, Sänger applied for a patent on an improved, closed regenerative coolant loop using supplemental coolants. In the main process fuel and lox are separately forced by high-pressure pumps through the injector into the combustion chamber, where they burn together and then expand across the nozzle and gain exhaust velocity. The supplemental cooling process handles about 2% of the reaction energy of the main process. Under a pressure of about 250 atm water as supplemental coolant is pumped at the nozzle throat into the cooling channels of the thrust chamber heated by combustion gases; the water circumferentially

circulates several times towards the nozzle exit and is tapped off as superheated steam under high pressure to expand across a turbine down to about 5 atm. In a lox-cooled condenser, the exhausted steam turns to water and thereby preheats the lox

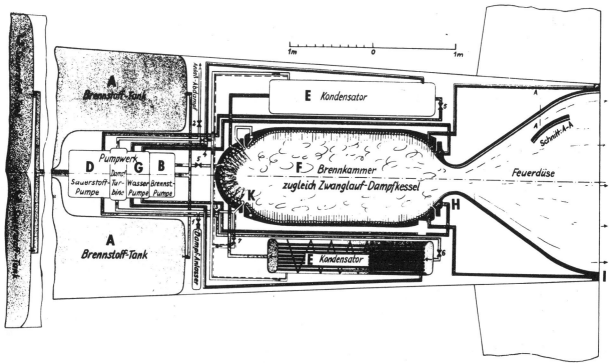

FIGURE 1.—Schematic representation of the main components of the rocket engine, shown installed in the interior of the rocket bomber proposed by Sänger (see reference 14). Its operation is as follows: The fuel goes from the fuel tank (A) to the fuel pump (B), where, compressed to 150 atm, it is then fed continuously through valve 5 to the injection head of the combustion chamber. The oxygen goes from the thin-walled uninsulated oxygen tank (C) into the oxygen pump (D), where it is compressed to 150 atm, then forced through valve 6 and the tubes of the condensers (E) into the injection head of the combustion chamber (F), after being warmed to 0° C. In the combustion chamber the propellants burn at a constant pressure of 100 atm, and a temperature of 4000° C, producing an exhaust velocity of between 3000 and 4000 m/sec, with a thrust of 100,000 kg and a propellant consumption of 245–327 kg/sec. It was proposed that the aircraft carry a 90,000-kg propellant supply and that the rocket engine operate for from 275 to 367 seconds.

The turbopump assembly is driven by steam generated through the cooling of the combustion chamber (F). The water pump (G) delivers

about 28 kg/sec of water, under 250-atm pressure, into the coolant tubes at the nozzle throat (H) whence the water flows toward the nozzle exit (I), being heated to 3000° C in the process. Still above the critical pressure, the water is then forced through the tubes of the combustion chamber (J) where it vaporizes in the critical pressure range. Finally, the resulting highly compressed, superheated steam is removed at the injector head (K) and used to drive the steam turbine. In the process, the steam expands to about 6 atm and passes into the liquid-oxygen-cooled condensers, where the steam is condensed back into water, giving up considerable energy to the oxygen, and then repeats the cooling cycle by again passing through the water pump (G). The steam turbine drives all three pumps from the same shaft. During the process valves 3, 4, 5, and 6 are open; 1 and 2 are closed; while 7 serves as a safety valve against too high rotation of the turbine. The pumping process is started with the aid of an external steam generator, which produces by chemical means the small amounts of steam required; in this process the valves 3 and 4 are closed and 1, 2, 5, 6, and 7 are opened.

by transmitting a considerable amount of residual heat. In a closed loop, the water finally is taken in by the pump. The steam turbine drives the fuel-, lox-, and water-fed pumps mounted on a common shaft.

The patent, "Verfahren zum Betrieb eines Raketenmotors mit Dampfkraftmaschinenhilfsantrieb" (Procedure for Operating a Rocket Engine with a Supplemental Steam-Driven Prime Mover), was granted on 15 March 1940, and filed as German secret patent 380/40, class 46 g. It contained 5 claims (the concepts described in this patent are shown in Figure 1):

1. Procedure for operating a rocket engine, the propellants of which are entirely carried on-board the propelled vehicle, with cooled thrust-chamber walls and supplemental steam-driven prime mover for feeding propellants and coolants, characterized by a combustion-chamber coolant which evaporates solely by cooling the combustion-

chamber wall and is then used to power the supplemental steam-driven prime mover.

2. . . . by circulating in a closed loop the coolant used for cooling the chamber wall and driving the steam engine.

3. . . . by exhausting the coolant for the chamber walls and the steam engine into the open directly after exiting from the steam engine or after passage through the thrust chamber.

4. . . . by a coolant which cools the chamber wall, drives the steam engine, consists of rocket propellants and, after having performed its turbine work, is fed into the rocket engine combustion chamber to burn.

5. Process according to claims nos. 1 and 2, characterized by using a coolant with high thermal conductivity; for example, mercury.

On 9 January 1939, assembly began of a test stand for the first rocket engine with 1000-kg thrust and regenerative forced-flow cooling; and on 24 February 1939, the test area G 1 was officially turned over to Sänger. On 27 June 1939—still with pressure-fed propellants—the first test firings with

FIGURE 2.—Supersonic exhaust gases from the nozzle of 100-kg experimental rocket motor using aluminum dispersed in diesel oil fuel.

diesel fuel and lox began on the test stand (Figure 2) at Trauen. On 28 August 1939, a high-pressure lox tank with a capacity of 56 tons was put into operation. On 3 February 1940, a test series was started for the development of a high-pressure pump for lox, based on Sänger's design. Earlier, on 11 November 1939, Sänger had his drafting shop make the first drawings for a planned 100,000-kg engine. On 1 August 1940, the first test firings began of the 1000-kg engine with both propellants pump-fed (Figure 3). The official log books of this time remained with the German Research Institute for Aviation in Braunschweig and may have been lost during the war or due to other circumstances.

Excerpts from Sänger's personal notes taken in the years 1940–41, however, permit an overview of the tests which were of decisive importance for the

realization of his plans for the development of rocket propulsion systems.

8 January 1940: Up to this time, thrust chambers designed for combustion pressures of 15 atm ($d'/d = 0.56$) were actually operated at 60 atm; therefore, only a $775/870 = 0.89$ portion of the exhaust velocity amounting to $c = 2700/0.89 = 3040$ m/sec could be realized.

2 February 1940: Gear pump tests with lox successful up to 2200 rpm.

5 February 1940: For first time, lox gear pump—with no bearing in lox—run at 1200 rpm.

8 February 1940: For first time, lox gear pump—with no bearing in lox—run at discharge pressure of 5 atm. First successful Roots-type lox pump run!

12 February 1940: Decided to build: (1) helical impeller pump for diesel fuel and aluminum powder; (2) centrifugal impeller pump for lox to permit direct turbine drive for both pumps.

14 February 1940: Helical impeller pump run at 200 rpm with diesel fuel and aluminum powder!

FIGURE 3.—Overall view of a 1000-kg, high-pressure combustion chamber experiment using cooling by evaporation. Propellent tanks are above the roof, to the left. The propellant pumps are directly underneath. Combustion chamber is in operation in center. Note the cloud of condensed cooling agent. The observation stand is above on the right.

15 February 1940: Helical impeller pump run at 9000 rpm with diesel fuel and aluminum powder and a discharge flow of 2 kg/sec.

29 February 1940: First successful Roots-pump run with diesel fuel and aluminum at 12,000 rpm (30% aluminum powder).

1 March 1940: First successful centrifugal pump run with lox.

22 March 1940: First successful test with combination of rotating water-ring and centrifugal pump serving as lox boost pump.

2 April 1940: First high-pressure lox pump run! (Combination of water-ring and gear pump $\Delta p_1 = +0.5$ atm, $\Delta p_2 = +10$ atm abs (atü), $\Delta p_3 = +95$ atm abs).

26 April 1940: Successful lox pumping tests with a customary centrifugal pump; a water-ring pump takes in gaseous oxygen from the first stage of the centrifugal pump (Apollo-pump MK 30; 1450 rpm). . . . Lox pump tests conducted so far show that lox can be fed by any standard high-pressure system (centrifugal, gear), if temperature influences and chemical properties are taken into account for the setup; especially no grease and no steel are acceptable; instead, copper alloys must be used and initially developing gaseous oxygen (gox) be removed, e.g., by subcooling through prepressurization (gravitational head, high

flow rates, Edur-pump, Sihi-pump or boost pump) or by pumping gox (Apollo-pump).

FIGURE 4.—Experimental high-pressure 6-stage rotary pump for liquid O_2 pump. At 15,000 rpm it pumps 5 kg/sec of liquid O_2 at 150 atm.

FIGURE 5.—Rocket motor test stand. This motor produced 1000 kg of thrust for a duration of 5 min.

14 May 1940: Reviewed layout for rocket of 100,000 kg thrust!

22 July 1940: Smooth test run of first lox pump (6 radial stages) discharging at 150 atm abs [see Figure 4].

1 August 1940: First test at a thrust of 1000 kg during 120 sec, both propellants fed by high-pressure pumps.

11 August 1940: Decided to operate 100,000-kg thrust engine from the very beginning with mercury coolant and steam turbine with system-contained waste heat.

19 September 1940: 1000-kg thrust under stable operation for 5 min! [see Figure 5]. Measured data: $t = 304$ sec, $p' = 1000$ kg, $p_o = 40$ atm, $p_{fuel} = 55$ atm, $p_{ox} = 100$ atm.

24 October 1940: First long duration test at combustion pressure of 75 atm!

28 October 1940: Water-coolant velocity for combustion chamber 31.8 m/sec, for nozzle 30.5 m/sec.
($O_2 =$ side: 2 x 7 holes of 2.8 mm Ø; fuel-side: 1 x 7 holes of 1.5 mm Ø; $p_{ox} = 100$ abs atm, $p_{fuel} = 90$ atm abs, ratio fuel/$O_2 = 1:10$)
First test: 300 sec., $p' = 500$ kg, $p_o = 38$ atm abs.
Second test: 240 sec., $p' = 800$ kg, $p_o = 93$ atm abs.

29 October 1940: ($O_2 =$ side: 2 x 7 holes of 2.8 mm Ø; fuel-side: 1 x 3 holes of 3 mm Ø; $p_o = 110$ abs atm, $p_{fuel} = 90$ atm abs); $t = 40$ sec., $p' = 1000$ kg, $p_o = 80$ atm abs.

7 November 1940: Water-coolant velocity for combustion chamber 25.5 m/sec (2 paths), for nozzle 33.5 m/sec (1 path)
($O_2 =$ side: 2 x 7 holes of 2.8 mm Ø, fuel = side: 1 x 3 holes of 3 mm Ø; $p_{ox} = 110$ atm, $p_{fuel} = 95$ atm, $p' = 7.25$ cm²).
First test: 45 sec, $p' = 900$ kg, $p_o = 80$ atm.
Second test: 66 sec, $p' = 1000$ kg, $p_o = 83$ atm.

17 November 1940: Water-coolant velocity for combustion chamber 24.5 m/sec, for nozzle 32 m/sec.
First test: 40 sec, $p' = 800$ kg, $p_o = 77$ atm.

Second test: 45 sec, $p' = 1100$ kg, $p_o = 89$ atm.

20 November 1940: Third test: 40 sec, $p' = 1100$ kg, $p_o = 89$ atm.

30 November 1940: Long duration test of 510 sec at $p' = 800$ kg and $p_o = 90$ atm.

14 February 1941: First combustion chamber for 100-kg thrust with cast outer wall successfully tested! Test data: $t = 120$ sec, $p' = 750$ kg, $p_o =$ up to 65 atm.

18 February 1941: ¾-liter thruster with combustion pressure of 1 atm abs (gauge) cooled for first time by steam at 100 atm and 400° C! Test duration 8 min (copper coolant tubing).

19 February 1941: ¾-liter copper thruster cooled by steam at 125 atm and up to 450° C for 15 min.

26 February 1941: Test runs of ¾-liter steel thruster with steam at
130 atm and 250° C for 2 x 5 min at $p_o = 1$ atm abs;
120 atm and 450° C for 2 x 5 min at $p_o = 1$ atm abs;
130 atm and 250° C for 2 x 5 min at $p_o = 1$ atm abs;
130 atm and 410° C for 2 x 5 min at $p_o = 1.5$ atm abs;

5 March 1941:
130 atm and 410° C for 2 x 10 min at $p_o = 31$ atm abs;
130 atm and 410° C for 2 x 10 min at $p_o = 31$ atm abs;

7 March 1941: ¾-liter steel thruster, wound tubing with circular cross-section and 1-mm wall thickness, run with steam at 100 atm and 410° C for 5 min at 1 atm abs; test run completely stable and without trouble.

18 March 1941: Firing of 1000-kg-thrust rocket engine (nozzle: Cu-tubes, 1 mm thick, 2 paths; water coolant velocity ~ 45 m/sec; combustion chamber: Cu-tubes, 3.5 mm thick, 2 paths; water coolant velocity ~ 30 m/sec).

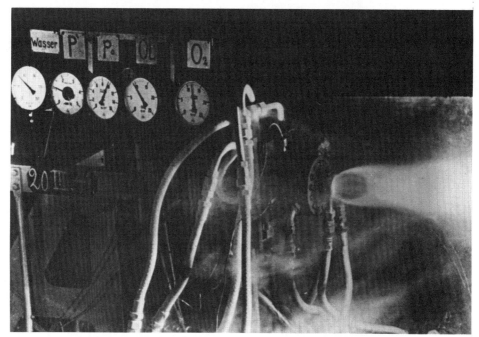

FIGURE 6.—Instruments and propellent lines during a test on 20 March 1941: chamber pressure 100 atm, thrust 1100 kg, duration 3.5 min.

Test results: t = 70 sec, p' = 830 kg, p_0 = 80 atm; k = 1.31, mixture ratio 1:3.9 (nozzle tubes buckled by combustion pressure).

19 March 1941: Firing of 1000 kg thrust rocket engine (nozzle: profiled Cu-tubes, 4 mm thick, reduced to 2.85 mm for throat area, 1 path, water coolant velocity 40 m/sec; combustion chamber: same as on 18 March 1941).

Test results: t = 195 sec, p' = 989 kg, p_0 up to 87 atm, k = 1.46, mixture ratio 1:3 (combustion chamber melted in places of great material concentration).

20 March 1941: Firing of 100-kg thrust rocket engine (nozzle and coolant data same as of 19 March 1941, but wall thickness of throat tubes reduced to 2.50 mm; combustion chamber data same as of 18 March 1941, but water coolant velocity ~ 28 m/sec)

Test results: t = 218 sec, p' = 1085 kg, p_0 up to 100 atm, k = 1.4, mixture ratio 1:3.9; during steady state operation: mixture ratio 1:4.8, c = 2060 m/sec. [see Figures 6 and 7].

16 May 1941: Fired 1000-kg thrust engine, steam cooled: p_0 = 10 atm; t = 10 sec.

4 June 1941: Fired 1000-kg thrust engine, steam cooled: p_0 = 20 atm; t = 20 sec (steel injector started to melt).

17 June 1941: First 1000-kg-thrust engine with steel injector; steam cooled: p_0 = 50 atm; t = 120 sec, injector heat separated; bolts too weak.

3 November 1941: Mailed to German Air Ministry request to authorize printing of manuscript "Raketenbomber" (Rocket-Propelled Bomber).

13 November 1941: Fired 1000-kg-thrust engine with high-pressure combustion chamber: (injector head made of wound Cu-tubes, combustion chamber of chromium-nickel alloyed steel and aluminum shell; nozzle consisting of 10-path Cu-tubing). Water coolant flow rate 1.1 liter/sec, p_0 = 80 atm abs, t = 200 sec with increasing thrust and highly oxygen-rich (about 1:10); water coolant temperature of 280° C under pressure of 80 atm.

24 November 1941: During discussions showed Mr. Brisken (German Air Ministry) completed forms for winding tubes of 100,000-kg-thrust rocket engine [see Figure 8].

11 December 1941: First 1000-kg-thrust engine with high-pressure combustion chamber. Test results: t=140 sec, p_0 = 36 atm abs; water coolant temperature 240° C at 100 atm abs pressure; wound steel tubing of combustion chamber showed signs of melting at locations of maximum water coolant temperature for water velocity of 11 m/sec.

12 December 1941: First 1000-kg-thrust engine with high-pressure combustion chamber. Test results: t = 200 sec, p_0 = 40 atm abs; water coolant: 200°C, 60 atm abs, 15m/sec.; wound-steel tubing showed signs of melting at locations of maximum water temperature.

19 December 1941: Reached conclusion that combustion chambers using evaporating coolants burn through on combustion-gas side because centrifugal forces displace portion of liquid coolant to opposite side of tube wall.

February 1942: Development of a coolant evaporator, the tubing of which is convexly bent towards the combustion gas side.

March 1942: Construction of 1000-kg-thrust, high-pressure combustion chamber equipped with new coolant evaporator.

27 April 1942: Termination of firing on large rocket test stand at Trauen.

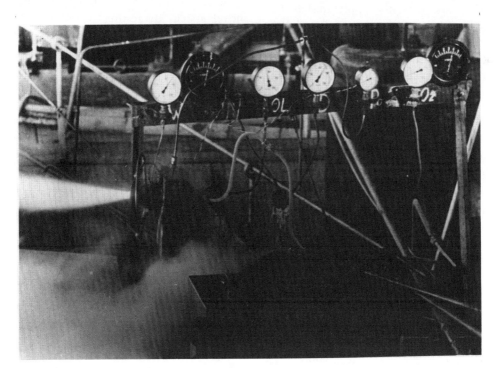

FIGURE 7.—Small water-cooled combustion chamber and test instrument in duration test. Water was heated at 400° C at 100 atm pressure in the cooling system.

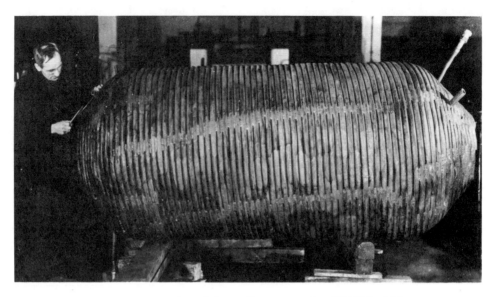

FIGURE 8.—Experimental construction of the cooling system of a 100,000-kg high-pressure combustion chamber.

Summary

Walter Dornberger appropriately wrote in his book *V 2*: "Man's technical progress does not come only from men with great ideas, but almost as frequently from those who first apply unshakable faith and tireless energy to an idea's materialization." [27]

Besides patentable intellectual authorship, investigations of priority claims to technical inventions should consider two more achievements which are almost equivalent to mental conception but require such entirely different human talents that priority in all three phases of a forthcoming invention is seldom combined in one and the same engineer. The process of transforming the mental concept of an invention into a design suitable for production represents a second step, and its successful solution also is an original accomplishment. The same holds true for the next step; to demonstrate successfully the manufactured hardware of a novel system by testing is also no routine work, but a pioneering feat. In technically defining these three steps, each has its own designation, namely "Research," "Development," and "Testing," which in turn require different skills from the technologist.

Considering these facts, a timetable on priorities of the most important cooling methods for liquid rocket powerplants would, as far as is known, stand as follows:

LIKELY PRIORITIES FOR DEVELOPMENT OF DYNAMIC, REGENERATIVE COOLING METHODS FOR LIQUID-FUEL ROCKETS

	Internal cooling	*External surface cooling*	*External forced-flow cooling*	*Combined regenerative cooling with steam*
Conception	Oberth 1923	Tsiolkovskiy 1928	Sänger 7 February 1934	Sänger 9 May 1934
Patent	nothing known	nothing known	Sänger 9 February 1935	Sänger 25 October 1938
Hardware	Pöhlmann 1938	Walter Riedel and Arthur Rudolph winter 1932 (or perhaps spring 1931)	Sänger 20 March 1934	Sänger August 1940 (probably earlier)
Testing	Peenemunde team 1939	Walter Riedel, von Braun, Dornberger 21 December 1932	Sänger 7 May 1934	Sänger 18 February 1941

The development of a successful cooling method for the liquid propulsion systems of space rockets was lengthy and troublesome. In the first place, most of the senior rocket pioneers took somewhat amateurish approaches, aiming more or less at short-duration demonstration flights of their small rockets. Naturally, they were mostly interested in rocket flight behavior or stability, guidance, and mass properties, whereas the thrustor, if considered at all, was thought to be a necessary but secondary obligation. Powerplants of the past remained mostly anonymous, whereas rocket stages received from their fathers the finest names of fantasy. If the pioneers dealt with powerplant problems at all, they concentrated on propellant feeding, atomization, and conditioning. Very few recognized the fundamental importance of cooling for the development of a ground-tested rocket powerplant; most inventors started to take care of cooling problems only after there was no other way out.

For example, in the November-December 1929 issue of *Die Rakete* (The Rocket), certainly in self-criticism, it is stated: "Up to the end of 1928, the term heat transfer hardly exists in the literature on space travel:" From this insight, however, no conclusions result as to cooling methods related to the heat transfer from combustion gas to chamber wall; only those heat fluxes between combustion gas and atomized liquid important for propellant conditioning are considered. It is amazing how little information on cooling methods is contained in the old 1932 test reports; this type of information is more or less accidentally mentioned and then only in subordinate sentences.

This is true even with Goddard, who in his famous papers "A Method of Reaching Extreme Altitudes" (1919)[28] and "Liquid Propellant Rocket Development" (1936)[29] does not even mention cooling methods for liquid rocket engines. His first treatments of cooling methods are found in the U.S. patents 2,016,921, 8 October 1935, "Means for Cooling Combustion Chambers," and 2,122,521, 5 July 1938, "Cooling Jacket Construction."

In his early layouts, the pioneer of spaceflight technology, K.E. Tsiolkovskiy, also assessed the dangers to the outer skin of his rocket from aerodynamic heating as clearly more important than the still neglected risks of an uncooled rocket engine. It took him 43 years—from 1885 until 1928—until he published a rocket design indeed embodying at the same time dynamically and regeneratively cooled combustion chambers.

The Swiss researcher Josef Stemmer, perhaps somewhat unjustly neglected, is an exception; with his privately financed ground and flight tests, starting in 1934 (somewhat later than but certainly independent of Sänger), he used force-flow cooling for models of combustion chambers and rockets.

NOTES

To Ruth von Saurma, of the George C. Marshall Space Flight Center Plans and Resources Control Office, and to Hans G. Paul, chief of the MSFC Astronautics Laboratory Propulsion and Thermodynamics Division, the editors express gratitude for their assistance in checking and revising the translation of this paper. Throughout, the abbreviation "at" has been translated as atm (atmospheres) and atü as atm abs (atmospheres absolute (excess) pressure). PS is understood to equal 0.9863 hp, equals 0.735 kw.

1. Leipzig: Verlag Hachmeister & Thal, 1932.

2. H. Oberth, *Die Rakete zu den Planetenraümen* [The Rocket into Interplanetary Space] (Munich and Berlin: R. Oldenbourg, 1923), p. 27.

3. Ibid., pp. 53–54; and Oberth, *Wege zur Raumschiffahrt* [Methods of Space Travel] (Munich and Berlin: R. Oldenbourg, 1929), pp. 241–42.

4. Ibid., p. 5.

5. Ibid., p. 5.

6. R. Nebel, *Raketenflug* [Rocket Flight] Mitteilungsblatt des Raketenflugplatzes Berlin Nr. 7, Raketenflugplatz Berlin, December 1932, pp. 27–28.

7. Max Valier, *Raketenfahrt* [Rocket Journey] (Munich: R. Oldenbourg, 1930).

8. W. H. J. Reidel, "Ein Kapitel Raketengeschichte der neueren Zeit." *Weltraumfahrt*, no. 3, July 1953.

9. Op. cit. (note 8).

10. W. Ley, *Rockets, Missiles, and Men in Space* (New York: The Viking Press, 1968), ed. 3, p. 134.

11. Op. cit., note 6, pp. 16–17.

12. Op. cit., note 10, pp. 126–28.

13. W. Dornberger, *V2—der Schuss ins Weltall* [V2—The Shot into Space] (Esslingen: Bechtle-Verlag, 1952), p. 26.

14. Werner Brügel, *Manner der Rakete* [Rocket Men] (Leipzig: Hachmeister & Thal, 1933), p. 129.

15. Op. cit. (note 6), p. 28.

16. Op. cit. (note 14).

17. Ibid.

18. Ley, op. cit. (note 10), p. 146.

19. In Brügel, *Manner der Rakete* (see note 14).

20. Alexander Boris Scherschewsky, *Die Rakete für Fahrt und Flug* (Berlin: C. J. E. Volckmann, 1928), p. 106.

21. Ley, *Rockets, The Future of Travel beyond the Stratosphere* (New York: The Viking Press, 1944), p. 157.

22. Op. cit. (note 13), p. 26.

23. Ibid., pp. 31–32.

24. Ibid., pp. 60–61.

25. See note 6.

26. [Rocket Flight Technique] (Munich and Berlin: R. Oldenbourg, 1933).

27. Op. cit. (note 13), p. 28.

28. *Smithsonian Miscellaneous Collections*, vol. 71, no. 2, 1919.

29. *Smithsonian Miscellaneous Collections*, vol. 95, no. 3, 1936.

REFERENCES

In addition to those sources cited in the footnotes, the following were used in the preparation of this paper.

1. A. Ananoff, *Des premières fusées a la V2, 14 problèmes.* Paris: Edition Elzevier, 1947.

2. A. Ananoff, *L'Astronautique.* Paris: Librairie Arthème Fayard, 1950.

3. P. von Dresser, "The Rocket Motor – a Survey of Known Types," *Astronautics*, no. 33 (March 1936), p. 8.

4. R. Engel, CERVA-Report No. 6, 1954.

5. I. Essers, *Max Valier – ein Vorkämpfer der Weltraumfahrt.* Düsseldorf: VDI-Verlag, 1968.

6. H. Gartmann, *Weltraum-ABC.* Düsseldorf: ECON-Verlag, 1958.

7. H. Gartmann, *Träumer – Forscher – Konstrukteure.* Düsseldorf: ECON-Verlag, 1955.

8. C. P. Lent, *Rocket Research – History and Handbook.* New York: The Pen-Ink Publishing Co., 1945.

9. W. Ley, *Grundriss einer Geschichte der Rakete.* Leipsig: Hachmeister & Thal, 1932.

10. *Die Rakete*, Offizielles Organ des Vereins für Raumschifffahrt e.V., 2, 1928.

11. W. H. J. Ridel, "Ein Kapitel Raketengeschichte der neueren Zeit," *Weltraumfahrt*, no. 3, July 1953.

12. E. Sänger, "Neuere Ergebnisse der Raketenflugtechnik," *Flug*, special issue 1, Wien: Verlag Flug, 1934.

13. E. Sänger, "Der Verbrennungsraketenmotor," *Schweizer Bauzeitung* vol. 107, no. 2, 11 January 1936.

14. E. Sänger and I. Bredt, "Uber einen Raketenantrieb für Fernbomber" [A Rocket Motor for Long-Range Bomber], Deutsche Luftfahrtforschung UM 3538, Ainring, August 1944. (Translated into English by M. Hamermesh, Radio Research Laboratory, and reproduced by Technical Information Branch, BuAer, United States Navy Department, as Translation CGD-32. A condensed version of this translation was published by Mr. Robert Cornog, 990 Cheltenham Road, Santa Barbara, California, on 16 November 1952).—Ed.

15. I. Sänger-Bredt, *Entwicklungsgesetze der Raumfahrt.* Mainz: Krausskopf-Flugwelt-Verlag, 1964.

16. I. Sänger-Bredt und K. Reiniger, *Requiem für Eugen Sänger* Herausgeber L. Bölkow (to be published).

22

Development of Winged Rockets in the USSR, 1930-39

YE. S. SHCHETINKOV, *Soviet Union*

The work of the winged-rocket team of the Group for Study of Jet Propulsion (GIRD) and of the Jet Propulsion Research Institute (RNII) was performed under the guidance of the author of this paper during the period 1933–37. Naturally, this work covered a range of problems allied to those carried out by other teams of workers, employed at the Gas Dynamics Laboratory (GDL), GIRD, and RNII, who designed and investigated solid-propellant winged rockets, liquid-propellant rocket engines, aircraft boosters, etc. Moreover, when it was necessary, the efforts of different teams and groups were temporarily combined.

Thus, it would be wrong to dwell on the history of the work done by only one team engaged in research on liquid-propellant winged rockets without mentioning the work of all other groups of workers engaged in allied fields. It would also be wrong to overlook the conditions prevailing in our country, and even in the world, which prompted our work, for in that case the general picture would be incomplete and lacking in breadth.

When discussing the origin of ideas on the use of jet engines on winged vehicles, one must first speak of F. A. Tsander. It was he who suggested the use of wings on rocket vehicles. His "Flights to Other Planets" was completed in 1924 and was published in the magazine "Technology and Life" appearing that same year.[1] A similar suggestion can be also found in the work of K. E. Tsiolkovskiy, published in 1926, "Investigation of Outer Space by Means of Reactive Devices," in which he mentioned the use of hydrodynamic lift force to reduce the required liquid-propellant-engine thrust (inclined trajectory flight).[2] Influenced by these ideas, a special winged-rocket team (the fourth team) was formed in GIRD in 1932, under S. P. Korolyev.

There were, however, other circumstances which urged us to study winged rockets. The 1930s in a certain sense were critical in the development of aviation. A piston engine with a propeller was the main and only type. The absolute world speed records established during the aircraft races for the Schneider-Creuzot prize were close to 700 km/hr. The rise in the speed of aircraft registered every year, if shown diagramatically, would produce a curve asymptotically approaching the limit of 700–800 km/hr.

Much more favorable prospects could be seen for liquid-propellant rocket engines, whose weight increased in proportion to the second, not the third, power of the speed, as was the case with a piston engine. From this point of view better characteristics were to be obtained for ramjet engines, their theory having been worked out by B. S. Stechkin.[3] And I remember very well lively discussions among the members of our team caused by G. A. Crocco's article about the flight performances of ramjet aircraft.[4]

Mathematical calculations of the flight performances of the liquid-propellant rocket engines demonstrated that flight speed "limits" posed by the piston engine could be readily overcome. Flight altitude limits could be overcome as well. It seemed feasible to build a liquid-propellant rocket aircraft which could be used to improve considerably world speed and altitude records. Such aircraft, used as an interceptor, would also be of interest from the military viewpoint. Moreover, winged flight vehicles with liquid-propellant rocket engines or ramjet engines could be considered as the first step toward spaceships. F. A. Tsander also drew attention to this prospect. Such was the sequence of arguments of the engineers and enthusiasts in the field of rocketry who worked jointly in GIRD. All of us were young and full of optimism. Financial troubles and hardships could not frighten us. And though our country was experiencing hard times, we were ready to work, ignoring our own discomforts, although we were aware that our strenuous labor would not soon bear fruit.

The first calculations of optimum parameters for the liquid-propellant rocket aircraft (we then called them "rocket planes") showed that maximum flight altitudes were obtained when the ratio of thrust to takeoff weight was slightly less than unity.

In 1933 liquid-propellant rocket motors available at GIRD had a thrust of 30–50 kg; therefore, dynamic flight parameters of rocket-propelled aircraft closest to the optimum values could be obtained only if the takeoff weight of winged rockets was less than 40 to 60 kg. Thus, we came also to think of designing pilotless free-flight models which could be used to study the flight dynamics of rocket planes.

Later, in the period 1935–36, a separate team (group) engaged in studying solid-propellant winged rockets was formed in RNII to investigate the possibilities of their use as guided antiaircraft rockets.

As indicated above, at GDL, and later at RNII, another trend of great importance arose in the field of winged flight vehicles with rocket engines: that is, the use of solid-propellant booster rockets to reduce the takeoff run of overloaded aircraft. Experimental investigation in this area was carried out from 1930 until the war broke out.

All the above-mentioned three main areas of interest, i.e., the rocket aircraft, pilotless winged rockets, and aircraft takeoff boosters were investigated by various departments of RNII. Their work was based on the same scientific interests. In particular, certain problems—the flight dynamics of winged vehicles acted upon by a reactive force, the effect of a jet on the control system and strength of structure—were treated as common in all areas. This fact contributed to the mutual interests in the scientific results obtained by the various departments.

In addition, it should be noted that the organizational structure of the departments dealing with winged rockets in RNII was not stabilized during the period 1934–38. For example, the author of this report had to take part, one way or another, in the work carried out in all above-mentioned three areas as different times.

Now, let us proceed with a consideration of the actual work on winged rocket vehicles performed at GIRD and RNII.

Rocket-propelled Aircraft

In 1932–33 GIRD attempted to design the OR-2 alcohol-oxygen engine with a thrust of 50 kg and to mount it on the BICh-11 tailless glider designed by B. I. Cheranovskiy. The work was headed by S. P. Korolyev.

This RP-1 rocket aircraft is shown in Figure 1, together with a diagram of its engine fuel-supply system. Tanks, valves, and other equipment were manufactured and mounted on the RP-1 rocket aircraft during that period, and it underwent test trials in an engine-off gliding flight. After GIRD and GDL were merged, the work on this rocket aircraft stopped because the glider was worn out.[5]

In 1936 research on rocket-propelled aircraft was resumed. Figure 2 shows a general view of the RP-218 two-seated experimental rocket aircraft with a cluster of three nitric acid-kerosene engines having a total thrust of 900 kg, a takeoff weight of 1600 kg, a wing area of 7.2 m²; a climbing speed of 850 km/hr, a ceiling of 9(20) km from a ground takeoff, and 25(37) km from a TB-3 aircraft at an altitude of 8 km (figures in parentheses indicate the ceiling for a single-seat variant). The project was under the guidance of S. P. Korolev and Ye. S. Shchetinkov.

During the first stage of the RP-218 project, attempts were made to mount an ORM-65 nitric acid-kerosene engine, with a maximum thrust of 175 kg, on the SK-9 glider and to undertake test flights. Work on this rocket-propelled aircraft, known as RP-318 (Figure 3a–c) was headed by S. P. Korolev. Its takeoff weight was 660 kg, the wing area was 22 m², and weight of propellant 75 kg. During 1938–39 the ORM-65 engine was modified and came to be known as the RDA-1-150 engine, with maximum and minimum thrusts of 150 kg and 50 kg, respectively. The fuel-supply system was of the gas-pressurizing type, and the thrust control was performed by throttling.

To ensure full safety of the pilot, both the fuel supply system and the engine underwent most careful bench tests over a period of three years (1937–40). Altogether, several hundred bench tests and 16 preliminary flight experiments were undertaken. The chief engineer on the engine installation was A. V. Pallo.

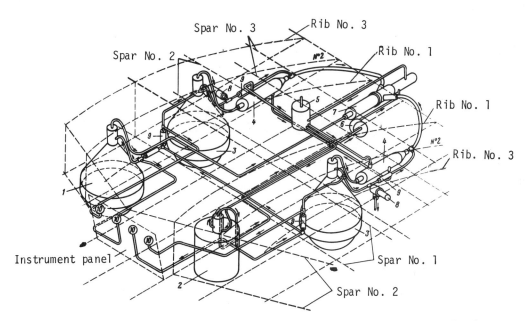

FIGURE 1.—Rocket-propelled aircraft (Raketoplan) RP-1 (top) and schematic diagram of rocket engine system for RP-1.

On 28 February 1940 the pilot V. P. Fedorov performed the first powered flight with the RDA-1-150 cut in. The RP-318-1 rocket aircraft was towed aloft by a P-5 aircraft. After disengagement, the rocket engine was cut in at 2600 m with a thrust of 90 kg; the speed increased from 80 to 120 km/hr, while the altitude increased by 300 m (Figure 3d).

(Due to wear of its structural members the speed of the rocket aircraft was limited to 160 km/hr.)

The entire operating time of the engine amounted to 110 sec. It was the first manned flight of a liquid-propellant flight vehicle accomplished in the Soviet Union. Repeated flights confirmed the design flight data of the RP-318 and showed the

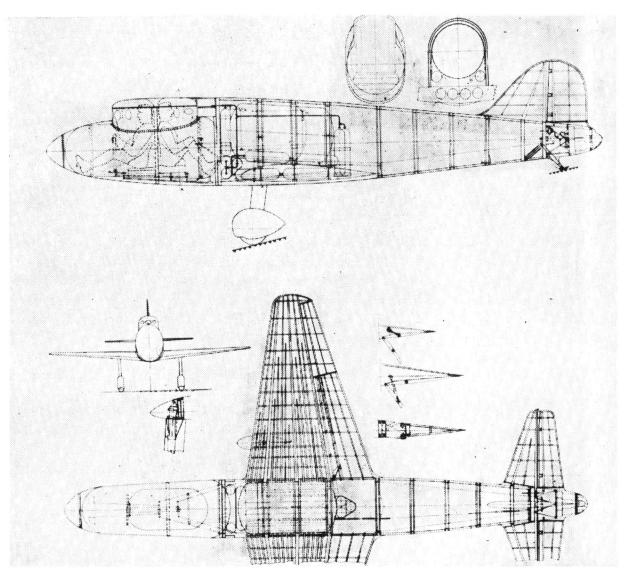

FIGURE 2.—Layout of RP-218.

reliability and safety of the power plant.

The work on the rocket aircraft was carried on at the design office headed by V. F. Bolkhovitinov, where an experimental model of the BI-1 rocket fighter (Figure 4) was designed and manufactured. The fighter was fitted with a powerful nitric acid-kerosene engine with thrust of over 1000 kg.

During the war, in 1942, the BI-1 fighter was flown by the pilot G. Ya. Bakhchivandzhi.[6]

Pilotless Winged Rockets

The 06/I—the first winged rocket—was a smaller geometrical model of the RP-7 rocket aicraft. It was

fitted with an 09 oxygen engine having a maximum thrust of approximately 50 kg. The rocket weighed 30 kg. Research on the 06/I–06/III was guided by Ye. S. Shchetinkov.

The rocket takeoff was similar to that of an aircraft, i.e., it was performed from horizontal guide rails.

The winged rocket was expected to climb along an inclined trajectory (at an angle of about 60° to

FIGURE 3.—a, Layout and b, tail surfaces of RP-318; c, rocket engine for the 318; d, RP-318–1 in flight, 28 February 1940.

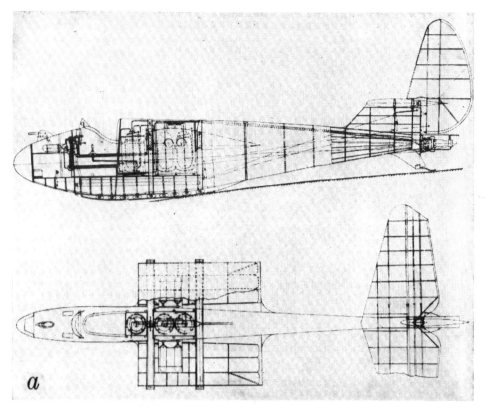

a

b

c

d

FIGURE 4.—Rocket fighter plane BI-1.

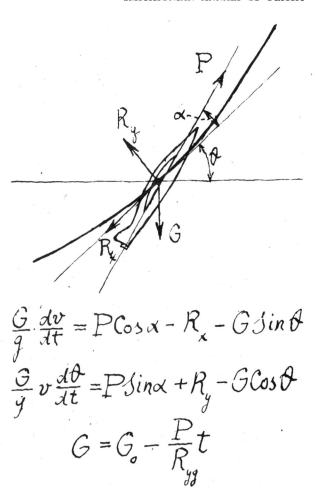

$$\frac{G}{g} \cdot \frac{dv}{dt} = P \cos \alpha - R_x - G \sin \theta$$

$$\frac{G}{g} v \frac{d\theta}{dt} = P \sin \alpha + R_y - G \cos \theta$$

$$G = G_o - \frac{P}{R_{yg}} t$$

FIGURE 5.—Equations used for flight trajectory calculations.

the horizon) and after the engine stopped, to pass on to a gliding flight. For this purpose the rocket was provided with an automatic device, of a fairly primitive type, to deflect the elevators as predetermined by a prescribed time program. The first flights, however, performed in May 1934, showed that the 06/I rocket motion was unstable. The rockets caused it to do loops, barrel-rolls, and other aerobatic figures but the design trajectory could not be obtained.

Therefore, the next 06/III winged rocket (known later as a 216 rocket) was provided with ailerons in addition to elevators. For this purpose a two-axis gyroscopic autopilot was specially designed at RNII under the guidance of S. A. Pivovarov.

The methods of trajectory calculation in 1934–35 could be understood by referring to a system of equations (Figure 5) which were to be solved mathematically. Later, in 1936–38, the methods of calculating dynamic flight were considerably improved by engineer B. V. Raushenbakh; the rocket motion relative to the center of gravity acted upon by the autopilot was given special attention; and dynamic stability of the rocket was also considered.

Characteristics of the 216 rocket were: Takeoff weight, 80 kg; maximum thrust of the 02 alcohol-oxygen engine (OR-2 modified), 100 kg; propellant weight, 12 kg; wing area, 1.5 m²; takeoff speed, 36 m/sec; and maximum flight speed, 180 m/sec.

Figure 6a shows a full-size 216 rocket under wind-tunnel tests. Figure 6b shows the main power plant elements mounted on the rocket thrust frame, also the wing-mounted oxygen tanks, a cylindrical alcohol tank, an 02 engine, and tanks of air to force the propellants out of the tanks and to drive the autopilot servo units. Figure 6c shows the GPS-2 gyroscopic two-axis autopilot.

The 216 rocket was fired from a special catapult (Figure 6d) which was, essentially, a launching trolley, complete with one or three solid-propellant rockets, that slid on guide rails over a distance of 60 m. Figure 7 compares the design and experimental results for two launchings of reduced-size mockups of the 216 rocket.

During the test flights, motion pictures of the takeoff were taken to determine the speed at which the rocket left the trolley. Special recording devices were employed to register the movement of the elevator and ailerons. Some of the rockets were provided with sodium flares to indicate flight trajectories.

Four 216 winged rockets were tested between 9 May and 4 November 1936, but only two firings went relatively successfully off the trolley. One of the rockets began to make a dead loop because of

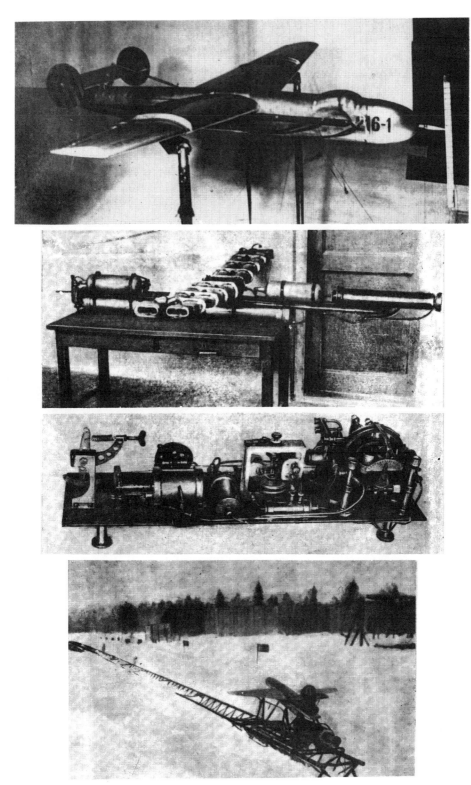

FIGURE 6.—*a,* Model of the 216 winged rocket (1933–36) mounted in wind tunnel; *b,* basic components of the 216 winged rocket; *c,* gyroscopic autopilot GPS-2 for the 216 rocket; *d,* catapult for winged rockets 216 and 212.

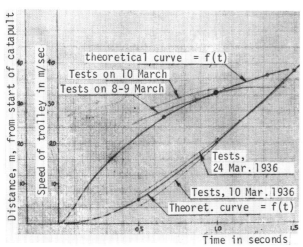

FIGURE 7.—Takeoff performance of 216 rocket on catapult.

FIGURE 8.—a, Winged rocket 212 (1934–39); b, gyroscopic autopilot GPS-3 for 212 rocket.

apparent autopilot failure. The second rocket, moving along an ascending straight-line trajectory, reached an altitude of about 500 m and then fell off on the right wing with the motor still running.

Even before tests of the 06/III-216 rocket were completed, the decision was made to start designing a 212 winged rocket of greater efficiency with three-axis GPS-3 autopilots and an ORM-65 nitric acid-kerosene motor. Provision was made for rocket recovery by means of a parachute. This work was headed by S. P. Korolyev.

Figure 8a shows the 212 rocket, the main design characteristics of which were: takeoff weight, up to 230 kg; wing area, 1.7 m²; thrust of liquid-propellant engine, 150 kg; and maximum speed in horizontal flight, 280 m/sec. Figure 8b shows the GPS-3 autopilot mounted in the body compartment.

Several hundred preliminary tests of both the propellant supply system and the control system were carried out. In contrast to the operations with the 216 rocket, static firing of engine with the on-board supply system was performed. Accelerographs and other measuring instruments were also used.

Test flights of the full-scale rocket were not made until 1939. Two rockets were tested, and in each all the systems of rocket engine, boost, and takeoff were activated normally. However, the designed ascent trajectory was achieved only in the initial part of the flight path. In the first case, the parachute was prematurely opened at an altitude of about 250 m and in the second, stability of the flight was disturbed. No further experiments of the 212 rocket were made.

Solid-propellant winged rockets were developed at RNII under the guidance of M. P. Dryazgov. Initially, the rockets were thought to be a simple and cheap means for carrying out experiments on a large scale to solve the problems of control and stability of liquid-propellant winged rockets (model 48).

Very soon, however, the rockets proved to be of special interest as antiaircraft rockets (model 217). At the same time we considered the fact that by 1936–37 the means of radio guidance and homing of flight vehicles were being developed in the Soviet Union.

Variants of rockets, types 48 and 217 are shown in Figure 9, and a 217/II rocket in the launching position in Figure 10. It can be seen that by that time, RNII was developing symmetric four-wing configurations providing good airborne maneuverability of rockets. Aircraft-type configurations were also de-

FIGURE 9.—Winged rockets 48 and 217 using solid propellant (1935–38).

veloped with various wing contours. Special mention should be made of delta wings, which recently have come to be widely used in aviation.

Of interest is the 217/II rocket. Based on a four-wing pattern, its characteristics were: total wing area, 0.74 m²; wing aspect ratio, 0.83; takeoff weight, 120 kg; weight of charge of TNT propellant, 17.5

kg; engine thrust, 1850 kg; design flight speed, 260 m/sec; design altitude of ballistic flight, 3300 m.

As to its flight stability, the tests of the 217/II rocket proved it to be fairly satisfactory. No tests of that rocket together with the control systems were carried out.

Rocket-assisted Takeoff for Aircraft

The airfield experiments on the use of solid-propellant rocket engines for aircraft takeoff started at GDL in 1930 (they had been suggested by V. I. Dudakov and V. A. Konstantinov as far back as 1927). The work was continued at RNII under the guidance of V. I. Dudakov. The author of this paper contributed to this work only from time to time.

Figure 11 shows the first Soviet rocket booster unit mounted in the U-1 light training aircraft. When the experiments proved to be successful in 1931, the decision was made to install rocket boosters on the TB-1, a heavier type aircraft (Figure 11 bottom) whose weight was 7 tons. During the period 1931–33 theoretical and experimental research to determine optimum sizes of rocket boost-

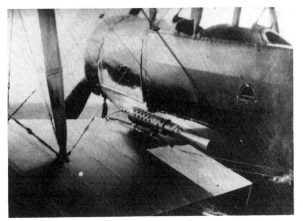

FIGURE 10.—Winged rocket 217/II on the launcher.

FIGURE 11.—Takeoff-assist rocket on the U-1 aircraft and (bottom) in operation on TB-1 aircraft.

ers and where to locate them was conducted, a study of the dynamics of rocket boosters for aircraft was being made, and methods to obtain more rigid structural members were being sought.

The final tests, carried out in October 1933, disclosed that due to the boosters, the runway length for aircraft of 7-ton takeoff weight was reduced from 330 to 80 m, and for the 8-ton weight the corresponding figures were 480 and 110 m. This result was achieved with six chambers mounted on the wings and connected to each other by a crossover tube. The total weight of the powder grain was 60 kg. The average thrust amounted to 10,400 kg during a period of 2 seconds.

The following years saw a number of aircraft of other types equipped with rocket boosters. The studies were also continued to make rocket boosters more sophisticated and, in particular, to reduce their weight. The above-mentioned rocket booster employed on the TB-1 aircraft was quite heavy because its weight amounting to 470 kg (the weight required to strengthen the aircraft structural members being also taken into account).

Conclusions

From a purely practical point of view, of the three main areas of winged-flight-vehicle development at GDL, GIRD, and RNII up to 1939, only aircraft rocket boosters received their "start in life" directly from RNII before 1939, i.e., began to be used by other organizations and teams of scientific workers. Rocket-propelled aircraft and winged rockets came into wide use only after 1939.

Such a conclusion, however, would be narrow and one-sided. The work of teams of scientific workers concerned with the rocket-powered winged flight vehicles in the period of 1930–38 should be also assessed and viewed from different aspects—scientific, historical, and engineering.

From the scientific and historical viewpoint, the following basic dates should be noted:

1. The takeoff of the first Soviet U-1 aircraft assisted by a solid-propellant rocket engine occurred in May 1931. In October 1933, rocket boosters were adjusted and tested on the TB-1 aircraft.
2. The first flight of the 06/I unguided winged vehicle with a liquid-propellant rocket engine occurred in the Soviet Union on 5 May 1934.

The first flight of the 216 winged vehicle equipped with an autopilot was accomplished on 9 May 1936.
3. The first flight of the Soviet 48 unguided winged vehicle of aircraft-type configuration with a solid-propellant rocket engine was made in January 1935, and the flight of the 217/II four-wing vehicle of axis-symmetric configuration took place on 19 November 1936.
4. The first flight of the Soviet RP-318 rocket glider with a liquid-propellant engine was accomplished by V. P. Fedorov on 28 February 1940.

From the engineering viewpoint, the following main results should be noted:

1. The tehnical feasibility of safe manned flight on a glider equipped with a liquid-propellant rocket engine was experimentally proved.
2. A number of pilotless winged vehicles, equipped with oxygen and nitric-acid liquid-propellant rocket engines and gyroscope autopilots were tested. Automatic takeoff of rockets from a catapult trolley was realized, and stable flight was obtained in the initial part of the ascent trajectory.

    Reliability of all the elements of the rocket was one of the main problems in the development of the winged vehicles. There cannot be any doubt that if the number of firings had been greater (e.g., 15–20) a 212 winged rocket would have completed the entire prescribed flight trajectory.
3. Engineering methods were developed to calculate flight performances of rocket aircraft and winged rockets. The possibility of obtaining record speeds and flight ceilings for aircraft with a liquid-propellant engine was theoretically proved.
4. Antiaircraft solid-propellant winged rockets with axis-symmetric and with delta-type two-wing configurations, both adapted for automatic control, were developed and approved.

    Methods of calculating the dynamic stability of winged rockets were worked out.
5. Aircraft solid-propellant boosters were tested and developed to the operational stage. Recommendations on designing and selection of optimum parameters of rocket boosters were worked out.

6. Small gyroscopic autopilots were designed and tested in laboratories and on winged vehicles in flight. Methods of calculating the dynamic stability of winged rockets were developed.

From 1927 on, a number of young engineers, enthusiasts in rocketry, were involved in research and designing on jet-propelled, winged flight vehicles. In the course of this research, their experience and knowledge became far more profound. As a result, in the period of 1934–39, RNII produced highly-skilled specialists in winged rockets who made significant contributions to the development of Soviet rocketry.

NOTES

Under the title *Razvitie krylatykh apparatov v SSSR v 1930–1939*, this paper appeared on pages 179–93 of *Iz istorii astronavtiki i raketnoi tekhniki: Materialy XVIII mizhdunarodnogo astronavticheskogo kongressa, Belgrad, 25–29 Sentyavrya 1967* [From the History of Rockets and Astronautics: Materials of the 18th International Astronautical Congress, Belgrade, 25–29 September 1967], Moscow: Nauka, 1970.

1. F. A. Tsander, "Perelety na drugiye planety," *Tekhnika i Zhizn* [Technology and Life], 1924, no. 13, pp. 15–16.

2. K. E. Tsiolkovskiy, *Issledovaniye mirovykh prostranstv reaktivnymi priborami*, Kaluga, 1926.

3. B. S. Stechkin, "Teoriya vozdushnogo reaktivnogo dvigatelya" [Theory of Air-breathing Jet Engines], *Tekhnika Vozdushnogo Flota* [Air Force Technology], 1929, no. 2.

4. G. Arturo Crocco, "Iperavmazione e Superaviazione," *L'Aerotecnica*, vol. 2, October 1931, pp. 1173–1220—Ed.

5. Additional information on the RP-1 rocket aircraft appears in the paper by A. I. Polyarny in this volume and in *Problems of Flight by Jet Propulsion: Interplanetary Flights*, by F. A. Tsander and L. K. Korneev, NASA-TT-F-147, 2 ed., 1964, 401 pp., a translation into English of *Problema poleta pri pomoshchi reaktivnykh apparatov: mezhplanetnye polety*, Moscow: Gos. Nauchno-Tekhn. Izd. Oborongiz, 1961.—Ed.

6. Additional details on the BI-1 aircraft are found in *The Soviet Encyclopedia of Space Flight*, G. V. Petrovich, ed. (Moscow: Mir Publishers, 1969), pp. 54 and 104; and in "Red Rocket: William Green Relates the Little Known Story of the Development, Production, and Flight Testing of a Rocket Interceptor in the Soviet Union During 1942," by William Green, *Flying Review International*, June 1969, pp. 79–81.—Ed.

REFERENCES

The following references, appearing at the end of this paper in the Russian publication cited above (p. 193), are to material in the Archives of the USSR Academy of Sciences.

1–3. See footnotes 1–3, respectively, above.

4. Calculations, rocket plane 318 (1937). Arkhiv AN SSSR, razr. 4, op. 14, d. 103.

5. Reports on tests, 318-1 and 218-1 (1937). Arkhiv AN SSSR, razr. 4, op. 14, d. 104.

6. Calculations, objectives for 218 and 318 (1936–1939). Arkhiv AN SSSR, razr. 4, op. 14, d. 105.

7. Initial report of experiments on rocket plane 818 (1940). Arkhiv AN SSSR, razr. 4, op. 14, d. 106.

8. Calculations, winged rocket 06 (1934). Arkhiv AN SSSR, razr. 4, op. 14, d. 79.

9. Winged rocket 216, reports, calculations, experiments, photographs (1936). Arkhiv AN SSSR, razr. 4, op. 14, d. 81.

10. Winged rocket, objective 212 (1936). Arkhiv AN SSSR, razr. 4, op. 14, d. 82.

11. Winged rocket, reports and photographs (1935–1936). Arkhiv AN SSSR, razr. 4, op. 14, d. 83.

12. Objectives, 312. Calculations, reports on testing of objectives 312, 212, 216. Arkhiv AN SSSR, razr. 4, op. 14, d. 84.

13. Winged Rocket. Reports, objective 212 (1938). Arkhiv AN SSSR, razr. 4, op. 14, d. 85.

14. Winged Rocket. Reports, objective 212 (1938). Arkhiv AN SSSR, razr. 4, op. 14, d. 86.

15. Winged Rocket. Acts and reports on object 212 (1938). Arkhiv AN SSSR, razr. 4, op. 14, d. 87.

16. Calculations on acceleration of airplane No. 25 (1933–34). Arkhiv AN SSSR, razr. 4, op. 14, d. 110.

17. Diary of experiments on acceleration of TB-1 (1932). Arkhiv AN SSSR, razr. 4, op. 14, d. 111.

23

Wilhelm Theodor Unge: An Evaluation of His Contributions

Å. Ingemar Skoog, *Sweden*

In Sweden as in most European countries, the first small steps towards rocketry were taken when Congreve rockets were introduced in 1810. But giant steps were taken at the end of the 19th century when Wilhem Theodor Unge started working with rockets—at the same time as Konstantin Tsiolkovskiy in the U.S.S.R. and about 10 years before Robert H. Goddard in the United States of America.

Wilhelm Theodor Unge (Figure 1) was born in Stockholm in 1845. He graduated from the College of Technology and started his military career in 1866. As a very promising young officer he was appointed to the Military College and afterwards he was attached to the General Staff. Soon his technical education became predominant and he started a career as an inventor in the field of military technology. His first patented invention was a telemeter, in 1887, and in a short time he patented several improvements for an automatic rifle.

In the late 1880s Unge became interested in artillery and he regarded rocketry as a possible way to improve artillery and to use the new sensitive high-explosive nitroglycerin as a war-head in artillery shells. Unge made contact with Alfred Nobel in 1891 and managed to get him interested in his ideas. In 1892 Unge formed his company, called the Mars Company, with Nobel and the Swedish King among the shareholders. The purpose of the company was to develop, manufacture, and sell the inventions of Captain Wilhelm Theodore Unge. As a matter of fact, the company soon became a workshop for developing ideas brought to light through an extensive collaboration between Unge and Nobel. All this work was financed by Nobel until his death in 1896, and after that for five more years by his estate. During the first five years Alfred Nobel invested about 20,000 dollars in the Mars Company.

The first rocket, tested in 1892 (Figure 2a), was made of brass, with a diameter of 20 mm (0.8 in.), 1-mm wall thickness (0.4 in.) and a length of 150 mm (6 in.). The conical burning area was placed with the base at the top of the rocket, which meant that the gas had to turn 180° in order to accelerate the rocket forward. The turning of the gas was achieved by a cupola at the top of the rocket. The greatest disadvantage of this rocket was the heating of the cupola and even the body, when the gas stream was forced to turn. Unge also found that this type of rocket had already been patented in England.

The next two types of rockets were very like those of William Hale, but they had only two instead of three exhaust pipes at the rear end. In one (Figure 2b), the exhaust pipes were cut along the center axis opposite each other and bent at the ends to form a "spoon" which would cause rotation of the rocket when the gas streams passed through. Unfortunately the rotation was not great enough to stabilize the rocket, and it did not help to make two combustion chambers inside the rocket (Figure 2c). In order to improve the rotation in the initial part of the trajectory the launch tube was replaced by a rotation gun. Other methods to create rotation were also used, but none was sufficiently effective.

New designs were tried, and one of the more significant details were oblique exhaust orifices. These were first uniformly thick (Figure 2d), but soon Unge tested rockets with conical orifices (Figure 2e). The rocket of the first type had already been patented by Hale, and besides it did not have the characteristics required by Unge and Nobel. The second modified type was also fitted with a guidance tube with a length of about 300 mm (12 in). This modification, with its "guideline stick," might suggest the Congreve rocket but in

FIGURE 1.—Wilhelm Theodor Unge, 1845–1915. Photo from Kungl. Armémuseum Archives, Sweden.

fact the conical orifice is the first step to the final solution to the problem of stabilization by rotating the rocket.

A few years earlier, in 1888, Gustaf de Laval had made the first sketches of the later well-known Laval nozzle, and in 1892 the approved patent was published in a paper. This new idea, which showed how to get maximum force out of a high-pressure gas stream, was obviously soon adopted by Unge. His efforts to find a way to impart the proper revolution to the rocket gave excellent results when, in 1896–

97, he finally designed the turbine shown in a drawing (Figure 3) from Swedish patent 10,257.

The description makes clear Unge's ideas for this new and unique invention. The gas turbine was fitted with exhaust outlets so designed that they would create the most effective pressure for combustion. The rounded central portion of the turbine transformed the centered stream of gas from the combustion chamber into a hollow stream distributed without shock to the periphery of the turbine by means of two or more gas canals through the

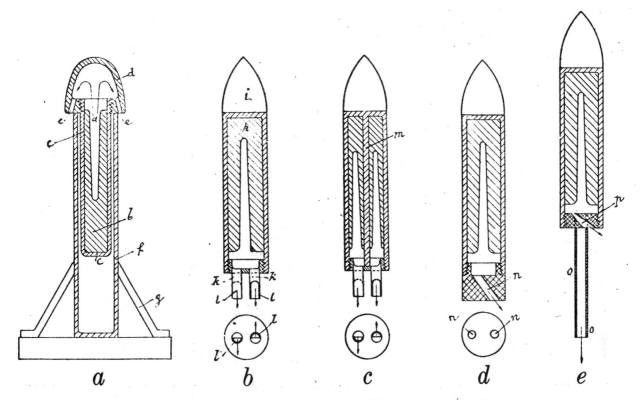

FIGURE 2.—Unge's early rockets: *a*, First rocket tested in 1892. *b*, Second type, with two exhaust pipes and one combustion chamber, diameter 50 mm (2 in), length 300 mm (12 in). *c*, Third type, with two combustion chambers. *d*, Type with uniformly thick, oblique exhaust orifices. *e*, Modification, with conical, oblique exhaust orifices and a 300-mm (12 in) guidance tube.

turbine "consisting of conical inlet canal (a) and likewise conical outlet canal (b), which at (c) encounter the smaller section (minima-section)," according to the patent. This is also the definition of the de Laval nozzle, even if the construction was not as finished and complete as today, but it was the first time the de Laval nozzle principle had been used in rocketry by a designer who knew why it was applied to the rocket. Patents on this gas turbine were approved in 12 countries.

A calculation, using the dimensions of the turbine and the pressures to be found in one of Unge's notebooks, gives the exit mach number as $M = 2.9$. Unge scaled the dimensions of the turbine to fulfill the requirements of an isentropic expansion usable in all three types of rockets he had in production.

This invention turned out to be so effective that the use of a rotation gun was no longer necessary. Unge therefore designed new types of lightweight launching tubes, consisting simply of a number of cylindrically arranged guides (Figure 4). The sim-

plification of the launch tube made the field handling of the rocket much more sophisticated, and there were no longer any restrictions on the designing of bigger rockets.

The name "aerial torpedo" was for the first time officially used in this turbine patent of 1897. Two years after this invention Dr. Gustaf de Laval joined the board of the Mars Co., which even more stresses the fact, that Unge was well aware of the de Laval nozzle principle through early contacts with its inventor.

Parallel with the work on the stabilization problem, Unge gave his attention to improving the rocket propellant. In the first types of rockets Unge used a propellant consisting of ordinary gunpowder, but his collaboration with Alfred Nobel gave rise to an extensive series of experiments to improve ballistite, invented by Nobel in 1888. The first known "successful" firing of a ballistite rocket (Figure 5) was made on 12 September 1896 in Stockholm.

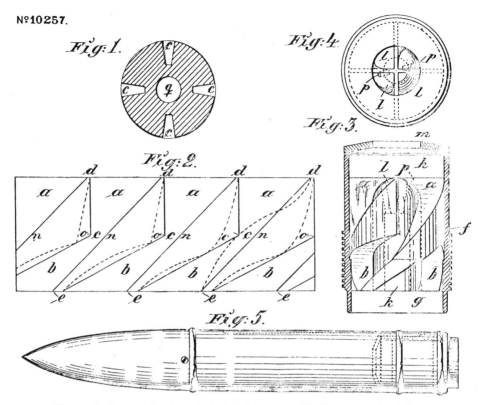

FIGURE 3.—Gas-turbine for which Swedish patent 10,257 was received in 1897.

After having completed the design of the gas turbine and made a number of tests on this one, Unge found that the ballistite propellant was difficult to handle and, most of all, it did not provide as much gas an gunpowder. The results of the ballistite experiments forced Unge back to a propellant composition of 78.3% niter, 8.4% sulphur, and 13.3% carbon. Later on this composition was changed to 81.3% niter, 5.4% sulphur, and 13.3% carbon. These compositions made optimum use of the qualities of the turbine, but they gave Unge yet another problem to solve. It turned out to be impossible to store a charged rocket because the propellant shrank and cracked during drying, and this resulted in an explosion because of the increase in the burning area. The first idea tried, in which it was intended to retain the moisture with gypsum, turned out to be useless, because even if the gypsum swelled in absorbing the water, it, too, shrank after 3 or 4 days.

Tests over several years at the turn of the century finally solved the problem: when mixed with 0.1–0.6% of a nonvolatile oil, the propellant always tried to expand after having been pressed into the rocket-body. To prevent the propellant charge from expanding along the central axis of the rocket, a plate with the same geometrical form as the end surface of the propellant was fastened immediately after the propellant had been pressed into the rocket body. This technique was patented in most countries in 1903.

To simplify manufacturing of the rocket, the propellant in its final form was shaped in small cylindrical pieces (cartouches) covered with paper or felting soaked in oil (Figure 6 and 7). This cover served three purposes: first to make the charge elastic when pressed into the body, second to protect the propellant when transporting and handling the rocket, and third, to provide a heat insulation around the charge. Rockets fitted with this propellant could be stored for years unaffected by temperature changes between −25°C and +30°C (−15°F and +85°F), and still deliver the same thrust when fired. Unge heat tested the propellant from −20°C to +80°C (−5°F to +175°F) without any trouble. The use of the gas turbine and the new storage propellant also brought into use higher pressures than before, and this forced Unge to give

FIGURE 4.—The lightweight launching barrel consisting of cylindrically arranged guides. Photo from Armémuseum Archives, Sweden.

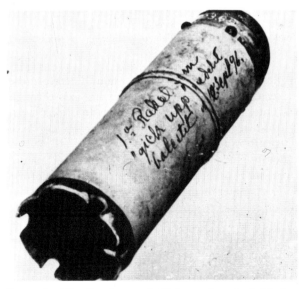

FIGURE 5.—The first known ballistite rocket, fired 12 September 1896 in Stockholm. In Tekniska Museet, Stockholm.

FIGURE 6.—Rocket manufactured according to the cartouche system. Photo from Armémuseum Archives, Sweden.

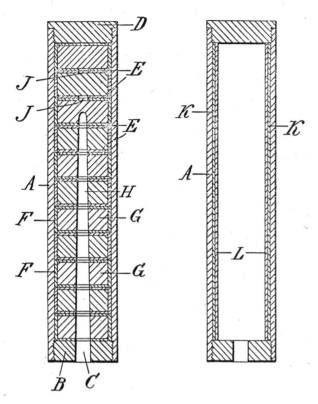

FIGURE 7.—Drawing from Swedish patent 19,130, showing Unge's system of manufacturing the propellant in cylindrical pieces.

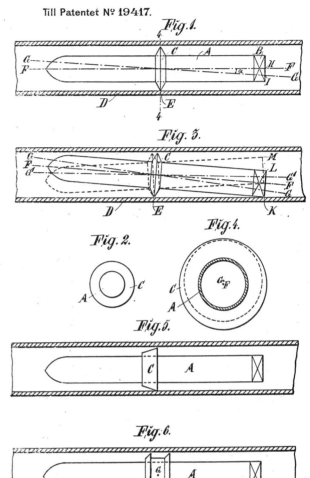

FIGURE 8.—Drawing from Swedish patent 19,417, showing the final solution to the problem of stabilizing the trajectory.

up the use of brass and aluminum for the rocket-body. He changed its material to steel, which could withstand the high pressures encountered in manufacturing the rocket charge.

The improvements of the rocket in all the above-mentioned respects were still not sufficient to make it a complete success, for the rocket made sudden, quick changes of direction at the beginning of its trajectory. The reason for this deviation was that while inside the launching barrel the rocket rotated around its geometric axis, but as soon as it left the barrel it started rotating around the axis through its center of gravity. If these axes did not coincide, the change in its axis of rotation caused it to move in spirals proportional to the speed of rotation.

This difficult problem was solved very simply by fitting the rocket with a balance-ring of copper or brass (Figure 8) at the center of gravity, or close to it. The outer diameter of the ring was made large enough so that the tip of the turbine could not touch the walls of the barrel when the rocket swung

inside the barrel during its rotation. Therefore the rocket could rotate freely around the axis through its center of gravity, after a few revolutions, even if it started rotating around the geometric axis, when still in the barrel.

Because of imperfections in the rocket manufacturing it could be assumed that the center of the outer diameter of the balance ring would not always fall on the axis through the center of gravity. Therefore the balance ring was made out of a soft material, like copper or brass, with a wedge-shaped cross section that could wear down during its rotation, so that the center of the outer diameter would eventually coincide with the axis through the center of gravity.

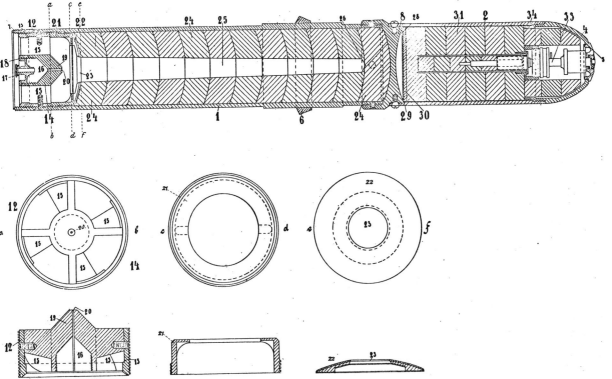

FIGURE 9.—The 20-cm rocket of 1905: 1, Rocket body. 2, Warhead. 4, Rounded tip. 5, Front cover of tip. 6, Balance ring. 7, Threads for cover of propellant during storage. 8, Intermediate wall. 12, Ring which transfers the propulsion thrust from the turbine to the rocket body. 13, Edge on which the turbine rests. 14, Turbine. 15, Exhaust orifices. 16, Space for igniter. 17, Igniter cover. 18, Holder of igniter. 19, Rounded center body of the turbine. 20, Ignition channel. 21, Ring for holding the end-plate. 22, End plate of combustion chamber. 23, Orifice of combustion chamber. 24, Cartouches. 25, Combustion chamber. 26, End cone of combustion chamber. 28, Edge to carry felt plate (29) and wooden plate (30). 31, Charge of explosive. 33, Impact fuse. 34, Ring for holding the charge.

The rocket as completed (Figure 9) showed good accuracy at test launchings. The maximum range was about 4 kg (2.5 mi) for the 10-cm rocket and 7 km (5 mi) for the 30-cm rocket. The spread was generally within an area of 100 m (300 ft) times 50 m (150 ft), 50 m along the trajectory. Measurements and dimensions of the rockets were as follows:

Model	Rocket Caliber (cm)	Length (cm)	Warhead	Weight (kg) Propellant	Total	Launch barrel Length (m)	Weight (kg)
1905	10	90	2	4.4	17	2.5	64
1909	10	88	4.1	5.1	18.3	1.7	66
1905	20	155	15.8	30.9	135.5	4.6	235
1905	30	235	58.0	116.0	363.5	7.0	708

New types of barrels were designed for such different purposes as mountain artillery and man-carried artillery. The prices were about 60 dollars for the 10-cm rocket and up to 600 dollars for the 30-cm rocket. The price of the barrel for the 10-cm rocket was about 240 dollars. Though different countries expressed some interest, no large-scale production was started, mainly because the Swedish military authorities were completely indifferent.

The German company Friedrich Krupp in Essen became interested in the rockets designed by Unge, and in 1908 Krupp bought all seven rocket patents and a large number of rockets from Unge for tests at their Meppen testing ground in Germany. A few years later Krupp ceased the experiments with Unge's rockets because of their inaccuracy, according to information of questionable accuracy given to Unge by Krupp.

After the unlucky affairs with Krupp, Unge continued his experiments with lifesaving rockets, which had begun in 1907. The work was based upon two patents, one for a new ignition system and the other for "improvements in or relating to the means for connecting lines, cables or the like to rotatory projectiles for conveying them through the air" (Swedish patent 26,991, received in 1908). Test launchings were made not only in Sweden but also in England for the Board of Trade, and Unge managed to sell some of these life-saving rockets (Figure 10) to England, India, Australia, and Greece. The weight of the system, including one rocket (based upon the 10-cm rocket), 400 m of line (400 yd), line-holder, and the transportation box with launch barrel was 105 kg (230 lb). The usable range was 300 m (900 ft) with very good accuracy, even in storms. The price for a set-up was 80 to 100 dollars.

Unge spent a lot of effort on improving manufacturing methods. A way to make a more inexpensive rocket body was introduced in 1912. The cartouches, the turbine, and the forward wall of the combustion chamber were pressed together into the final form of the propellant charge by means of a hydraulic press, and then a steel band was wrapped around the propellant and fastened at the ends to the turbine and to the forward wall by screws. Another idea, tried with great success, was the manufacturing of a very inexpensive turbine out of clay. Most of the smaller rockets tested after 1912 were produced with the clay turbine. The turbine was also modified to provide greater thrust by means of a conical hole in the central portions of the turbine. The dimensions of the 10-cm rocket

FIGURE 10.—Complete lifesaving rocket system, manufactured by the Mars Company. Photo from Armémuseum Archives, Sweden.

were changed to a new model called the 10.8-cm rocket.

New ideas for the use of the rockets were developed by Unge when he started to calculate how the heavy guns on armored vessels could be replaced with batteries of his aerial torpedoes. Fixed batteries for coast defence were also suggested, as well as rocket-armed dirigibles. However, most of the experimental work during 1913 and 1914 was with the life-saving rockets.

One of Wilhelm Theodor Unge's later ideas was a system to propel and guide rockets, aeroplanes, and airships by using the reaction force of a jet of gas. Unfortunately this idea will be a secret forever, because it is only to be found in a 1909 patent application which Unge did not carry through; the application is therefore marked secret, according to the patent law of that time.

Wilhelm Theodor Unge, retired as lieutenant colonel from the Army, died in 1915. Subsequently, in 1917, the Mars Company went into liquidation, and was dissolved in 1922 after having been managed by his sons.

REFERENCES

1. Unge, *Fliegender Torpedo* (Stockholm, 1907).

2. Swedish Patents 5,556, 10,036, 10,257, 19,113, 19,130, 19,417, 19,946, 26,814, and 26,991.

3. Unge's notebooks from 1899–914 in Swedish Kungl. Armémuseum Archives.

4. The correspondence between W. T. Unge and Alfred Nobel, 1891 to 1896, in Nobel Foundation Archives.

24

Some New Data on Early Work of the Soviet Scientist-Pioneers in Rocket Engineering

V. N. SOKOLSKY, *Soviet Union*

Recent advances in space exploration have aroused considerable interest in the history of cosmonautics as well as in the people who founded this science and developed theories on interplanetary travel.

Among the pioneers in rocketry in the first third of the twentieth century, a prominent place is occupied by the Soviet scientists Kostantin Eduardovitch Tsiolkovskiy (1857–1932), founder of theoretical cosmonautics, Fridrikh Arturovich Tsander (1887–1933), one of the pioneers of Soviet rocketry, Yuri Vasilyevich Kondratyuk (1897–1942), a gifted scientist and inventor. Because of their talents and efforts, as early as in the first third of the century the Soviet Union had made substantial contributions toward the development of interplanetary travel.

In their works are encountered many interesting proposals, among which the following deserve special mention:

1. Employment of liquid-propellant rocket engines.
2. Use of highly reactive metal-base fuel.
3. Use of other kinds of energy (atomic and electro-thermal rocket engines, solar light pressure).
4. Creation of intermediate interplanetary bases utilizing artificial satellites of the Earth and other celestial bodies.
5. Employment of multistage rockets and development of their theory.
6. Use of rocket structures as an additional source of fuel.
7. Fitting the first rocket stages with airfoils, and employment of airfoils for re-entry to Earth or for a gliding descend onto planets possessing an atmosphere.

8. Use of other planets' gravitational fields to increase the velocity of space vehicles.

A study of the scientific legacy bequeathed by these founders is of great scientific and cognitive interest, for it enables us to trace the development of this branch of engineering and provides for a better insight into the psychology of the scientific creativity of these outstanding scientists, engineers, and inventors.

Recently, a group of Soviet historians of rocket and space engineering have studied the scientific legacy of Tsiolkovskiy, Tsander, and Kondratyuk, the founders of rocket engineering. Space limitations do not permit us to deal at great length with all the results obtained; we shall therefore dwell only on those aspects associated with the initial period of the activities of each of these scientists, as well as on several fundamental principles that will permit us to clarify certain points in the history of rocket engineering.

Until recently in many works and especially in foreign publications, it has been said that Tsiolkovskiy devoted himself to problems of interplanetary travel only in the late 19th and early 20th centuries, having been influenced by scientific fiction, particularly that of Jules Verne.

In reality, he was interested in this problem as early as 1873–76, during his stay in Moscow, when he conjectured that cosmic velocities could be achieved by utilizing the properties of centrifugal force.

During the years 1878–79, Tsiolkovskiy began to compile his astronomic drawings. In the same years he proposed a device for investigating the effect of gravitational acceleration on living organisms.

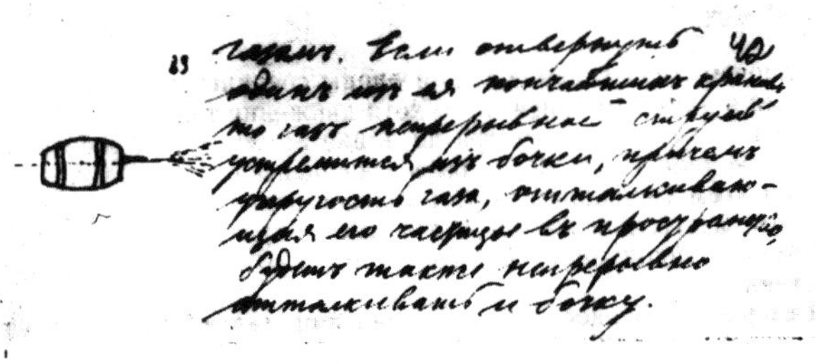

FIGURE 1.—Excerpt from 1883 manuscript, in which Tsiolkovskiy discusses the reactive effect of gasses, saying, in part, "If we open one of the . . . [illegible] valves, gas will flow in a constant stream from the barrel; moreover the elasticity of the gas forcing its particles into space will also steadily repel the barrel as well."

Four years later, in 1883, in his manuscript "Free Space." Tsiolkovskiy stated for the first time the possibility of using reaction as a propulsive force for motion in outer space (Figure 1). This manuscript, not published during his lifetime, is of considerable interest to those who study his work, for it contains the embryos of many ideas expressed in a general way and developed in his later works.

In this manuscript, Tsiolkovskiy analyzed the simple cases of mechanical motion in space without any attraction and resistance, gave a schematic drawing of a spacecraft (Figure 2), and proposed the use of a simple gyroscopic device to stabilize the spacecraft in flight. In the same work, he considered such problems as the conditions required for the existence and growth of vegetation and living organisms in interstellar space—their forms and sizes.

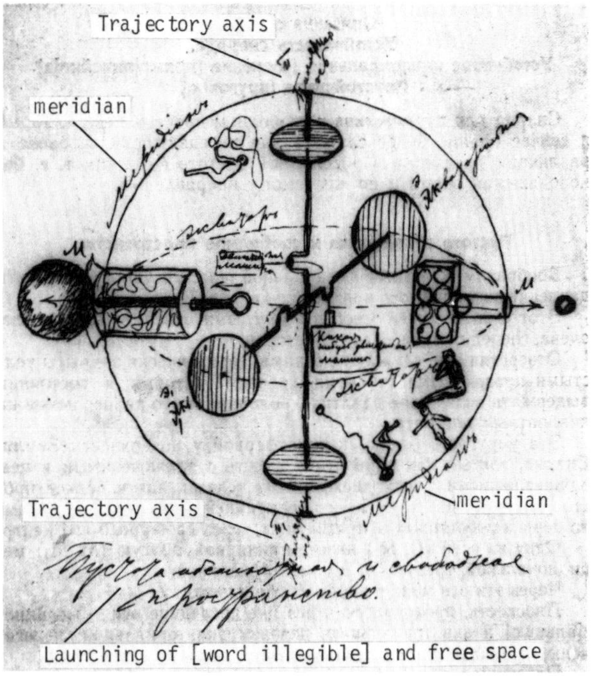
Trajectory axis
meridian
Trajectory axis
meridian
Launching of [word illegible] and free space

FIGURE 2.—Schematic diagram from 1883 manuscript.

There are no quantitative data in this manuscript, and therefore all the conclusions are based on qualitative deductions. Besides, it does not consider possible means for overcoming the Earth's gravity and placing a spacecraft into a near-Earth or near-Sun orbit. However, the necessity of using jet reaction was clearly understood and formulated in the manuscript. Therefore, as noted by Professor A. A. Kosmodem'yanskiy, one of the experts on K. E. Tsiolkovskiy, the earlier works of Tsiolkovskiy were undoubtedly associated with his fundamental work, "Investigation of Outer Space by Means of Reactive Devices," published in 1903.

His ideas about interplanetary flights found further development in his scientific fiction, namely, "On the Moon" (1893) and "Visions of the Earth and the Sky, and the Effects of Universal Gravitation" (1895). In the latter work he expressed the novel idea of creating an artificial Earth satellite and clearly posed the problem of "imparting to a body the velocity required to generate a centrifugal force that would overcome Earth's gravity when this velocity amounted to 8 versts per second [10,675 m/sec]." [1]

In 1896 Tsiolkovskiy began the theoretical study of the problem of interplanetary flights by means of rockets. A perusal of his papers in the Archives of the USSR Academy of Sciences, shows that Tsiolkovskiy's well known equation was derived as far back as 1897 (Figure 3).[2]

Of undoubted interest is the design of his first rocket. As is known, his paper "Investigation of Outer Space by Means of Reactive Devices," published in the "Scientific Review" (St. Petersburg, 1903) did not contain any figures or drawings, although they are referred to in the text.

A drawing of K. E. Tsiolkovskiy's rocket was published for the first time in the periodical "Herald of Aeronautics" (No. 19, 1911) under the heading "Summary of the First Paper." Most authors have attributed this drawing to the time when the first paper was written and considered this drawing to be the "schematic drawing of Tsiolkovskiy's rocket of 1903" (Figure 4*b*). This conclusion, however, is erroneous, for during the past few years researchers

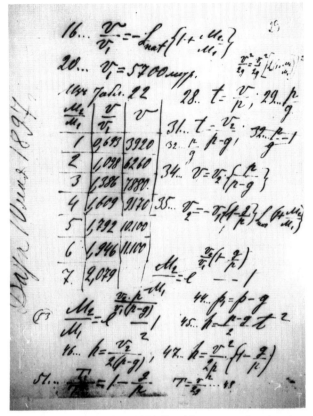

FIGURE 3.—Excerpt from Tsiolkovskiy manuscript bearing date 10 May 1897.

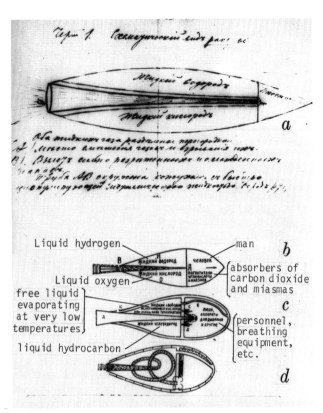

FIGURE 4.—Sequence of Tsiolkovskiy's spacecraft designs.

studying Tsiolkovskiy's manuscripts have discovered a thus-far unknown drawing of Tsiolkovskiy's rocket dated 1902 (Figure 4a).[3] The drawing, in his own hand, fully agrees with the description given in the paper of 1903. Thus, it has finally been established what was actually the design of the rocket described by Tsiolkovskiy in 1903, and the sequence of the other spacecraft versions proposed by him in subsequent years (see Figure 4).

In prerevolutionary Russia, in addition to Tsiolkovskiy, several other scientists and inventors worked on the problem of interplanetary travel. Among them, F. A. Tsander deserves special mention. He was the first engineer in our country to devote himself to the problem of interplanetary flights. He was the only scientist among the first generation of Soviet pioneers in cosmonautics (before the 1930s), who undertook practical realization of his ideas in the field of rocket engineering.

A study of Tsander's work is of considerable interest, although it is greatly hampered by the fact that the majority of his manuscripts (over five thousand pages) in the Archives of the USSR Academy of Sciences are in shorthand and are difficult to decipher because he employed an obsolete system.

Besides, until recently part of Tsander's papers were in the scientist's personal archives, in the custody of his family, and inaccessible to researchers. It was only in 1968, when a commission was set up to study Tsander's works, that his daughter, Astra Fridrikhovna Tsander, released these papers to the Archives of the USSR Academy of Sciences, which now contains almost all his papers.

Among these materials, of great interest are his first working notebooks, wherein he wrote down his observations, experimental results, calculations, and estimates, as well as his views on various problems.

These notes indicate that as early as in 1907 Tsander conceived the notion of interplanetary travel. For example, on 23 June 1907, he made an entry in his notebook on the motion of a body propelled by the reaction of issuing particles. On 10 November of the same year he made a brief mention (see Figure 5) of the problems associated with

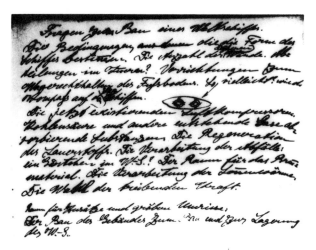

FIGURE 5.—Excerpt (translated in the text) from Tsander manuscript dated 10 November 1907.

creation of a spacecraft ("Fragen zum Bau eines Weltschiffes") as follows:

Conditions which determine the shape of the spacecraft. Number of outside walls. Bays in . . . [illegible]. Appliances for keeping the floor of the frame in horizontal position. Can it be so? [a drawing is appended] as a gyrocompass on seagoing ships? Present-day air compressors. Substances which absorb carbon dioxide and other gases which develop. Regeneration of oxygen. Conversion of wastes: a small garden in the spacecraft. Fuel storage. Utilization of solar heat. Selection of propulsive force. Construction of a hangar for building and accommodation of the spacecraft.[4]

On 8 February 1908 Tsander returned again to the design of a spaceship and in autumn 1908, he set aside a special note-book for spacecraft design calculations (see Figure 6) entitled "Die Weltschiffe

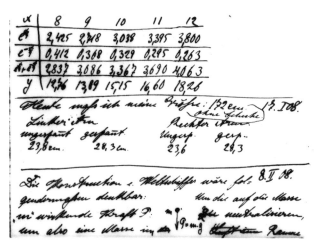

FIGURE 6.—Spacecraft calculations by Tsander in 1908.

(Ätherschiffe) die den Verkehr zwischen der Sternen ermöglichen sollen. Die Bewegung im Weltenraum" (Spacecraft (Ether craft) Will Make Possible Interstellar Travel. Movement in Space).[5]

In that notebook, he poses such problems as a determination of the energy required to reach any star, work needed to move a certain mass to a particular distance from the Earth, the amount of oxygen required for man's existence in a spacecraft, etc. He also considers the question, in how many flight days can Mars or Venus be reached? and he also sets himself the task of theoretically determining the conditions of motion in space under (1) minimum energy, and (2) in the shortest possible time. From page 8 onward, the notes are in shorthand and have not yet been deciphered.

In 1909, Tsander expressed for the first time the idea of utilizing the solid structural material of the rocket as an additional fuel, and between 1909 and 1911 carried out further calculations on a jet engine and the work required for boosting a spacecraft to great heights.

The third Soviet researcher who worked on the problem of interplanetary travel was Y. A. Kondratyuk, whose life and activities have not thus far been studied in detail.

Kondratyuk began working on interplanetary travel problems during World War I. At that time the only works published on this subject were Tsiolkovskiy's papers (1903, 1910, 1911–12, and 1914) and a paper read by R. Esnault-Pelterie in 1912 and published in 1913 in France.[6] At that time R. H. Goddard, H. Oberth, and F. A. Tsander were already carrying out investigations in the field of rocket engineering and cosmonautics, although their papers had not yet been published.

It is evident that Kondratyuk could not have known the results obtained by the above-mentioned scientists.[7] Neither was he aware, according to his own statement, of the papers published by Tsiolkovskiy and Esnault-Pelterie. Consequently, in his investigations Kondratyuk often repeated some of the statements already made by others. Generally he proceeded along his own special and unique path, and evolved different methods for solving one and the same problem.

While studying Kondratyuk's manuscripts, one can trace how his views on problems associated with conquering outer space were gradually formed over a number of years. It is apparent how from his first conclusions, which were not yet mature in every detail and were sometimes even naive, Kondratyuk developed the views expressed in his book "Conquest of Interplanetary Spaces," published 10 years later (1929).

The first version of Kondratyuk's manuscript on interplanetary travel (as yet unpublished)[8] is in the form of preliminary notes and cannot be considered a complete work. In these notes, written in the form of a diary wherein the author is sometimes in error, he argues with himself, and in a number of cases re-writes and re-calculates separate sections of his work. However, even in the early notes, a number of interesting statements can be encountered.

Like Tsiolkovskiy, Kondratyuk first of all endeavored to find out whether one could make an interplanetary flight by a reactive device, using currently available materials. Having completed the calculations, he derived independently and in a different way Tsiolkovskiy's basic equation for rocket flight.

Having been convinced that flight by rocket was in principle possible, Kondratyuk started refining a number of problems associated with flight in outer space. In his first manuscript he considered the effect of gravitation and resistance of the environment, acceleration and launching methods, arrangement of various parts of the spacecraft, its controllability and stability, conditions of flights within the solar system, creation of intermediate interplanetary bases, etc. And he made a number of proposals which are of considerable interest even today, with due regard to present achievements in cosmonautics. In particular, the sequence of first steps in conquering outer space that Kondratyuk presented in his manuscript undoubtedly deserves our attention. He envisaged the following (from page 25 of the first version): (1) to test out the operation of the equipment for ascent in the atmosphere; (2) flight to near-Earth distances for several thousands of versts; (3) flight to the Moon without landing, i.e., a circumlunar flight; (4) flight to the Moon with landing thereon.

Of considerable interest is his method of sending an expedition to the Moon and to other celestial bodies. He clearly understood that the amount of energy required for landing and subsequent take-off from some celestial body, is directly proportional to the mass of the spacecraft. Therefore, he proposed, when arranging a flight to some celestial body (e.g., the Moon), first to place the spacecraft into lunar orbit, with the subsequent separation of a special bay which should alight on the Moon.

In the section "The Theory of Landings" (page 18 of the first version of his manuscript) Kondratyuk wrote:

Landing on some other celestial body in no way differs from a takeoff and landing on the Earth, except for the magnitude and the potential. In order to avoid too much consumption of the active substance [fuel, as opposed to "non-active part," the spacecraft without fuel], it is possible not to land the whole rocket, but only to reduce its velocity to such a degree that it would revolve uniformly around and as near as possible to the body on which landing must be made. Then, the non-active part should be detached with such an amount of active substance needed for the non-active part to make a landing and subsequently to return to the rest of the rocket.

He formulated this more distinctly on page 126 of the second version of the manuscript, wherein he wrote:

For landing on some planet, it is necessary to multiply the ratio for takeoff from and return to the Earth by the respective ratio for the other planet. Therefore, it is more advantageous not to land the whole rocket on the other planet, but to turn it into a satellite [around the planet], while the landing should be made with such part of the rocket as is required to land on the planet and to return back and join the rocket.

The second version of Kondratyuk's manuscript, which is a refinement of the previous work, differs from the first in being a more systematized and detailed presentation. Also, several new sections were included in the second version, such as "Active Substance and its Combustion," "Orientation Instruments," "Acceleration Indicator," "Shape of the Rocket to Provide for Atmospheric Landing and Landing Control," "Utilization of the Relative Motions of Celestial Bodies," "Electric Gun," etc.[9]

Kondratyuk's manuscripts of this period are characterized by a great number of spectacular and interesting ideas not quite comprehensively developed from the technical point of view. Among them are his proposals of jettisoning the unnecessary passive parts of the rocket mass, creation of electric rockets (see Figure 7) and nuclear engines, use of solar energy, utilization of the Earth's atmosphere during re-entry, creating some intermediate bases in the form of an artificial lunar satellite, using gravitational fields and the relative motions of celestial bodies, etc.

In evaluating the early works of Kondratyuk

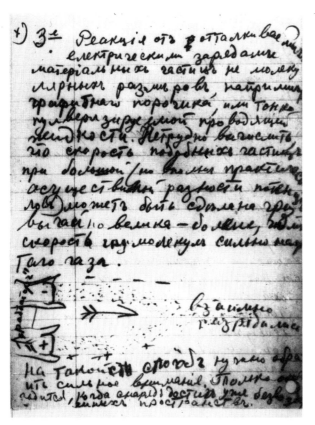

FIGURE 7.—Excerpt from Kondratyuk's second manuscript, in which he discusses "Reaction from repulsion by electrical charges of material particles . . . . Based on such a method, I am thinking of inventing a powerful vehicle. Only suitable when the rocket reaches the void of outer space."

interplanetary travel after 1914, and returned to these problems only in 1923 after the publication of H. Oberth's *Die Rakete zu den Planetenräumen* (The Rocket into Interplanetary Space).

In fact, this last statement is erroneous, as evidenced by the unpublished notes, "Extension of Man into Outer Space," dated 1921. Until recently, these notes were probably not within the reach of researchers, because they were kept, not with his manuscripts devoted to the problems of reaction propulsion and interplanetary travel, but with his manuscripts on the universe. They came to light only when a research group of the Institute of the History of Natural Science and Technology of the USSR Academy of Sciences began a systematic study of all his manuscripts.

These notes cannot be considered as completed work. Rather, they are rough drafts which nevertheless are of considerable interest, for they evidently represent the first attempt made by Tsiolkovskiy after the first world war to return to the problems of conquering outer space with reaction (jet-propelled) vehicles.

In the very beginning of the manuscript (dated 21 September 1921), Tsiolkovskiy enumerated the possible methods for attaining cosmic velocities. He points out that the following means can be used to achieve this aim:

1. Repulsion of gases, solids, and liquids (reaction vehicles).
2. Electric flux . . . . Outflow of negative or positive electricity.
3. Pressure of light rays.
4. Radiation of matter, for example, radium . . . .[10]

Somewhat later (11 October 1921), Tsiolkovskiy returned to this problem again and answered his own question (what can the engines be used for?) as follows:

1. Direct light-pressure provides motion in space, making it possible to move away from the Sun, to approach it, to restore velocities.
2. Motors serve for movement in gaseous medium, to obtain a velocity or the first impulse . . . .[11]

It is notable that here Tsiolkovskiy touches upon the use of various types of engines. He points out that for the purpose of overcoming gravity and atmospheric resistance, use should be made of reaction engines operating on chemical fuel, but once the spacecraft travels beyond the Earth's gravitational field and is in a dynamically balanced state, it is more appropriate to make use of low-

from the viewpoint of their importance to the history of science and technology, it should be borne in mind that these manuscripts were not published in time, and their contents did not become known earlier than 1925. Consequently, before 1925, they could not have had any influence in the development of rocket engineering, and, as far as that period is concerned, they are of interest only as part of the evolutions of ideas of interplanetary travel.

Let us now return to Tsiolkovskiy's works. As is known, they were published in 1903, 1911–12, and 1914 (we are considering here only his research works, not his scientific fiction). Then, after a ten-year interval, in 1924, his first work (1903) was republished as a separate brochure, with minor corrections and additions. This caused some historians to suppose that Tsiolkovskiy had ceased working on the problems of rocket engineering and thrust engines. A fortnight later (27 October 1921), he made the following entry: "Writing of the complete rocket theory should be started." [12]

Evidently associated with the same record and dated 23 October is the outline of an article entitled "The Rocket," [13] in which he suggested considering a number of problems of reaction-propulsion flights in free space as well as within the atmosphere.

In the same manuscript, Tsiolkovskiy for the first time poses the problem of transportation using an "air cushion." Thus far, biographers of Tsiolkovskiy have believed that his interest in the problem of transportation using an air cushion arose in 1926, when he was working on the manuscript "Gas Friction," [14] and that it found expression in his work "Air Resistance and an Express Train," published in 1927.

It now appears that Tsiolkovskiy already was aware of this principle and clearly understood it in 1921, this being evident from the above-mentioned work "Extension of Man into Outer Space," where, in the section "Rapid Translational Motion on the Earth," he points out that "gliding on a liquid or a gas," (Figure 8) as one of the possible means of movement, when the movement of ground (or water) transportation is achieved as the result of gliding of a carriage on an elastic air cushion created by powerful engines. He mentioned that "With polished surfaces, the gas layer between such surfaces may be very thin. This resembles flight." [15]

Later on, the air cushion idea found further development in his works "An Express Train" and "General Conditions of Transportation."

In conclusion, I would like to trace how the attitude toward Tsiolkovskiy has changed over the years. Before the October Revolution he was considered to be an eccentric, an unsuccessful but gifted self-educated man without a degree. After the revolution, this attitude underwent radical changes. He was elected a member of the Socialist Academy, was allotted a personal pension, and had the opportunity to set aside teaching and devote himself completely to research. However, he devoted his activities to the development of aviation at that time. The State allotted a personal pension to him, "in view of the great merits of the scientist-inventor, an expert in aviation and aeronautics." No mention whatever was made about his research in rocket engineering and interplanetary travel.

More than ten years passed. K. E. Tsiolkovskiy's

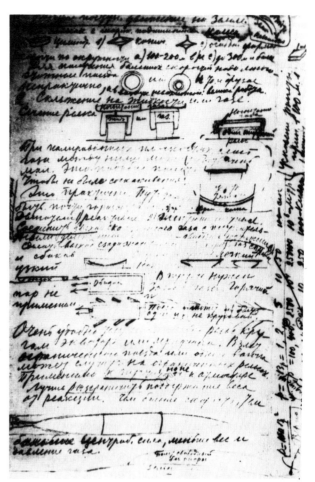

FIGURE 8.—Excerpt, dealing with "rapid translational motion on the Earth," from manuscript of Tsiolkovskiy's unpublished notes of 1921 on "Extension of Man into Outer Space."

ideas in rocket engineering were converted to reality and the number of adherents to his concepts increased in number. The first liquid-propellant rockets were launched in our country, as well as abroad. In various parts of the world, organizations were set up to study rocket engineering and interplanetary travel. For these people and organizations, Tsoilkovskiy was a spiritual leader, a pioneer in rocket engineering and a patriarch of interstellar navigation. This attitude can be seen in the greetings sent him on his seventy-fifth birthday by the German Verein für Raumschiffahrt (Society for Space Travel). It read:

Dear Sir,

Since the day of its foundation the Society for Space Travel, has always held you to be one of its spiritual leaders, and has never missed any occasion to point out—orally, as well as in the Press—your merits and your indisputable priority in the development of this great idea.[16]

The same sentiments were expressed in letters from the Head of the Reactive Scientific Research Institute, in one of which it was stated:

It is no mystery that most of the workers now engaged in rocketry became acquainted for the first time with the fundamentals of reaction propulsion in your wonderful books, learned from them, were infected with your enthusiasm and confidence that our cause will be crowned with success.[17]

But for most people the name of K. E. Tsiolkovskiy was, as before, associated principally with aeronautics and dirigibles. Such an estimation of his activities can be seen in the press report on his death (19 September 1935).[18] His works in the field of rocket engineering were not mentioned either in this press report or in the decision of the government on the perpetuation of the memory of K. E. Tsiolkovskiy.[19]

Another decade passed. The attitude toward rocket engineering changed fundamentally. World War II, which had just ended, clearly showed what possibilities were associated with solid-propellant and, to a greater extent, with liquid-propellant rockets. Then only was the great scientist mainly referred to as the founder of the theory of jet propulsion and a pioneer in rocket engineering, whereas his involvement in the problems of aeronautics was almost buried in oblivion.

Another 10 to 15 years passed. The notion about the potentialities of rocketry during this time changed fundamentally again. What seemed, even recently, to be a matter of a very distant future, became a today's reality. Artificial Earth satellites and spacecraft, were launched in the USSR and USA, automatic stations were sent toward the Moon, Mars, and Venus, and man's flight into outer space was ultimately realized.

So the notion about Tsiolkovskiy changes again. Before us, in all its grandeur, arises the figure of the founder of cosmonautics, of the first man who had the courage to announce that "mankind will not stay on the Earth forever," and who proved this point scientifically. Now K. E. Tsiolkovskiy is mainly spoken of as a man who has shown the way to the Universe, as the founder of the theory of interplanetary travel, and his works on the theory of reaction propulsion are considered only as a specific problem in the theory of cosmonautics.

Perhaps this, too, may not be the final assessment of the creative work of this amazingly gifted and truly inexhaustible scientist. It is quite possible that a time will come when our notions about him will again undergo radical change. As our knowledge of the Universe increases, a time will come when more attention will be paid to his works on the cosmos, and his works on the theory of interplanetary travel will be considered only as a specific problem in the general theory of mankind's conquest of the Universe.

NOTES

1. K. E. Tsiolkovskiy, *Grezy o Zemle i neve i effekty vsemirnogo tyagoteniya* [Visions of the Earth and the Sky, and the Effects of Universal Gravitation] (Moscow 1895), p. 50.

2. Arkhiv AN, SSSR [Archives, USSR Academy of Sciences], f. 555, op. 1, d. 32. 1.

3. Arkhiv AN, SSSR, f. 555, op. 1, d. 32. 1.

4. From Tsander's working notebook. Arkhiv AN, SSSR, f. 573, op. 2.

5. Arkhiv AN, SSSR, f. 573, op. 2.

6. R. Esnault-Pelterie. "Consideration sur les résultats de l'allégement indéfini des moteurs" [Considerations concerning the results of the indefinite lightening of motors]. *Journal de Physique Théoretique et Appliquée.* ser. 5, vol. 3, March 1913, pp. 218–30.

7. From autobiography of Yu. V. Kondratyuk in "Interplanetary Travel" (in Russian), by N. A. Rynin (Leningrad, 1932), issue 8.

8. The manuscripts of Yu. V. Kondratyuk were released by the author to the well-known historian of aviation B.-N. Vorob'yev in July 1938. They are now kept in the Institute of History of Natural Science and Technology of the USSR Academy of Sciences.

9. This work was published for the first time in 1964. See *Pioneers in Rocket Engineering: Kibal'tchitch, Tsiolkovskiy, Tsander, Kondratyuk. Selected Works* (in Russian), compiled and edited by B. N. Vorob'yev and V. N. Sokolskiy (Moscow: Nauka, 1964).

10. Arkhiv AN, SSSR, f. 555, op. 1, d. 246, l. 11 ob.

11. Ibid., l. 11 ob.

12. Ibid., l. 18.

13. Arkhiv AN, SSSR, f. 555, op. 1, d. 39.

14. Arkhiv AN, SSSR, f. 555, op. 1, d. 12.

15. Arkhiv AN, SSSR, f. 555, op. 1, d, 246, l. 6 ob.

16. Translated from the German. The original is published in *Konstantin Eduardovitch Tsiolkovsky, 1857–1932* (in Russian), a jubilee collection dedicated to K. E. Tsiolkovskiy's 75th birthday and the 40th anniversary of the publication of his first works on dirigibles (Moscow-Leningrad, 1932), p. 55.

17. From the correspondence between K. E. Tsiolkovskiy and the Reactive Scientific Research Institute. Arkhiv AN, SSSR, f. 555, op. 3, d. 108, l. 14.

18. *Izvestiya*, no. 220 (5773), 20 September 1935.

19. *Izvestiya*, no. 221 (5774), 21 September 1935.

25

Early Developments in Rocket and Spacecraft Performance, Guidance, and Instrumentation

ERNST A. STEINHOFF, *United States*

Introduction

Late in 1938, I was invited to join Dr. Wernher von Braun at Peenemunde, Germany, to take over the development of guidance and control systems for rocket vehicles and to direct activities in the areas of test instrumentation, flight testing, and flight performance measurements. My selection was based on the recommendation of Dr. Hermann Steuding at Peenemunde, a colleague and former head of the Flight Mechanics Department at the Deutsche Forschungsanstalt für Luftfahrt (DFS—German Research Institute for Motorless Flight) at Darmstadt, Germany. He felt that the work I was doing at DFS was directly applicable to the control of rockets and spacecraft.[1]

The work performed in the period 1936–38 at DFS by myself and my teammates dealt with conceptual studies for guidance of high-volume-to-surface-ratio, rocket-propelled guided missiles; the analysis of strap-down gyro references on flight-path-oriented reference signals; and the study of the coordinate transfers required. We also worked on sensors for acceleration, rate of speed change, aerodynamic angle of attack; on measurement methods of angular rate and angular acceleration, and on the compensation for effects of angular rate and angular acceleration on flight-measurement equipment. Also conducted were experiments with autopilots and flight-control systems using these sensors; wind tunnel experiments with sensors in the flow field of the main body; tests of hydraulic amplifiers for control actuators in flight-control systems; and flight tests in aircraft of such systems suitable for missile application. About this time it became recognized that rate and acceleration measurements were needed to control with repeatable accuracy the flight paths of unmanned vehicles. Among the concepts worked on which found application and actual use in the post-1938 era were low-altitude recovery of missiles by using the rate of pitot pressure change to initiate the recovery sequence; use of angle-of-attack vanes to limit air loads under wind shear; the application of acceleration and rate sensors in addition to displacement sensors along with hydraulic servomotors to achieve the high response rates needed for repeatable guided-missile trajectories; and the use of the integration of acceleration for precision propulsion cut-off. Much of the pre-1938 flight-performance measurement, data acquisition, and evaluation at DFS were directly applied to subsequent rocket and missile work.

As a student working at DFS, I followed up earlier rocket-powered glider experiments of Friedrich Stamer.[2] While employed there, my group supported flight-performance measurements on a prototype of what later became the Me 163 of Alexander Lippisch (Figure 1).

Sensor Developments

The need to determine stability parameters for the flight performance of powered and unpowered aircraft became more and more urgent at DFS during the period 1936–38. The need for more accurate flight test instrumentation became obvious particularly under flight-test conditions, when an aircraft was towed by another aircraft to an altitude of from 3,000 to 4,000 meters, so that performance and stability parameters, independent of propeller interference, could be determined in the subsequent

FIGURE 1.—Model of DFS-194, a further development of the DFS-39 which was flown by R. Opitz without engine in 1937. The next model, DFS-40, since the H_2O_2 rocket engine was not ready yet, was equipped with an Argus aircraft engine in 1938 and flown by H. Dittmar. The follow-on, DFS-194, was flown by H. Dittmar in the winter of 1938–39 and became the forerunner of the Me 163. Alexander Lippisch was the designer of all of these planes. Photo courtesy R. Opitz.

glide flight. Dr. Werner Spilger, one of my teammates, developed a linear accelerometer (Figure 2), sensitive to a single measuring axis only, which deflected the mirror of an Askania 4-element optical recorder. The link between the mirror and the accelerometer mass consisted of a small metal channel with flexures of specific axis of rotation, so as to minimize the effect of the linkage of inertial components on the measured acceleration. These flexures caused real problems owing to the fatigue resulting from high frequency vibrations caused by boundary-layer separations.

Dr. Spilger at that time invented a link, consisting of a very small beryllium-copper alloy channel, flexible on the suspension points at each end. This solution proved very successful, and not only permitted measurement of large variations in linear acceleration, but also reproduced the fine structure of acceleration and vibration. These accelerometers (used in triplets with their axes mutually perpendicular to each other) were later used at Peenemunde for early rocket flight-path and velocity-control purposes. Because electric outputs rather than optical light-beam deflections were needed to produce the control signals for flight-control equipment, pickups were developed which used a differential change in capacity ratio or

differential impedance to produce the desired signal.

While he was at Darmstadt Institute of Technology, Dr. Helmut Schlitt, later at Peenemunde, originally used the same type of accelerometer to develop a lateral inertial flight-path control for missiles. However, he changed the pickup to an a.c. current-modulation system, the current was proportional to lateral acceleration and the integral of the current proportional to the lateral velocity.

For stability measurements, of interest were not only deviations in attitude and the easily determinable damping increment—to determine deviation from linear behavior during flight-path oscillations —but also the angular rates, angular accelerations, and angle of attack. Also important were changes in pitot pressure during, for instance, a complete Phugoid oscillation cycle, and changes in actual attitude to account for all effects either observed or recorded.

Although rate gyros were initially satisfactory to determine pitch, yaw and roll rates, their own deflection introduced errors due to their finite spring constants. Introduction of angular accelerometers—in which was measured the torque of an inertial mass constrained to movement in one axis of rotation—permitted resolving errors of angular rates and attitudes. Since, particularly for Phugoid analysis, angles of attack were of importance, a dual-vane angle-of-attack meter was developed. Due to the inertia of the vanes, this instrument was sensitive to angular accelerations and gave reading errors proportional to the instantaneous acceleration; it also tended to oscillate. To eliminate this effect, a rotating mass of equal inertia was installed, with its steel wire pulleys reversing the sense of rotation of the compensating mass torque. If no aerodynamic forces were acting, and only angular acceleration tended to displace the angle-of-attack meter, the inertia of the compensator prevented any deflection. In the event of the presence of aerodynamic forces, these permitted proper rotation of the angular acceleration compensation and the angle-of-attack meter. With this arrangement, angular acceleration effects on angle-of-attack measurements were satisfactorily eliminated, but its overall inertia to aerodynamic forces was twice as high as that of the vane alone.

In order to measure the actual pitch displacement, either optical cinetheodolite measurements

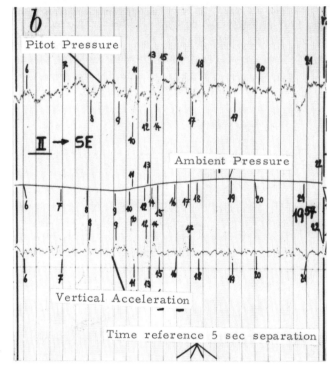

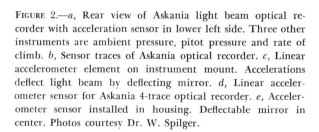

FIGURE 2.—*a,* Rear view of Askania light beam optical recorder with acceleration sensor in lower left side. Three other instruments are ambient pressure, pitot pressure and rate of climb. *b,* Sensor traces of Askania optical recorder. *c,* Linear accelerometer element on instrument mount. Accelerations deflect light beam by deflecting mirror. *d,* Linear accelerometer sensor for Askania 4-trace optical recorder. *e,* Accelerometer sensor installed in housing. Deflectable mirror in center. Photos courtesy Dr. W. Spilger.

of high resolution or barometric measurements of equally high (or even higher) resolutions were needed. Neither existing altimeters nor rate-of-climb indicators were adequate at that time to measure vertical displacement of the order of only a few feet or meters. To solve this problem, the author started the development of a rate-of-climb indicator in which the pressure gauge consisted of a single grounded corrugated beryllium-copper diaphragm (Figure 3). This diaphragm acted as a variable capacitance insulated between two electrodes, the measuring volume of which was connected with the ambient pressure source, and the other volume was connected with a 250-cc reference air volume within a thermos bottle. Both volumes were interconnected by a capillary such that the time constant of the rate indicator was in the order of 10 milliseconds. The capillary could be closed off so that a sensitive statoscope could be obtained which permitted horizontal flight within a meter of a reference altitude.

The same technique was applied to obtain either a pitot pressure rate-of-change indicator or a stagnation pressure variometer. This type of instrument

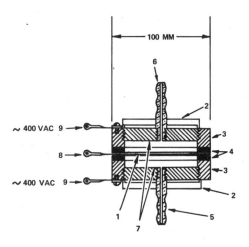

1. COPPER–BERYLLIUM DIAPHRAGM
2. ADJUSTABLE ELECTRODES (ALUMINUM)
3. MAIN SENSOR BODY, ALUMINUM, ANODIZED OUTER SURFACES
4. INSULATING RINGS (BAKELITE TYPE PLASTIC)
5. HOSE CONNECTOR, AMBIENT PRESSURE
6. HOSE CONNECTOR, TO REFERENCE AIR VOLUME OF 250 CCM THERMOS BOTTLE
7. ANODIZED ELECTRODE SURFACES
8. GROUNDED ELECTRODE CONNECTOR (DIFFERENTIAL ZERO)
9. OUTER CONNECTORS (VARIABLE CAPACITY ~400 VAC)

FIGURE 3.—Sketch of principle of variable capacitance pressure differential sensor for electronic variometer. Pressure range +0–1 to 0–10 mm H_2O. Pressure adjustable; orifice- or capillary-type pressure gradient elements for 0.1-second response time. Photo courtesy Dr. W. Spilger.

was later used at Peenemunde to arm the parachute recovery system of A-5 missiles during the ascent flight path; it released the brake and later the main parachute at certain stagnation pressure conditions, based on the rate of change of pitot pressure rather than fixed altitude. This method proved more dependable and desirable than using an altimeter to initiate the recovery sequence.

While stabilized platforms were under development for missile use during this period—at Kreiselgeraete, under the direction of Captain Johan M. Boykow [3]—these were too bulky to be installed in the aircraft we had to test. We therefore attached to the vehicle (strap-down system) conventional single- and two-axis-free gyros, mounting them in three mutually perpendicular axes (directional and horizon gyro arrangement). To resolve gyro readings and to determine actual displacement angles referred to the flight path (rather than the inertial reference axes), coordinate transfer equations were derived and published. These equations established the relation between gyro read-out and actual attitudes with reference to the flight path. Later, in 1939 and 1940 at Peenemunde, this system was further expanded to determine proper propulsion and cut-off velocities through reference axes fixed to the body axes.

At that time the author proposed to improve such systems by use of thrust-control to make the trajectories more reproducible and to reduce the range errors of such systems. This approach compensated for the effect of time variation on cutoff velocity, as proposed at that time by Dr. Walter Schwidetzki. Much of the refinement of the theoretical analysis of these techniques was later performed by the Institute of Practical Mathematics of the Darmstadt Institute of Technology under Professor Dr. Alvin Walther, and at Professor Wilhelm Wolman's Electronic Institute at the Dresden Institute of Technology. Also Dr. Steuding, one of my colleagues at Darmstadt, continued much of his work at Peenemunde and made major theoretical and practical contributions to the state of the art of that time. One of the results of his work was that, for the A-series type of missile (A-3 to A-8), positive stabilization and flight control was introduced in the period 1938–39. The originally considered mode of spin stabilization was abandoned, because of its sensitivity to wind shear in ascent and descent.

During measurement of aircraft flight performance, knowledge of the actual angle of attack is of great value for the analysis and interpretation of flight-performance data. In addition, angle-of-attack meters can also be used to limit or control the range of angle of attack. While working at DFS at Darmstadt, I used the above-described angle-of-attack meter to limit the angle-of-attack range during high-speed cruise, which reduced structural loads due to gusts. I also introduced the angle-of-attack reading to bias gyro displacements on an hydraulic or pneumatic autopilot. Another bias was the pitot pressure rate of change. Both techniques led to flight control modes more closely related to the pilot's feel of flying. Particularly, limitation of angle of attack to a prescribed range can reduce structural loads. Therefore this method was considered at Peenemunde to limit the angle of attack to reduce the structural weight of the missile. Since theoretical analysis showed that lateral forces, angle of attack, and speed or stagnation pressure have mutual relations, the angle-of-attack measurement was replaced by normal force measurement and the velocity measurement was replaced by electronic means. However, wind-shear reduction by installing angle-of-attack vanes for the bias of autopilots was later used again by my colleagues on the Redstone missile at Huntsville, Alabama.

Many of the thoughts derived in flight-performance testing at Darmstadt were actually put to use at Peenemunde by one of my colleagues, also from the Darmstadt Institute of Technology, Dr. Helmut Hoelzer. The use of accelerometers and rate indicators induced him to find electronic methods of integrating and differentiating sensor displacements, and to mix the results in accordance with stability requirements. His familiarity with Dr. Harry Nyquist's work then led to applications which, late in 1939, resulted in possibly the first electronic analog computer to simulate flight performance in the laboratories, rather than through tedious and time-consuming flight tests or static tests, and resulted in simplification of autopilots. This work eventually led to the A-4, or V-2, autopilot, which was fully electronic.

Flight Control Developments

During the 1936–38 period, the author worked to improve flight and landing qualities of single-engine aircraft by using angle-of-attack meters in connection with pneumatic amplifiers. Experience with these techniques, and having observed the need for higher response rates in missile applications, later led me to use hydraulic amplifiers. During this period, close contact developed with Askania-Berlin in pneumatic as well as hydraulic servo applications. This cooperation led to the modification of hydraulic servomotors to meet response and torque requirements of control actuators on the A-4 and A-5 missiles at Peenemunde. The original servomotors were improved to torques several times their original torque rating through mutual programs which increased control response and dynamic range of controllability. The A-5, Wasserfall and A-4 flew with these servomotors. Parallel work with Siemens was also successful, permitting alternate use of Siemens actuators. Insight gained in flight performance testing also found application during the 1939–40 period in beam-riding systems flight tested in aircraft.

Flight Performance Measurements

Next in importance to sensor developments for facilitating measurement of flight performance, was the development of ground-based optical equipment—the ballistic cameras and cinetheodolites which later played an increasingly important role in missile and rocket development testing. Wilhelm Harth and Dr. Paul Raetjen who, at DFS during the period 1931–39, devoted considerable time to the improvement of optical precision equipment, sponsored the development of what became cinetheodolites for flight performance measurement. The original design was an intermediate of the ballistic camera and the well-known Askania cinetheodolite (Figure 4). In this design the target was tracked and superimposed on a precision-grid fixed background, as shown in Figure 5. In order to achieve the required high resolution, the graduation of a hollow hemisphere required a mechanical skill available in only a few precision mechanics. This was a biggest obstacle to serial production of these cameras. Harth's efforts and Askania's design capabilities led to the later well-known Askania ballistic cameras and the Kth 39 and Kth 41 models used at Peenemunde and later at many other missile proving grounds.

However, the use of on-board recording and

FIGURE 4.—First Askania cinetheodolite, used at the DFS-Darmstadt, Germany, 1935–39 for flight performance measurements. Photo courtesy R. Opitz.

ground-tracking led to another technological development of even greater importance. While at DFS (1931–33 and 1936–39), I worked on airborne communication transponders and transmitters for transmitting messages from aircraft to aircraft, and aircraft to ground. The transmission of instantaneous

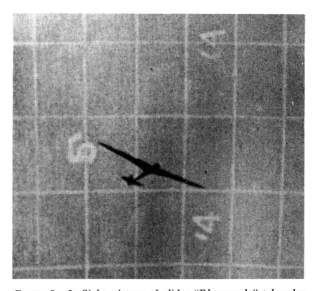

FIGURE 5.—In-flight picture of glider "Rhoeneagle" taken by Askania cinetheodolite. The grid indicates azimuth and elevation angles, under which picture was taken. For flight performance measurements, two to three stations were used. Photo courtesy R. Opitz.

sensor data was the next step to make flight performance measurement more efficient. At Darmstadt we only pondered how to combine these various techniques to achieve an autonomous data system. However, Dr. Gerhard Reisig at Peenemunde, together with Dr. Rudolf Hell at Berlin-Dahlem, developed the first missile-borne recorder, using a picture tube to electronically present sensor data by sub-commutating it to read-out, and to photograph traces of a multitude of sensor data. The next step was to be radio transmission to the ground.

Even prior to World War II, work on pulse time, pulse code, AM-telemetry and possibly also AM/FM and FM/FM were not only on the drawing board, but in laboratory tests. Team members participating in this effort, which I coordinated from 1939 on, were Dr. Reisig, Dr. Hans-Heinrich Emschermann, Dr. Hans J. Rittinghausen, and Dipl. Ing. Helmut Gröttrup.

In 1938 one of the tasks we handled in our flight performance group was the engineless prototype (see Figure 1) of what later became the Me 163.[4] This prototype aircraft, designed by Alexander Lippisch and his team, did not yet have its rocket engine. While waiting for the completion of its development, it underwent considerable flight testing with Rudi Opitz as test pilot. During one of these test flights, Opitz had extreme difficulties in recovering the aircraft from a spin, and had to bail out at an altitude below 100 meters. My colleagues and I saw the parachute blossoming at the time Opitz disappeared in the forest surrounding our test center. We were amazed to find him alive, although badly shaken emotionally. He told us later that because his parachute did not sufficiently decelerate his fall, he spread himself out during the fall and tried to catch some branches of the fir trees he was falling through; these he managed to hang on to until the parachute lines started to stretch. The force of the impact would still have been too great, however, if the moss and soft soil had not further moderated his impact. The German Army officers, arriving at the scene, asked Opitz if they could be of any help. Opitz replied: "If you should have a cigarette, it will help me most." We were glad to see him alive. Rudi Opitz has recently recovered from a severe helicopter accident, which he sustained while a test pilot at Lycoming. His 14-year-old son, like his father, is an ardent glider pilot and looks forward to becoming a test pilot.

First Personal Involvement with a Missile

It must have been in 1937 or 1938 when my team was asked to look into conceptual solutions for an air-to-surface missile which would be dropped out of the bomb bay of a conventional bomber, and which would be controlled or could be guided to its target. Being familiar with our institute's prior work with rocket propulsion (Friedrich Stamer's pioneering work at the Wasserkuppe),[5] we decided that this vehicle could be either rocket-propelled or unpropelled, since space available and other dimensional constraints indicated that no wings could be used. In contrast to Lippisch's approach, we selected solid-fueled motors of the type used by German Army units for rocket propulsion. About two years later I used the same type for missile firings from my brother's submerged submarine.[6] Instead of using the conventional body of revolution approach, we selected a low-aspect-ratio (AR = 0.5) lifting-body configuration operating within the subsonic speed range. The project never went beyond its initial conceptual analysis because I left for Peenemunde soon after the beginning of this work. However, other solutions were later dealt with by various DFS personnel. Alexander Lippisch's Me 163 rocket airplane became one of the major projects to be tested in subsequent years at Peenemunde.

Flight Dynamics Aspects of Flight Testing Work

Many of the problem areas which later became key issues in missile developments, hinted at their importance early in the flight-performance work at the DFS because of the considerable attention given to flight handling qualities; to judgment of interaction between configuration peculiarities, flight performance, and flight handling; as well as to mutual interference between powerplants, aerodynamics, and stability. The realization that many parameters other than attitude, speed, and altitude represented the complex dynamic behavior of missiles and aircraft, led to the development of many types of sensors in order to obtain a better insight into areas of flight dynamics, the importance of response rates, and the requirements on control parameters. Consequently much work was going on during the 1936–38 period in quite a few laboratories. Dr. Oppelt at the DVL, Dipl. Ing. Waldemar

Moeller at Askania, Dr. Wilfried Fieber and Dr. Gerald Klein at Siemens, all worked on different solutions to the same problems, and they were able to fill in the gaps we found at Peenemunde one to two years later.

Also during this time, as the theory of flight dynamics was perfected, it was learned that with higher speed and required tighter flight-path control, the response rate of contemporary autopilots was insufficient. The importance of the higher derivatives of sensor displacement became more and more obvious. The need to reduce lag in the control circuits and to improve damping coefficients became increasingly accepted. Dr. Oppelt, Prof. Dr. Maximilian Schuler, Prof. Dr. Kurt Magnus, and Dr. Steuding were key individuals in developing the theoretical background needed to assist Dr. Hoelzer and his team in finding the electronic circuits most suitable to meet these requirements.

The Challenge of Inertial Reference Systems

At the time that Dr. Paul von Handel, Dr. Johannes Plendl, and others conceived fundamental radio navigation systems, it became obvious that these systems could not cover all the needs of the advancing fields of rocketry and aeronautics. At a time when we found that radio propagation through rocket exhaust had its problems, Dr. von Braun and Captain Boykow discussed the potential of fully inertial platforms and the use of Professor Schuler's earth radius pendulum for rocket and spacecraft navigation.[7] At the DVL, tests of aircraft navigation devices showed that the most difficult areas of technological requirements were those involving gyro drift and inaccuracy of accelerators. I am told that an aircraft, departing from Adlershof near Berlin and approaching the Netherland border, indicated "Australia" on its navigation system as the current position.

Drift rates of gyros produced at Kreiselgeraete, Berlin, reduced drift rates to below a degree per hour; platform designs, using "Schulerloops" progressed subsequently to the point to be flown in V-2s during 1943. While strapdown systems, as initially used at Darmstadt, appeared to be no match to gyro-stabilized space-reference systems, there are many applications in which these still hold their own. Progress made in digital computers has contributed much to their improvement, individual gyro and accelerometer performance being of equal importance in each application. Also the two original modes of air- and fluid-suspended gyros are still in competition with each other, the former originally sponsored by Kreiselgeraete and the latter by Siemens.

Much of the research in the area of gyro-platform improvement and error-source analysis has been performed by an outstanding U.S. scientist, Dr. Charles S. Draper, and his team, who, as the current president of the International Academy of Astronautics, is the chairman of this Symposium. The current state of the art in this field owes much to Dr. Draper and his group at the Massachusetts Institute of Technology.[8] I am proud to pay him this tribute at this time and place.

Rocket Engine Developments at Kummersdorf

While I personally was not involved in rocket-engine development, I became involved in the instrumentation and analysis of rocket-engine tests and data transmission to a central recording station near the end of the period covered in this presentation. In this connection, I would like to report on the development work of some of my colleagues at Kummersdorf and Peenemunde which I think was fundamental in rocket-engine development and therefore deserves mention on this occasion.

From 1937 through 1939, a 1500-kg thrust high-pressure rocket engine (750 psi or 50 kg/cm²) was developed in which aluminum was used for the combustion chamber and exit nozzle. This required cooling of the entire chamber and nozzle. In order to accomplish this, transpiration cooling was introduced to produce a fuel-rich, cool envelope surrounding the hot combustion gases (2200° to 2400°C depending on the fuel and oxidizer selection), to protect the chamber itself. The introduction of this technique, to be credited to Dr. Walter Thiel, Klaus Riedel, Dr. h. c. Arthur Rudolf, Mr. Albert Püllenberg and others, is one which brought rocket-engine technology a substantial step forward and could be classed the first modern rocket engine.

My team's involvement toward the end of our work at Peenemunde also dealt with flame temperature measurements, exhaust gas composition measurements and causes of radio-transmission blackout. For some of this work, my organization issued research contracts to groups of universities, supporting our work. Use of sodium-D line reversal

technique to determine flame temperature was one of the new techniques in which Dr. Martin Schilling was instrumental.

Summary

The preceding paragraphs are an historical account of the developments and contributions made by the author and his team to the instrumentation, flight testing, flight dynamics, guidance, and control of missiles. Broad technological fields provided initial answers to many technical and developmental problems; they also outlined the avenues along which much of the subsequent research would have to be directed before it could meet the increasingly difficult requirements resulting from supersonic flight through dense and rarefied atmospheres.

It is not possible to credit every person who was involved in this effort. My account must be a tribute to those who were not individually named, but whose contributions provided the multitude of scientific and engineering building blocks. As to my own contributions, I was at all times supported by dedicated teams and colleagues of exceptional training for the tasks assigned to them.

In addition to particularly crediting Dr. Draper, I feel compelled to give credit to Dr. Wernher von Braun, whose broad engineering abilities, exceptional insight into the entire spectrum of missile and spaceflight, and whose broadminded leadership permitted me, subsequent to 1938, to implement the many solutions found prior to that time for missile and spaceflight guidance applications.

NOTES

Under the title *Razrabotka sistem upavleniya ismeritel'noy apparatury i metodov opedeleniya letnykh kharakteristik pervykh raketnykh letatel'nykh apparatov*, this paper appeared on pages 169–78 of *Iz istorii astronavtiki i raketnoi tekhniki: Materialy XVIII mezhdunarodnogo astronavticheskogo kongressa, Belgrad, 25–29 Sentyavrya 1967* [From the History of Rockets and Astronautics: Materials of the 18th International Astronautical Congress, Belgrade, 25–29 September 1967], Moscow: Mauka, 1970.

1. For accounts of Dr. Steinhoff's employment and first day at Peenemunde, see Wernher von Braun, "Reminiscences of German Rocketry," Henry J. White, ed., *Journal of the British Interplanetary Society*, vol. 15, no. 3 (no. 70), May-June 1956, p. 138; and Walter Dornberger, *V-2*, James Cleugh and Geoffrey Halliday, translators (New York: The Viking Press, 1955), p. 15.—Ed.

2. The early tests by Friedrich Stamer and Alex Lippisch

on the Wasserkuppe, one of the Rhön Mountains in Western Germany, are described in Willy Ley's *Rockets, Missiles, and Men in Space* (New York: The Viking Press, 1968), pp. 419–21.—Ed.

3. For information on this inventor see George R. Pitman, Jr., ed., *Inertial Guidance* (New York: John Wiley & Sons, 1962), p. 10 ("Introduction," by John M. Slater) and p. 34 ("V-2," by Dornberger).—Ed.

4. For a summary of the evolution of this aircraft, see William Green, *Famous Fighters of the Second World War* (Garden City, New York: Hanover House, 1960), pp. 124–28.—Ed.

5. See note 2.

6. Dornberger, V-2 (see note 2), p. 245.—Ed.

7. For Professor Maximilian Schuler's classic paper on his earth radius pendulum, see Pitman, op. cit. (note 3), pp. 443–54: Appendix A, "The Disturbance of Pendulum and Gyroscopic Apparatus by the Acceleration of Vertical," by Maximilian Schuler, translated from the German by John M. Slater; the article originally appeared in *Physikalische Zeitschrift*, vol. 24, July 1923, pp. 334–50.—Ed.

8. Charles S. Draper, Walter Wrigley, and John Hovorka, *Inertial Guidance,* (New York: Pergamon Press, 1960), 130 pp.; and Sidney Lees, ed., *Air Space and Instruments: Draper Anniversary Volume* (New York: McGraw-Hill, 1963), 516 pp. —Ed.

26

From the History of Early Soviet Liquid-Propellant Rockets

M. K. Tikhonravov, *Soviet Union*

Thirty-five years is a very long time, but for us it is a part of our lives which we lived through and we still recall in every detail the events of so distant a past.

My presentation covers the story of GIRD, or, to give its full title, the Group for Study of Jet Propulsion.

The history of GIRD, organized in 1931, is somewhat similar to that of the Society for the Study of Interplanetary Communication (OIMS), which had been founded in 1924. Both GIRD and OIMS began as public organizations to unite enthusiasts in rocketry and cosmonautics. The task both groups established for themselves was that of spreading Tsiolkovskiy's ideas and of helping to bring these ideas into practice.

Both organizations contacted K. E. Tsiolkovskiy and he kindly gave them advice. The members of GIRD and OIMS were people who profoundly believed in the vast future of rocket technology and cosmonautics.

In spite of general similarities, however, the results of the activities of the two societies were quite different. OIMS managed to successfully conduct publicity programs and meetings for the general public,[1] but it was not able to undertake practical research work or obtain equipment for construction of experimental devices. After having existed for less than a year, it disbanded. On the other hand, GIRD, which had acquired facilities for experimental work and had rallied a considerable engineering staff, achieved great success not only in programs of public interest but also obtained practical results with experimental rockets and components. Approximately two years after it was formed, GIRD, having merged with the Leningrad Gas Dynamics Laboratory (GDL), was converted into a higher level organization, the Jet Propulsion Research Institute (RNII). The different fates of both OIMS and GIRD were partially due to the different conditions existing in the Soviet Union at the time of their formation.

The Soviet Union, an agrarian country in 1924, had become an industrial nation by the beginning of the thirties. By this time, the heavy machinery and aviation industries were developing throughout the USSR.

By the 1930s the future course of aircraft development was already beginning to be clearly visible. Even then the limits of propeller driven planes were apparent. A number of young aviation workers, in search of how to go beyond these limits, concentrated their attention on the problems of jet propulsion. Consequently, even though they had accepted Tsiolkovskiy's ideas, they did so because of their aspiration to fly higher, faster and farther, rather than to fly to Mars as soon as possible.

It was particularly fortunate that these young people, in addition to their aspirations, had experience in aircraft engineering. Many had already developed their own aircraft designs and were planning further developments using rocket propulsion. They could use the aviation industry as a base for their work on reaction-propelled aircraft. Among these enthusiasts with aviation background was the chief of GIRD, Sergei Pavlovitch Korolyev, an outstanding designer who possessed profound scientific intuition and brilliant organizing abilities. Other individuals with backgrounds in aviation were the team leaders and most of the leading workers of GIRD.

From its inception, GIRD was given the complete support of the powerful mass organization, the Society for Assisting Defense and Aviation and

Chemical Construction in the USSR (Osoaviakhim). It should be noted that the greater part of GIRD's funds was obtained not only through the efforts of its leaders but also because these efforts met with complete understanding on the part of M. N. Tukhachevsky.

Thus, the establishment of GIRD as an organization to develop rocket technology was due to the rise of science and technology in the USSR. Several favorable factors influenced its development, but it was the members of GIRD who, by their hard work and dedication, brought about fulfillment of their historic mission as pioneers of Soviet liquid-propellant rockets.

The Moscow Group for Study of Jet Propulsion (MosGIRD) was established in August 1931. The decision to organize the group was preceded by S. P. Korolyev's work in creating a rocket-propelled aircraft with the OR-2 liquid-propellant engine designed by F. A. Tsander.

GIRD conducted a large-scale publicity campaign and on 13 November 1931, the Leningrad GIRD (LenGIRD) was formed. Subsequently OSOAVIAKHIM began to found GIRDs in other areas.

The Moscow GIRD became the central group (CGIRD), and directed all the other GIRD's. Early in 1932, CGIRD established courses, the first in the world, on jet propulsion, which contributed to training and education of rocket engineers in the USSR.

On 3 March 1932, at a meeting with Tukhachevskiy as chairman, the CGIRD leaders presented a report on jet propulsion problems. As a result a decision was adopted to establish the Rocket Research Institute, and to allocate to RNII the necessary funds. In April 1932, the decision was made to create the CGIRD Experimental Rocket Plant. S. P. Korolyev was appointed plant director, chief of CGIRD, and chairman of its technical council.

The CGIRD and local GIRD's had been open to all rocket and space-flight enthusiasts.[2] However, the Experimental Rocket Plant of GIRD accepted only specialists having the necessary background and training in rocketry. At first, all were voluntary workers, but later, as individuals became involved in the work, they were accepted on the GIRD staff. The funds allocated did not limit the work of GIRD to the field of rocket aircraft, thus enabling GIRD to begin work on a number of concepts suggested partly by S. P. Korolyev and F. A. Tsander,

partly by M. K. Tikhonravov, and by Yu. A. Pobedonostsev, who came to work in GIRD.

By the latter half of 1932, after a great many organizational difficulties had been solved, such as the search for premises and equipment and the arrangement of supply sources for materials, the GIRD plant became a research laboratory having four design teams and manufacturing workshops to serve them. The first team was headed by F. A. Tsander, the second by M. K. Tikhonravov, the third by Yu. A. Pobedonostsev, and the fourth by S. P. Korolyev. The concepts and projects developed in GIRD carried serial numbers preceded by zero (0), when the number was a single digit. Altogether, ten design and research projects were designated for development by GIRD.

It is my privilege to tell you about the work of the GIRD second team of which I was scientific leader. Our team worked on the following projects:

1. Project 03, the RDA-1 engine, with pump-fed propellants, designed for a rocket aircraft.
2. Project 05, A flight rocket for installation of the nitric-acid engine ORM-50 designed by the Leningrad Gas Dynamics Laboratory (GDL).
3. Project 07, A flight with a liquid oxygen/kerosene engine.
4. Project 09, A flight rocket using a semisolid (hybrid) fuel and liquid oxygen.

During the work on Project 03, attention was concentrated on the development of the liquid-oxygen-driven pump. The suggested fuel for this 100-kg-thrust engine was benzine. The pump was designed to operate on oxygen vapor created by evaporation of a portion of the oxygen in the tank. The majority of the oxygen was fed into the rocket engine from the pressure generated by its own vaporization in the tank. In 1932 the working drawings of the pump had been made, but actual fabrication of the pump was delayed because it had to be constructed in facilities other than those of GIRD.

Subsequently, the work was transferred to RNII, where a test stand for the pump was constructed. However, even here the manufacture of the pump could not be completed. By this time it was apparent that development of the combustion chamber would prove to be very difficult, and all efforts were concentrated on this problem. The work on the pump was temporarily stopped.

The 07 Project was the first flight rocket program

FIGURE 1.—Propellant tanks for Rocket 07.

to be undertaken by the second team. The engine of this rocket operated on liquid oxygen/kerosene. The propellant tanks were located in stabilizers with the rocket engine between them (Figures 1 and 2). The fuel was fed into the engine by oxygen pressure. However, development of the 07 rocket and its engine were not completed in GIRD. The project was passed on to RNII where the rocket was completed and later flown.

The next flight rocket for the second team was the 09 (Figure 3). It's engine operated on liquid oxygen and a semisolid (hybrid) fuel called "condensed benzine." This "condensed benzine," prepared in Baku, was a solution of colophony, a natural resin, in benzine. Under normal conditions, the condensed benzine had the consistency of grease and burned in successive layers. The heat of combustion of colophony is about 9,000 kg-cal/kg. The 09 rocket engine had a sheet-brass combustion

FIGURE 2.—Rocket 07 mounted on test stand.

chamber with a bronze injector head and a bronze socket for the exit nozzle. The nozzle was of steel. The inlet valve was screwed into the injector head and was directly connected with the oxygen tank, made from a duraluminum tube. The oxygen was fed into the combustion chamber by its own vapor pressure. A pressure gauge was fitted to the tank. The condensed benzine entered the combustion chamber between a special cylindrical metal grid

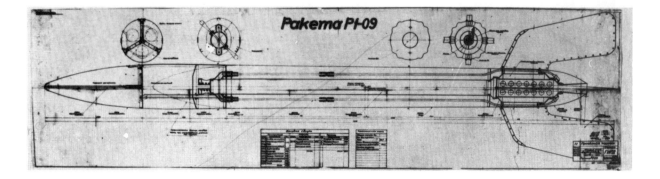

FIGURE 3.—Drawing of Rocket 09.

FIGURE 4.—Rockets 07 (left) and 09.

and the chamber walls. An aircraft spark plug screwed into the combustion chamber served as the igniter. The body of the 09 rocket, constructed of 0.5-mm-thick aluminum, contained the engine and the tanks. The fins were made of Electron, a magnesium alloy. The fully equipped rocket weighed 19 kg. Photos of it were repeatedly printed in technical and scientific publications (see Figure 4).[3]

The engine for the 09 rocket was developed during the spring and summer of 1933. The thrust, measured on a balancing beam test stand (Figure 5) averaged 37 kg. The first launching of the 09 rocket took place on 17 August 1933 and was a success. The rocket was launched vertically and reached an altitude of about 400 m. It is shown being loaded with liquid oxygen in Figure 6 and in flight in Figure 7. This was the first flight of a Soviet liquid-propellant rocket.

The 09 rocket was launched for the second time late in the fall of 1933. This time its thrust chamber exploded in the air, for an undetermined reason, when the rocket reached an altitude of about 100 m. RNII later made a series of six 09 rockets, designated series "13," which were successfully launched at various angles of elevation to investigate the

FIGURE 5.—Test stand for Rocket 09 engine tests.

FIGURE 6.—Loading a Rocket 09 with liquid oxygen.

FIGURE 7.—Launch of Rocket 09.

possibilities of using liquid propellant rockets for flights with low trajectories.

After the 07 and 09 rocket projects, work on the 05 rocket was begun. This rocket (Figure 8) was designed to use the nitric acid/kerosene ORM-50 engine developed by GDL. Design of the rocket was completed in 1933 when the Rocket Research Institute was being organized, and RNII continued its further development.

On the basis of the 05 rocket's design, RNII developed, under the sponsorship of the All-Union Aeronautic Research and Technical Society (Aviavnito) the stratospheric rocket "Aviavnito" (Figure 9). It used the 12-K liquid rocket engine which operated on liquid oxygen/96% alcohol and generated 300 kg thrust for a duration of 60 sec. However, the flat stabilizing fins of the 05 rocket were replaced with new, profiled hollow fins. The initial rocket weighed approximately 100 kg, of which 32 kg was propellant. The 12-K motor developed a specific impulse of 205-207 kg-sec/kg. The entire engine installation weighed 15 kg.[4] The rocket was designed to reach an altitude of 10,800 m and contained a parachute. An altimeter, of the barograph type developed by S. A. Pivovarov, was mounted on the rocket.

The initial launching of the Aviavnito rocket took place on 6 April 1936. Pravda published a article about the launching which included a photo of the rocket in the launching position prior to take-off. The correspondent described the rocket flight as follows:

The engineer has switched on the electric ignition plug. Gray smoke of evaporating propellant. Spark. And suddenly a dazzling yellow flame appeared at the base of the rocket. The rocket moved slowly up the guide rods of the launching frame, slipped out of its steel embrace and rushed upwards.

The flight was an extremely impressive and beautiful spectacle. A flame rushed out of the motor nozzle. The rapid flow of gas was accompanied by a low-pitched roaring sound. A parachute opened showing its white canopy after the rocket reached a low altitude and then landed smoothly on a snow field.[5]

For subsequent launchings a wooden tower was constructed with a guide, 48 m long, constructed from a narrow-gauge rail, which engaged the launching lugs of the rocket.

On 15 August 1937 an Aviavnito rocket reached an altitude of 3000 meters,[6] but on descent the parachute was torn from the rocket, and the rocket was severely damaged upon impact.

Some of the individuals working on the second team were, F. L. Yakitis, V. S. Suyev, V. N. Galkovsky, S. I. Kruglova, O. K. Parovina, N. I. Shul'gina, V. A. Andreyev, E. I. Snegireva, and N. I. Yefremov.

In summary, the results of the GIRD second team's activity were as follows:

1. Bringing about the flights of early liquid propellant rockets.
2. First use of liquid oxygen and other oxidants in combination with various fuels.
3. The first rocket to use liquid oxygen and a semisolid (hybrid) fuel.
4. Initiation of the development of a pump driven by liquid oxygen.
5. Developing and experimentally proving methods of calculating rocket design and performance.

All the above problems were studied experimentally and in most cases results were obtained which subsequently served as the basis for realistic tasks and development programs.

The main task of GIRD and its second team was to prove that the principle of jet propulsion was quite workable even with the state of the art of

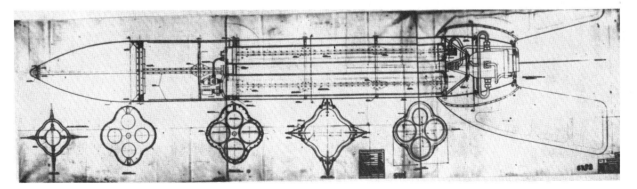

FIGURE 8.—Drawing of Rocket 05.

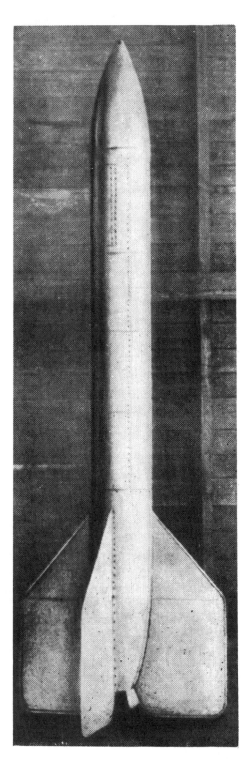

FIGURE 9.—The Aviavnito rocket.

those early years.[7] That was accomplished and the proof was convincing because it was done at a high scientific and technical level and in a surprisingly short time.

NOTES

Under the title *Iz istorii sozdaniya pervykh sovetskikh raket na zhidkom toplive*, this article appeared on pages 154–61 of *Iz istorii astronavtiki i raketnoi tekhniki: Materialy XVIII mezhdunarodnogo astronavticheskogo kongressa, Belgrad, 25–29 Sentyavrya 1967* [From the History of Rockets and Astronautics: Materials of the 18th International Astronautical Congress, Belgrade, 25–29 September 1967], Moscow: Nauka, 1970.

On 4 March 1974 Mikhail K. Tikhonravov died in Moscow. His obituary was carried in *The Washington Post*, 7 March 1974.—Ed.

1. Additional information on the formation of the Society for Studying Interplanetary Travel is presented on p. 377 of *The Soviet Encyclopedia of Space Flight* (translated from the Russian), G. V. Petrovich, ed., (Moscow: MIR Publishers, 1969); a reproduction of an OIMS meeting poster announcing a public debate of 4 October 1924 in Moscow regarding a reported launching of a moon rocket by Dr. Robert H. Goddard on the previous 4 August and an account of F. A. Tsander's participation in this debate appears on pp. 19–21 of F. A. Tsander's *Problema poleta pri pomoshchi reaktivnykh apparatov: Mezhplanetnyye polety* [Problems of Flight by Jet Propulsion: Interplanetary Flights], L. K. Korneyev, ed., 2nd ed., enlarged (Moscow: Gos. Nauchno-Tekhn. Izd. Oborongiz, 1961); translated from the Russian and published for the U.S. National Aeronautics and Space Administration and the National Science Foundation, Washington, D.C., by the Israel Program for Scientific Translations, ed. Y. M. Timnat, NASA TT F-147, (Jerusalem, 1964).—Ed.

2. "Soviet Engineers Constructing Two Rockets," *Bulletin of the American Interplanetary Society*, no. 15 (January 1932), p. 1.—Ed.

3. An 09 rocket on display is shown in Yu. A. Pobedonostsev, "Behind the Luniks," *Astronautics*, January 1960, p. 31; additional data on the 09 Project appears on pp. 126, 166, and 461 of *The Soviet Encyclopedia of Space Flight* (see note 1)—Ed.

4. A sectioned 12-K engine is shown in Pobedonostsev, "Behind the Luniks," p. 33.—Ed.

5. "Rocket Enters the Air," *Pravda*, no. 99 (6705), 9 April 1936.

6. An Aviavnito rocket on display is shown in Pobedonostsev, "Behind the Luniks," p. 32.—Ed.

7. M. K. Tikhonravov and Yu. V. Biryukov, "Expression of Ideas of K. E. Tsiolkovskiy in the Work of GIRD," *Proceedings of the First Symposium Dedicated to the Development of the Scientific Principles and to the Development of the Ideas of K. E. Tsiolkovskiy*, Moscow, 1967, pp. 5–15. Available in English translation as NASA TI F-0544, *Transactions of the First Lectures Dedicated to the Development of the Scientific Heritage of K. E. Tsiolkovskiy*, A. A. Blagonravov et al., ed. (Washington: NASA, April 1970), 117 p.—Ed.

REFERENCES

The following references appeared at the end of this paper (p. 161) in the Russian publication cited above:

1. Test data from tests of the Rocket 09 assembly and an account of the launch on 17 August 1933 of Rocket 09. Archiv AN SSSR (Archives of the USSR Academy of Sciences), razr. 4, op. 14; d. 50.

2. Test data from the testing of separate components for Rocket 07 (1933). Archiv AN SSSR, razr. 4, op. 14, d. 51.

3. Rocket Aviavnito, calculations and photographs (1935–1936). Archiv AN SSSR, razr. 4, op. 14, d. 57.

4. The work plan of "GIRD" for 1933–34 for all teams (1933–1934). Archiv AN SSSR, razr. 4, op. 14, d. 1.

5. Launching test of Rocket 05 and the test firing of the motor 0–10 (1934). Archiv AN SSSR, razr. 4, op. 14, d. 3.

6. *Pravda,* no. 99 (6705), 9 April 1936.

27

Annapolis Rocket Motor Development, 1936-38

R. C. Truax, *United States*

I was bitten by the rocket bug at a very tender age. As a high school student in the late 1920s and early 1930s, I avidly read all the material available in the local libraries in my home town of Alameda, California. This included, as I remember, Goddard's Smithsonian reports, the occasional articles in Sunday supplements and accounts of the exploits of Fritz von Opel and Max Valier which appeared in such magazines as *Popular Mechanics*. Of course, "Buck Rogers in the 25th Century" was my continuing inspiration.

My first venture into the field of hardware was to help a friend pry open shotgun shells to get out the powder. This we poured into a tube inside a very beautifully constructed balsa-wood rocket. When the rocket exploded in a shower of flying splinters and soda straws (rocket tubes), my friend proceeded to build another beautifully painted model, but I concentrated on making an engine that would work. I tried paper tubes, small metal carbon dioxide cylinders, etc., with the usual black powder and gum arabic propellant formulations. I also found old nitrate movie film to have interesting properties. The rocket case for this propellant was an old tooth-powder can. This one burst at a height of several feet and scattered strips of flaming celluloid all over my back yard.

My "thesis" in mechanical drawing during my sophomore year in high school was a drawing of a regeneratively cooled rocket motor, labelled Heylandt Liquid Rocket, which I had never seen, but of which I had read a description.[1]

I count my significant work in rocketry from the time I made my first engineering measurements on an operating rocket engine. These measurements were made during December 1937 on a thrust chamber constructed earlier that year. The essential features of the thrust chamber are shown in Figure 1.

During this period, I was a midshipman at the U.S. Naval Academy, subject to the severe restrictions of time and opportunity associated with studying at Annapolis.[2] There were, however, two compensating advantages; the Naval Academy had a machine shop, and across the Severn River from the Academy was the U.S. Naval Engineering Experiment Station.

During the 1935–36 period, I had designed a liquid propellant sounding rocket embodying a regeneratively cooled thrust chamber, tanks of seam welded, ¾-inch hard-rolled stainless steel, gyroscopic controls, etc.[3] The thrust chamber shown in Figure 1 was the first step toward development of this sounding rocket. As can be seen, the design involved regenerative cooling for the entrance section of the nozzle, water film cooling at the throat, and an uncooled metal diverging section.

The Naval Academy was not noted for the amount of free time it gave to midshipmen, and my rocketeering had to be sandwiched in between the termination of classes and evening formation. As a matter of fact, it developed that my time for building rocketeering devices was even more restricted because electric power in the shop was turned off at 5 p.m.

After I had completed the design of the thrust chamber in my room in Bancroft Hall, I went over to Isherwood Hall to the machine shop to get on with the job of fabrication. Mr. Harold Lucas, the machinist in charge, listened sympathetically as I explained my requirements for materials and then asked me whether or not I had the proper requisitions. Of course I had none, and after a somewhat crestfallen silence on my part, Mr. Lucas offered

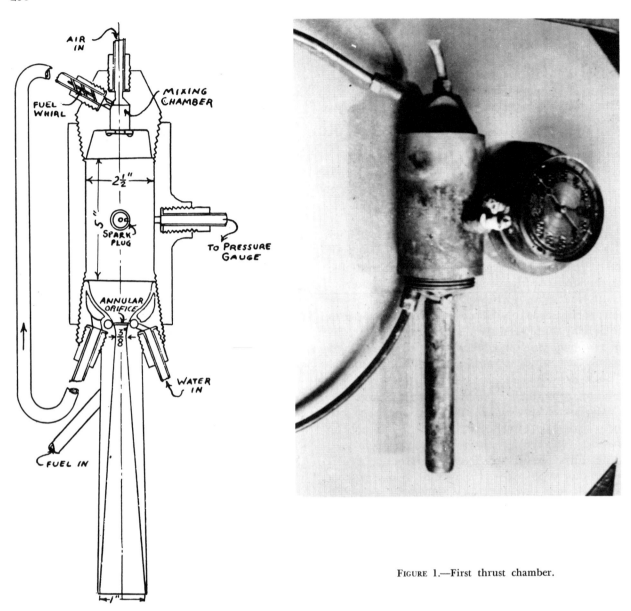

FIGURE 1.—First thrust chamber.

a way out. He led me down to the scrap box and said, "If you can find anything in there that can be used for your rocket, go ahead and take it." I selected as the main body of the thrust chamber a nickel-steel pinion gear. The hub of this gear appeared to be of proper thickness and quality to withstand almost any pressures which might be generated. I took the gear back to Mr. Lucas and asked him if I might use one of the machine-shop lathes. He asked me whether I had ever used a lathe before. When I replied that I had only that instruction given all midshipmen in shop work, he

led me down the long line of lathes to the smaller and older ones. He finally stopped in front of a ten-inch South Bend lathe, of about 1917 vintage, and told me that I was free to use that one.

In spite of the age and decrepit condition of the lathe, I am sure that Mr. Lucas' machinist's soul winced each time the lathe went clank, clank, clank with the cutter hitting the case-hardened teeth as I proceeded to machine them off the pinion gear. I am not sure whether I lost more teeth off the driving gears of the lathe or off the work in the chuck. At length, however, this task was completed.

I remember being so frustrated by the fact that the power was cut off at 5 p.m. that many times I would set up to take a cut, lose the power, and then pull the lathe through by hand. Under such circumstances, it is not surprising that it took about eight months to complete the first test combustion chamber.

When my masterpiece was completed, I took it to the head of the Marine Engineering Department and requested permission to set it up in the foundry and fire it. In perhaps justifiable concern over the future of Isherwood Hall, permission was denied. I found a much more receptive climate, however, across the Severn River at the Experiment Station. After a third-degree interrogation by several heads of departments, concerning in particular the safety of my proposed operations, it was decided to let me have a go at it. Not only was I given permission to work at the Experiment Station, but some assistance was provided in the form of materials.

In addition, a little welder named Sugar Evans was assigned to give me a hand in the construction of the rocket test stand.

In order to complete the test that I had programmed, I had to forego my September leave, and I was most annoyed to find that construction of an item as prosaic as a test stand required nearly half of my leave period. Nowadays, of course, construction of a rocket test stand requires upwards of 18 months and many millions of dollars. Sugar Evans and I took a very practical approach, although not a very elegant one. In making the propellant tanks, we went out to the stock rack, selected some steel pipe of approximately the right size, and pulled it out to what appeared to be about the right length. Sugar, whiz that he was with the cutting torch, then cut the pipe off at the proper length without even removing it from the stock rack. We then made closures for the tanks by burning circles out of boiler plates, welding them in, and providing them with gussets which appeared to both of us to be about adequate in thickness and strength. There was a tank for the fuel, a tank for the liquid oxygen, and since the thrust-chamber design utilized a nozzle cooled in part by an injection of water, there was also a tank for cooling water.

Instrumentation was characteristically simple and direct, involving the use of Bourdon tube pressure gauges, an Eastman Kodak timer, and best of all, a stock-room scale on which the thrust chamber was mounted in a nozzle-up position. In operation, the beam rider on the scale was set to the thrust desired, and the valves were opened until that thrust was obtained. The instruments were then photographed with a Boy Scout camera at intervals determined primarily by the time required to wind the film on the camera. The fuel consumption was measured by means of a boiler gauge glass.

Although such flow measurements were undoubtedly highly inaccurate, they were no more inaccurate than the measurement of the thrust itself. And at any rate, it was not accuracy, but the principle of the thing that counted at this stage of the game.

Tests of December 1937

Before completion of the test stand, I went to the Industrial Superintendent, Mr. John K. Amos, and announced that I was ready for my tests and would need an adequate supply of liquid oxygen and gasoline. I might as well have asked for an atomic bomb. Mr. Amos replied that the U.S. Naval Welding Regulations specifically forbade the use of oils or hydrocarbons in conjunction with oxygen of any kind, and there was no supply of liquid oxygen at the Experiment Station or any place in the vicinity. Mr. Amos volunteered, however, that there was an adequate supply of compressed air at very high pressure available from some torpedo air compressors, and that I would be allowed to use this compressed air as the oxidizer for the gasoline. This fact probably proved to be a very favorable turn of fate, since the compressed air supply allowed me to run my thrust chamber for relatively long periods of time. It also avoided the difficulties which undoubtedly would have been encountered in the use of liquid oxygen.

Figure 2 shows one of the first tests in progress. The thrust chamber rested on a beam balance with the nozzle pointed skyward. The thrust and mixture ratio were controlled by hand valves in the propellant lines.

Thrust and chamber pressure were the only variables of significance measured. The motor operated for several seconds but was initially very difficult to control. The maximum chamber pressure attained was 150 pounds per square inch. The thrust was about ten pounds.

FIGURE 2.—First test in progress.

With the first combustion chamber we made a considerable number of more-or-less successful tests at increasing thrusts, finally running the apparatus for periods as long as several minutes at a time. I would frequently run the tests during the lunch hour when the workmen from the shop would come out, gather around the rocket, and amuse themselves by throwing stones into the jet to see how high they would be hurled. I remember once two of the men got a large board and attempted to force it into the jet. Although the thrust of the rocket was only about 25 pounds, they found it difficult to hold the board in position against this force.

The tests were duly reported in the April 1938 issue of the journal of the American Rocket Society [4] and constitute some of the very earliest measurements on rockets ever described.

Tests of September 1938

After the first set of tests, it was obvious that a man with only two hands could not juggle three valves—air, gasoline, and water—simultaneously, especially since smooth combustion could be obtained only at certain very delicate settings of the mixture ratio. During the succeeding months, the chamber was modified to eliminate the water by using refractory nozzles. A continuously indicating thrust measuring device was provided and a gauge glass was added to the gasoline tank. A Kodak timer

was used, and the gauges were photographed by a still camera at intervals determined by the length of time required to wind the film. Figure 3 shows a typical photographic record of the instrument panel.

In September 1938, another series of tests was made, again using compressed air and gasoline. Three types of refractory nozzles were used: graphite, fireclay, and aluminum oxide cast from thermit slag. Except for the nozzle change, the motor was identical to that used previously. Only the aluminum oxide nozzle was found satisfactory; the others eroded too rapidly. With the Al_2O_3 nozzle, however, runs of many minutes could be made before the chamber became overheated.[5]

For record purposes, runs from 15 to 45 seconds were made. The data obtained in these September 1938 tests are summarized in the following tabulation:

FIGURE 3.—Instrument panel.

	Run number						
	1	*2*	*3*	*4*	*5*	*6*	*7*
S	300	300	300	300	300	400	400
P_a (psi)	100	110	140	160	200	—	—
P_f (psi)	100	160	200	225	250	—	—
P_c (psi)	70	90	100	120	170	180	190
T (lb)	6	7	10.4	15	16.5	22	25
t (sec)	19	15	20	15	13	45	20
f (lb)	0.12	0.065	0.13	0.11	0.09	0.40	0.20
v (fps)	2010	3250	3220	4260	4900	5000	5040
E_{th} (%)	6.5	16.8	16.6	29.0	38.0	40.0	40.3

A second design of thrust chamber was tested with lesser success. This chamber, shown in Figure 4, was regeneratively cooled by the fuel. It consisted of a tubular outer jacket, about 1½ inches in diameter, containing a combustion chamber and a long nozzle. The fuel was injected towards the head end on two sides of the chamber, and the oxidizer through an annulus surrounding the spark plug. Only intermittent combustion was obtained.

This same thrust chamber was later tested by the American Rocket Society using liquid oxygen and gasoline.[6] It was reported "the motor ran quite well for several seconds, developing about 20 lbs. of thrust before it burned out." This provided a rather charitable evaluation of its performance.

Tests of December 1938

Because two series of tests had been performed without loss of life or limb, Mr. Amos finally agreed to allow me to use gaseous oxygen in place of the compressed air. However, since the welding regulations so dictated, he specified that a welding regulator be used in conjunction with the oxygen bottles. The welding regulators available to me at the Experiment Station were far too small to permit passage of enough oxygen to give significant thrust, and I protested this restriction as strenuously as I could. Mr. Amos, however, felt that he had stuck his neck out far enough, and he insisted on the welding regulator. I found a way around the difficulty by the simple expedient of interchanging the high-pressure gauge commonly found on welding

FIGURE 4.—Tubular engine mounted on horizontal test stand.

FIGURE 5.—Oxygen test stand.

regulators with the outlet connection. In this fashion I was able to completely bypass the regulator, conforming to the letter, if not the spirit, of the rule book, giving the appearance (see Figure 5), at least to the casual observer, that the regulator was being employed!

For this series of tests, a new thrust chamber was built of light-gauge stainless steel, designed to be water cooled and equipped to accept interchangeable nozzles, either metal or refractory. With this chamber, and the test stand modified for the use of gaseous oxygen, a final program of tests was performed in December 1938. The initial tests were performed to evaluate refractory nozzles. Silica, alumina, and tungsten carbide were tried. Only the latter gave reasonable success, although it tended to oxidize. The tungsten carbide nozzle also cracked from thermal shock, but the pieces remained in place.[7]

FIGURE 6.—Thrust chamber tests, using gaseous oxygen with water cooling.

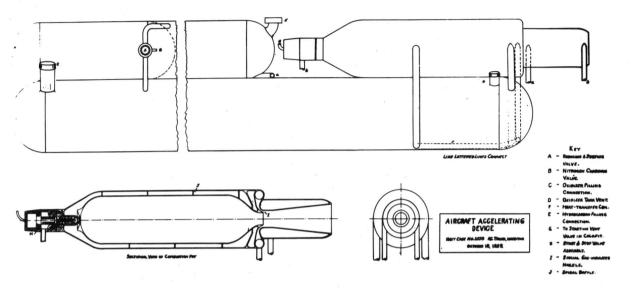

FIGURE 7.—Proposed rocket engine for aircraft take-off assist.

Figure 6 shows these tests in progress. Note the blow torch for igniting the motor, the natural convection water cooling jacket, and the different appearance of the flame under different operating conditions.

Tests of this nature were continued for five or six months into 1939 and culminated in operation of a motor having forced convective cooling with water. At this point, the U.S. Navy expressed an interest in the work, looking to the use of rockets to assist the takeoff of large flying boats. My design for such a rocket, prepared in October 1939, is shown in Figure 7. This particular drawing was used as an instrument for getting a development program started. This program, initiated two years later under my direction, continued the development of rockets for JATO and guided missiles throughout World War II.

NOTES

Under the title *Razrabotka raketnykh dvilateley v Annapolise v 1936–1938,* this paper appeared on pages 162–68 of *Iz istorii astronavtiki i raketnoi tekhniki: Materialy XVIII mezhdunarodnogo astronavticheskogo kongressa, Belgrad, 25–* *29 Sentyavrya 1967* [From the History of Rockets and Astronautics: Materials of the 18th International Astronautical Congress, Belgrade, 25–29 September 1967], Moscow: Nauka, 1970.

1. "Light Weight Rocket Motor Developed in Germany," *Bulletin of the American Interplanetary Society,* no. 8, March-April 1931, p. 14; and "German Rocket Car Tested," ibid., no. 9, May 1931, p. 1.

2. Robert C. Truax, "Rocket Development," *U.S. Naval Institute Proceedings,* September 1964, pp. 81–94.

3. Truax had written Dr. Robert H. Goddard during this time and received a reply with comments to his questions and suggesting that he obtain a copy of his "Liquid-Propellant Rocket Development" (Smithsonian Miscellaneous Collections, vol. 95, no. 3, 1936). See Esther C. Goddard and G. Edward Pendray, editors, *The Papers of Robert H. Goddard* (New York: McGraw-Hill Book Company, 1970), vol. 2, pp. 985, 988.—Ed.

4. Truax, "Gas, Air, Water," *Astronautics,* no. 40 (April 1938), pp. 9–11.

5. Truax, "Annapolis Motor Tests," *Astronautics,* no. 42 (February 1939), pp. 6–10.

6. John Shesta, H. Franklin Pierce, and James H. Wyld, "Report on the 1938 Rocket Motor Tests," *Astronautics,* no. 42 (February 1939), pp. 2–6.

7. Truax, "Addenda to September Report," *Astronautics,* no. 42 (February 1939), p. 10.

Index

303

☆U.S. GOVERNMENT PRINTING OFFICE: 1974 O—521–480